An Introduction to
Numerical Methods and
Optimization Techniques

An Introduction to Numerical Methods and Optimization Techniques

Richard W. Daniels

NORTH-HOLLAND·NEW YORK
NEW YORK • OXFORD

Elsevier North-Holland, Inc.
52 Vanderbilt Avenue, New York, New York 10017

Distributors outside the United States and Canada:
Thomond Books
(A Division of Elsevier/North-Holland
Scientific Publishers, Ltd)
P.O. Box 85
Limerick, Ireland

Library of Congress Cataloging in Publication Data

Daniels, Richard W., 1942-
   An introduction to numerical methods and
optimization techniques.

   Bibliography: p.
   Includes index.
   1. Numerical analysis.   2. Mathematical
optimization.   I. Title.
QA297.D37   519.4   78-6980
ISBN 0-444-00263-4

Manufactured in the United States

To Pat
for her encouragement and understanding

Contents

Preface

The availability of computers has revolutionized every field which depends on numerical calculations. The scientist or engineer can be greatly aided in his work if he knows how to enlist the aid of his new ally. The purpose of this book is to help the undergraduate student learn how to apply a computer to many different types of practical problems. The book is written in a manner that should instill enthusiasm in the reader and help convince him that the computer is one of the greatest labor saving devices ever to come along.

This book's philosophy differs from most others written on numerical methods or numerical analysis. In a typical numerical-analysis text, much time is spent on error analysis. However, in practical applications, usually little time is devoted to rigorous error analysis.

Instead of relying solely on error analysis to estimate the accuracy of answers, other methods are emphasized in this text. Observing how a process converges can give insight into its accuracy. Also, solving a problem two different ways can verify a solution. Although error analysis is not very practical as a tool for estimating accuracy, it does have other uses. It can be used to compare different numerical methods and demonstrate that, on the average, one is superior to another. Or a knowledge of error properties can be used to improve a numerical method.

Avoiding a lengthy investigation of error analysis allows time for the reader to become acquainted with optimization techniques. Numerical methods and optimization techniques are intimately related, but unfortunately they are not generally taught in the same course. However, since both numerical methods and optimization techniques are usually iterative procedures, they have a common philosophy and application. In fact, as demonstrated in this book, an optimization technique can be viewed as a collection of numerical methods which have been linked together in a specific way. Thus, once a student has become familiar with numerical methods the extension to optimization techniques is very natural.

This text does not attempt to be a complete catalog of numerical methods or optimization techniques—volumes would be needed for this. For a specific problem, the specialist can probably consult the literature and obtain a more efficient solution than presented in this book. If he uses his sophisticated program very often, his time is well spent. In fact, this text is not written for the specialist, but for the reader or student who will probably not have the luxury of spending days on research to save milliseconds of computer time.

Instead of overwhelming the reader with numerous methods for solving the same problem, attention is focused on one or two. If a person is familiar and confident with a specific method, he is much more likely to apply it than if he only has a nodding acquaintance. Just because a particular method has been included in this text, it need not be the best one available. The choices were influenced by the desire to have an *introductory* text which *links* numerical methods to optimization techniques. At the end of most chapters is a section entitled "Suggested Reading in Related Topics", which enables the enthusiastic reader to do additional research on topics not essential to an introductory course.

The typical student using this book for a formal course will be a junior or senior—a sophomore could understand the material, but might not appreciate the range of applications. A knowledge of differentiation and integration is essential for the course; the ability to solve differential equations would be helpful, but is not essential.

Because the application of many of the algorithms in this text requires the use of a computer, numerous programs are included. These programs are written in a version of time-sharing FORTRAN that is similar to FORTRAN IV. The programs were all run on a Control Data Cyber 70 computer system.

The programs that have been included in the text are written with the emphasis on clarity. Their purpose is to implement the methods described in the text and provide a means for the student to apply the algorithms. The programs have not been included in the hope that they will become widely used in various computation centers; they are ill suited for that purpose. The literature contains ample selections of programs that have been written with the emphasis on speed and accuracy. However, even though the programs in this book are relatively simple, they should be adequate for the problems encountered by students who are at this introductory level; and they provide a good basis for understanding the more sophisticated programs that abound in the literature.

The problems at the end of the chapters serve various purposes. Some help to extend the material presented in the text or to check the reader's knowledge of subtle points. Others illustrate the application of the programs or equations. Finally, many of the problems help the student become familiar with the computer so that it will become an ally in future endeavors.

The idea of combining numerical methods and optimization techniques into one text occurred to the author while teaching at Tennessee State University. My appreciation goes to those students who helped shape the early direction of the book. Also, I have the good fortune to have had many different experts review the text and offer numerous suggestions for its improvement. To two of my colleagues go special thanks: R. P. Snicer for his thorough review and detailed suggestions, and P. H. McDonald for her helpful hints on structured programming.

Chapter One

Introduction

1.1 "HISTORICAL" BACKGROUND

Scientists have been using numerical methods to help solve mathematical problems for many, many centuries. As an illustration of a numerical method, consider one that *could* have been used by Pythagoras to find the hypotenuse of a right triangle. Suppose his triangle had two sides of unit length, so that the hypotenuse was $\sqrt{2}$. The square root of two is an irrational number, so it cannot be calculated exactly, but it can be approximated by using the binomial expansion

$$(1+1)^{\frac{1}{2}} \approx 1 + \frac{1}{2} + \frac{\left(\frac{1}{2}\right)\left(-\frac{1}{2}\right)}{2!} + \frac{\left(\frac{1}{2}\right)\left(-\frac{1}{2}\right)\left(-\frac{3}{2}\right)}{3!} + \frac{\left(\frac{1}{2}\right)\left(-\frac{1}{2}\right)\left(-\frac{3}{2}\right)\left(-\frac{5}{2}\right)}{4!}.$$

$$(1.1)$$

If Pythagoras had used the first five terms in (1.1), he would have approximated the square root of two as 1.40. This is just one of many possible numerical methods that could have been used. A better (though equally simple) method is given in Problem 3.10 (Chapter 3).

The original numerical methods were first used when there were no computer systems, minicomputers, desk-top calculators, pocket calculators, mechanical calculators, or even any slide rules. It is, thus, not surprising that our present conception of a good numerical method may differ greatly from our ancestors'.

Originally, much effort was spent on systematically tabulating calculations so that a relatively untrained person could perform the drudgery required by a numerical method. In fact, because computers are a recent invention, that was true well into this century. Then, with the advent of computers, emphasis slowly shifted to writing the numerical method in such a way that a computer could do the tedious calculations.

1.2 NUMERICAL METHODS

Numerical methods are used to *estimate* answers to mathematical problems. Depending on the particular numerical method and the particular problem, the numerical answer may be very accurate or very inaccurate. That is, assuming an analytical answer could be determined, the numerical and analytical answer might be the same for many digits, or the numerical answer might have only a few meaningful significant figures.

One usually applies a numerical method because an analytical result either cannot be obtained or would require too much work. Since in the usual case direct comparison cannot be used to estimate the accuracy of the numerical result, an error analysis is often required. Texts that devote a considerable amount of space to error analysis are usually referred to as numerical-analysis texts, instead of numerical-methods texts.

The series expansion of a function is one numerical method with which the reader is probably already familiar. This can be used to estimate the value of a function by adding together a sufficient number of terms. Special attention will not be devoted to series solutions in this text, but they will often be part of an *iterative* solution. An iterative numerical method follows a definite set of rules—over and over and over again, until the desired accuracy is obtained. With high-speed computers, many iterations can be performed in a very short time. This has helped make many numerical methods practical which used to require too many manual computations.

EXAMPLE 1.1

Transient responses (i.e., responses that eventually disappear) occur in many engineering problems. For this example we will consider the voltage

$$v(t) = 7e^{-3t} + 3e^{-2t}, \tag{1.2}$$

where t represents time. This voltage is plotted (for positive times) in Fig. 1.1, which indicates that the voltage initially is equal to 10 and asymptotically decays to zero.

In theory it takes forever for a transient response to become zero. However, in practice the transient response soon becomes small enough so that it is negligible. In this example we will assume that a designer wants to determine when the voltage has decayed to one percent of its initial value. That is, we want to solve the following equation for t:

$$0.1 = 7e^{-3t} + 3e^{-2t}. \tag{1.3}$$

This is a nonlinear equation for which we cannot obtain an exact solution, but by "guessing" at the answer in a systematic manner we can obtain as accurate an answer as we desire. Chapter 3 will describe more sophisticated methods of solving nonlinear equations, but the following *interval-halving* method will be a good introductory example of an iterative method.

As a first guess, assume the solution is $t = 1.5$. The accuracy of this guess

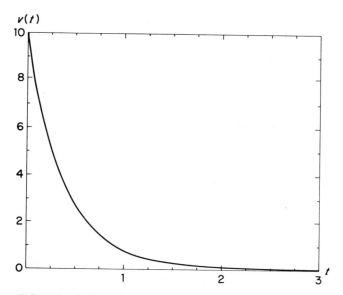

FIGURE 1.1. Transient response of an electrical network.

can be determined by evaluating the error, which is defined as

$$\text{error} = (7e^{-3t} + 3e^{-2t}) - 0.1. \tag{1.4}$$

Table 1.1 indicates that this error is approximately 0.1271. Since the error is positive, we know the solution must occur at a larger time, so the guess $t = 2.5$ is made. Table 1.1 indicates that this error is approximately -0.0759. Since the first error was positive and the second error was negative, the solution must be between $t = 1.5$ and $t = 2.5$. Therefore let the next guess be half way between $t = 1.5$ and $t = 2.5$.

The solution to (1.3) can be found approximately by iteratively halving the interval of uncertainty as illustrated in Table 1.1. Of course, halving the interval will never reduce the uncertainty to zero; but it may not take too many iterations before the error is negligible. For example, the fifth guess $t = 1.875$ yielded an error of -0.0042. (To four significant figures the solution is $t = 1.856$.)

Table 1.1
Interval-halving example

t	error
1.5	0.12712
2.5	-0.07591
2.0	-0.02770
1.75	0.02732
1.875	-0.00420

1.3 OPTIMIZATION TECHNIQUES

An iterative numerical method is often used to successively adjust a parameter until a desired result is obtained. For example, in Chapter 3, various methods are described for adjusting the parameter x so that the function $f(x)$ is made zero—that is, x is adjusted so that the roots of $f(x)$ are found.

Optimization techniques also adjust parameters so as to attain a desired result. In fact, it is often a matter of personal preference whether a process is termed a numerical method or an optimization technique. Usually, if the process adjusts only one parameter, it is termed a numerical method; if it adjusts more than one, it is termed an optimization technique.

The optimization techniques to be described in this book can simultaneously adjust many parameters to meet some specification optimally. Like the numerical methods, the optimization techniques will be iterative procedures. The optimum set of parameters will not be found by applying a set of computation rules just once; often many iterations will be required.

Because numerical methods and optimization techniques have a common philosophy and application, both will be treated in this book. In fact, an optimization technique can be viewed as a collection of numerical methods which have been linked together in a specific way. Thus, once a student has become familiar with numerical methods, the extension to optimization techniques is very natural.

1.4 COMPUTER PHILOSOPHY USED IN THE TEXT

Many programs and numerous examples have been included in the text. This is because it is difficult, if not impossible, to fully appreciate numerical methods without using them. For those who do not have access to a computer, the examination of examples will help by providing sample output. However, actually using the programs will be even more beneficial.

The actual choice of a computer language was difficult, since no choice will make everyone happy. The BASIC language was considered first, because it is an elementary language which is easily learned. However, almost every person who eventually does "serious computing" will discard BASIC for a more powerful language. Since more advanced languages can be learned without much added difficulty, it was decided not to use BASIC.

FORTRAN was chosen as the computer language for this text because it is the most universally used language. However, this does not imply it is the most readable language. In fact, unless care is taken, the flow of computation can be confused by many branching and GO TO statements. This has been avoided as much as possible in this text by simulating statements such as WHILE and UNTIL which are found in other languages. Also, the readability of the programs has been enhanced by including numerous comment statements, many of which cite equations used in the text.

Until recently, the majority of computer programs were run in the *batch mode*. This means that a batch of instructions was given to the computer, and then it proceeded without interruption until the job was terminated. Because computers only do exactly what they are told, this implies that the instructions they are given must be perfect or else the computations will not be correct. Because we humans are prone to make mistakes, it often requires many attempts at writing a program before it works correctly. Thus, many programmers have pondered the possibility that we have merely traded the drudgery of numerical calculations for the frustrations of program "debugging".

Instead of operating in the batch mode, it is now often feasible to run programs in the *interactive mode*. This implies that the user can directly interact with the computer by some means such as a teletypewriter or a keyboard. The degree of interaction varies from computer to computer. Some interactive computers are still essentially used in the batch mode: the job may be originated at a teletypewriter and the results printed out there, but there is no other communication between the user and the computer. At the other extreme, some interactive computers inform the operator that he has used the wrong syntax in a command even before he attempts to run the program.

When a computer is used in the interactive mode, it allows for much more flexibility from the user's viewpoint. The computer can request data, print out some intermediate results, and then request additional data. The user can examine the previous output and supply new data based on his observations. Of course, all this could be done in the batch mode, but not as conveniently.[1]

The purpose of this book is to help the reader become aware of what can be accomplished with numerical methods and optimization techniques. So that attention can be focused on the main concept in an algorithm, the programs have been kept as simple as possible. Writing the programs for an interactive computer helped to keep the programs simple. For example, less emphasis need be placed on providing "stop criteria" in a program. It should be reemphasized that it is not the purpose of this book to develop general-purpose, efficient programs that will be used at computing centers. Computer facilities come supplied with "canned" programs for standard problems such as solving sets of linear equations. In writing such

---

[1]Batch programs may still be desirable in many instances—for example, if a computer program requires a large amount of time for execution.

programs, much effort is spent in making the program both efficient and foolproof. Thus, in many situations the reader may find it wise not to "reinvent the wheel", but instead use what is already available. This book should help one obtain an understanding of the theory that is used in these programs.

If the reader understands the theory behind the programs in this text, he should then be in a position to assess realistically whether or not a particular program is sophisticated enough for his needs. Thinking about a problem before rushing off to solve it can save time (much more than a few milliseconds) in the long run. It should be kept in mind that in many applications computational efficiency does become important (e.g., in optimization problems that require many iterations).

In closing this section, a few of the author's programming habits will be mentioned. In order to simplify the programs, free-format input and output statements are frequently used. In a free-format **PRINT** statement, / (slash) causes a line to be skipped. Sometimes, more than one statement is included on one line, the symbol $ being used to separate statements.

Although it is not required by time-sharing FORTRAN, in this text statement numbers are always made the same as the corresponding line numbers. For example,[2]

$$98 \qquad 98 \qquad X = 5 + Y.$$
$$\uparrow \qquad \uparrow$$
$$\text{line} \quad \text{statement}$$
$$\text{number} \quad \text{number}$$

1.5 ERROR ANALYSIS

Numerical techniques are applied because, for a particular problem, an analytical answer is impractical or impossible to find. In any numerical method, there will be sources of error, so attempts will be made to estimate the amount by which the answer is in error. It must be emphasized that the error can only be *estimated*—if we could find the exact error, then we would know the exact answer.

Three sources of error will be discussed in this section: input error, roundoff error, and truncation error. Interspersed throughout the discussion will be hints on the use of the computer as an aid in error analysis.

The input data supplied to the computer may contain errors because the data are the result of imperfect measurements. For example, suppose we want to determine the area of a rectangle of which side *a* is measured as

---

[2]Note that in batch FORTRAN, there would be no line numbers, only statement numbers.

10.232 cm and side b as 8.417 cm. If we know that the measuring device has 0.1% accuracy, we might feel confident in stating $a = 10.23$ cm and $b = 8.42$ cm, but certainly we would not want to wager money on $a = 10.232$ cm versus $a = 10.231$ cm. In this case, we would say that $a = 10.232$ cm is accurate to four *significant figures*.

Errors in input data will cause errors in output (i.e., calculated answers); however, the amount of output error will vary from problem to problem. *Sensitivity analysis* can be used to determine how sensitive a result is to variations in a particular input parameter. For example, assume the output y is a function of three input parameters x_1, x_2, x_3. A 0.1% change in x_1 (x_2, x_3 assumed constant) is found to cause a 2% change in y, while a 0.1% change in either x_2 or x_3 causes only a 0.5% change in y. We would then conclude that the calculations are most *sensitive* to errors in x_1 and take extra precautions to insure an accurate value for x_1.

If the output is very sensitive to variations in the input, then the problem is said to be ill conditioned. An example is given in Problem 1.8.

The computer can, of course, serve as an aid in sensitivity analysis. One can run the same problem many different times, each time making a small change in one parameter and observing the effect on the output. In fact, sophisticated programs exist which simultaneously vary all input parameters by amounts determined by statistical properties of the data. These programs allow one to determine the probability that an answer is within a certain range of values.

The roundoff errors we will be concerned with result from the fact that a computer must represent numbers by using only a finite number of digits. For example, the fraction $\frac{1}{3}$ may be represented by a computer as 0.33333333. Since in practical problems we will not normally need more than eight significant figures in an answer, this might not appear to be a serious limitation. However, roundoff errors have a nasty tendency to accumulate. In a numerical solution to a problem, there may be thousands of calculations before the result is obtained. Many of these calculations may depend on previous calculations, so it is not difficult to conceive of roundoff errors growing until the final answer is meaningless.

Some computers let the user specify double-precision arithmetic. That is, throughout the program (or just in specific parts), twice as many digits as normal will be used by the computer. Using double-precision arithmetic reduces computation speed and also uses additional memory locations, so it should be avoided unless necessary. Its necessity can be determined by doing two computer runs: one with single precision and one with double precision in the critical parts of the program. Comparing the two results will indicate whether or not roundoff errors significantly influenced the result.

If roundoff errors are troublesome, it is often possible to modify part of the program and reduce their effect. An example of this is given in Problem 1.9. This problem indicates that roundoff errors are particularly troublesome if two nearly equal numbers are subtracted. For example, consider the difference $\frac{1}{3} - 0.333$. If $\frac{1}{3}$ is rounded to four significant figures (i.e., to 0.3333), then the difference will be calculated as 0.0003, while the actual difference is $0.000333\ldots$; thus the answer is only accurate to one significant figure.

As previously mentioned, roundoff errors can accumulate and eventually cause a final answer to be meaningless. Whether or not an error decays, stays approximately constant, or grows as the computations proceed will depend on the numerical method that is used. In fact, in some algorithms the roundoff errors exhibit exponential growth. An example of such an algorithm is given in Section 7.4.

Truncation error will be explained with reference to the Taylor series expansion of $f(x)$ about a reference point x_0,

$$f(x_0+h)=f(x_0)+f^{(1)}(x_0)h+\frac{f^{(2)}(x_0)h^2}{2!}+\frac{f^{(3)}(x_0)h^3}{3!}+\cdots, \quad (1.5)$$

where, for example, $f^{(3)}(x_0)$ represents the third derivative of $f(x)$ evaluated at x_0. This equation implies that for an increment size h, $f(x_0+h)$ can be determined exactly from the behavior at $f(x_0)$ (assuming all the derivatives exist).

It is impossible to sum an infinite number of terms with a computer, so an expression such as (1.5) must be *truncated*; that is, only a certain number of the terms can be used, and the rest must be discarded, resulting in a *truncation error*. For example, if the Taylor series is truncated after the second derivative, then (1.5) can be written as

$$f(x_0+h)=f(x_0)+f^{(1)}(x_0)h+\frac{f^{(2)}(x_0)h^2}{2}+\text{error}(h). \quad (1.6)$$

The error term can be expressed by the Taylor-series remainder theorem, but that will not be necessary for our purposes. We will be able to obtain sufficient information about the error just by noting how the error behaves for small increments h. For example, comparing (1.5) and (1.6) yields that, for h small enough, the error is proportional to h^3. That is,

$$\text{error}(h)\approx\alpha h^3.$$

EXAMPLE 1.2

Expanding $f(x)=e^x$ in a Taylor series about $x_0=1$ yields

$$f(1+h)=e^{1+h}=e+eh+\frac{eh^2}{2}+\frac{eh^3}{3!}+\frac{eh^4}{4!}+\cdots.$$

If this series is truncated after the third term, then the error is given by

$$\text{error}(h) = e^{1+h} - (e + eh + 0.5eh^2).$$

The error can be made arbitrarily small by making h small enough. For example error$(0.1) = 4.646 \times 10^{-4}$, while error$(0.05) = 5.735 \times 10^{-5}$. Since error$(0.1)/\text{error}(0.05) = 8.1$, we see that when h was reduced by a factor of 2 the error was reduced by approximately a factor of 8 which implies error$(h) \approx \alpha h^3$. Using error$(0.1) = 4.646 \times 10^{-4}$ yields that the constant of proportionality is approximately 0.46.

The previous work implies that if $f(x)$ is expanded in a power series as

$$f(x_0 + h) = a_0 + a_1 h + a_2 h^2 + \cdots + a_m h^m + \text{error}(h),$$

then for h small enough the error is proportional[3] to h^{m+1}. This is also stated as "the error is of the *order* of h^{m+1}" and written as error$(h) = O(h^{m+1})$.

Knowledge about the order of an error will be useful to us when we study numerical integration in Chapter 6. In that chapter we will obtain some formulas for approximating[4] $\int_{x_0}^{x_0+h} f(x)\,dx$.

We will now develop some tools that can be used to establish the order of the error of these (and other) approximations. Assume that a particular formula is *exact* for every second-degree function, but not for every third-degree function. That is, if an arbitrary function $f(x)$ is expanded in a power series as

$$f(x_0 + h) = a_0 + a_1 h + a_2 h^2 + \text{error}(h), \tag{1.7}$$

then the integral equation will be exact for the first three terms and only yield an error for the last term. Thus,

$$\text{Integral error} = \int_{x_0}^{x_0+h} \text{error}(h)\,dx = \int_0^h \text{error}(h)\,dh. \tag{1.8}$$

But for (1.7) error$(h) = \alpha h^3$, so that the integral error in (1.8) is of the order h^4.

Generalizing, if an approximation for $\int_{x_0}^{x_0+h} f(x)\,dx$ is exact for every mth-degree function, but not every $(m+1)$th-degree function, then the error is of the order of h^{m+2}.

---

[3] Assuming that the $m+1$ derivative of $f(x)$ is nonzero.

[4] Actually, some of the formulas will be of the form $\int_{x_0}^{x_0+ih} f(x)\,dx$ where i is an integer. However, the same conclusions apply for this case also.

EXAMPLE 1.3

In Chapter 6 the trapezoidal rule is given as

$$\int_{x_0}^{x_0+h} f(x)\,dx \approx \frac{h}{2}\left[f(x_0)+f(x_0+h)\right].$$

Any first-degree function can be written as $f(x)=a+bx$. For this arbitrary first-degree function it follows that the exact solution is

$$\int_{x_0}^{x_0+h} f(x)\,dx = \int_{x_0}^{x_0+h}(a+bx)\,dx = ah + b\left(x_0 h + 0.5h^2\right).$$

But applying the trapezoidal rule to this function gives

$$\frac{h}{2}\left[f(x_0)+f(x_0+h)\right] = \frac{h}{2}\left\{(a+bx_0)+\left[a+b(x_0+h)\right]\right\},$$

which is the same as the exact answer; thus the trapezoidal rule is exact for any first-degree function.

If we instead consider the second-degree function $f(x)=x^2$, then the exact integral is $x_0^2 h + x_0 h^2 + h^3/3$, while the trapezoidal rule yields $x_0^2 h + x_0 h^2 + h^3/2$, which is different from the exact answer.

Since the trapezoidal rule is exact for every first-degree function, but not for every second-degree function, it follows that the error for the trapezoidal rule is of the order of h^3. This is equivalent to saying that, for h small enough, the error for the trapezoidal rule is proportional to h^3.

The above type of error analysis can be used to compare two different methods for approximating integrals: if one has an error that is proportional to h^2 and another has an error proportional to h^4, the latter one is usually considered to be better. The reason for this is that halving the step size h for the process which has an error proportional to h^4 would reduce the error by a factor of 16, but only by a factor of 4 in the other process.

Notice that if a Taylor series approximation of $f(x_0+h)$ was accurate for every second-degree function, but not every third-degree one, then the error was of the order of h^3; while for the same conditions the integration error was of the order of h^4. An interpretation of this is that integration "smoothes" errors—positive and negative errors tend to cancel and aid the accuracy of the estimation. On the other hand, differentiation tends to magnify errors. By analogy to the previous work it can be shown that:

If sample points of separation h are used to estimate df/dx and the approximation is exact for every mth-degree function, but not every $(m+1)$th-degree function, then the error is proportional to h^m.

In many of the interactive numerical methods, h represents a step size—the solution advances from x_0 to $x_0 + h$ to $x_0 + 2h$, etc., until it finally reaches the desired point. We have just seen that for small step sizes the error may be proportional to h^m, where m is a positive integer. Thus by reducing the step size the error can be made arbitrarily small. The disadvantage of reducing the step size is that more steps must be taken from the initial value x_0 to the final value.

Reducing the step size is one way of determining the truncation error introduced by a numerical method. If the step size is halved and the new answer agrees for the first five digits with the previous answer, then it is fairly certain that the answer is accurate to five significant figures (assuming no input errors). This is one way the computer can be used to estimate the accuracy of solutions. In fact, as demonstrated in Problem 1.11, the computer can even be used to determine, for a paticular numerical method, the value of m in $\text{error}(h) \approx \alpha h^m$.

PROBLEMS

1.1 Round off the following numbers so that they are accurate to four significant figures:

$$n_1 = 12.3456, \qquad n_2 = 0.00126446, \qquad n_3 = 7846.51.$$

Which answers would change if the numbers had been truncated to four significant figures instead of rounded?

1.2 Express $10 \sin 45°$ as a number which is accurate to
(a) Three significant figures.
(b) Three digits after the decimal point.

1.3 If x_2 is used as an approximation to x_1, then the *absolute error* can be defined as $|x_1 - x_2|$.
(a) If $x_1 = 1.784$ is approximated as $x_2 = 1.78$, what is the absolute error?
(b) If the number $x_2 = 12.63$ was obtained by rounding to four significant figures, what is the largest the absolute error could be?
(c) If the number $x_2 = 12.63$ was obtained by truncating to four significant figures, what is the largest the absolute error could be?

1.4 If x_2 is used as an approximation to x_1 then the *relative error* can be defined as $|(x_2 - x_1)/x_1|$.
(a) If $x_1 = 1.98$ is approximated by $x_2 = 2.00$, what is the absolute error and what is the relative error?
(b) Repeat (a) for $x_1 = 198$ and $x_2 = 200$.

(c) Which gives more insight into the number of significant figures: the absolute error or the relative error?

1.5 (a) What is the relative error if $22 + 21$ is used to approximate $21.9 + 20.6$?

(b) What is the relative error if $22 - 21$ is used to approximate $21.9 - 20.6$?

1.6 What is the relative error if 100×200 is used to approximate 101×201?

1.7 Sensitivity coefficients can be used to indicate how much a particular input parameter x_i influences the output y. For example, if y is a function of two parameters, then the sensitivity coefficients are defined as

$$s_{x_1}^y = \frac{\partial y}{\partial x_1} \frac{x_1}{y}, \qquad s_{x_2}^y = \frac{\partial y}{\partial x_2} \frac{x_2}{y}.$$

Calculate the sensitivity coefficients for $y = 60x_1 - 1/(x_2 - 0.98)$. Let $x_1 = 1 = x_2$.

1.8 Division by a difference of large numbers can produce inaccuracies due to roundoff errors in computation or magnify input data errors. For this problem the output y is related to the input x via $y = 10/(x - 99)^2$. If x is increased 1% from its original value of 100, what is the percentage change in y?

1.9 The expression $(x - y)/(x^2 - y^2)$ can be written in a simpler form if the denominator is factored. This problem illustrates that the accuracy of the answer can depend on which form is used.

(a) Evaluate $(x - y)/(x^2 - y^2)$ for $x = 1.001$, $y = 1$. Use five significant figures in all calculations.

(b) Repeat (a) for $1/(x + y)$.

1.10 An approximation for $\ln(1 + h)$ is $\ln(1 + h) \approx h - 0.5h^2$.

(a) What is the error if $h = 0.1$?

(b) What is the error if $h = 0.05$?

(c) Calculate error(0.1)/error(0.05).

(d) For h small, error$(h) \approx \alpha h^3$. Find the value of α.

1.11 An approximation for $\sin x$ is $\sin x \approx x$, where x is in radians. What is the order of the error of this approximation? Check your answer by finding error(0.01)/error(0.005).

1.12 The trapezoidal rule can be written as

$$\int_{x_0}^{x_0 + h} f(x) \, dx \approx \frac{h}{2} \left[f(x_0) + f(x_0 + h) \right].$$

Let $x_0 = 1$ and $f(x) = x^3$.

(a) Find the error that results when the trapezoidal rule is applied with $h=0.1$.

(b) Repeat (a) with $h=0.05$.

(c) Find error(0.1)/error(0.05).

1.13 A simple approximation for the derivative at $x=x_0$ is

$$\frac{df}{dx}\bigg|_{x=x_0} \approx \frac{f(x_0+h)-f(x_0)}{h}.$$

(a) Show that this is exact for any first-degree function.

(b) Show that it is not exact for every second-degree function.

1.14 The approximation in Problem 1.13 has an error which is proportional to h. Verify this for the function $f(x)=e^x$ by comparing the exact derivative at $x=0$ with the approximate value. In particular, calculate error($h=0.1$)/error($h=0.05$).

Chapter Two

Solution of Linear Equations

2.1 INTRODUCTION

Unlike most chapters in this book, this chapter is concerned with finding an analytical solution—the solution of a set of linear equations. The methods described in this chapter will not be iterative; except for roundoff errors, they will yield exact answers. We will study the solution of linear equations because their solution is often required as *part* of a numerical technique. A specific example of this is the least-*p*th optimization technique, which is described in Chapter 10.

One first encounters the solution of simultaneous linear equations in a study of algebra. A popular method of solution introduced there is Cramer's rule, which is expressed in terms of determinants. This method is reviewed briefly in the next section—briefly because it is inefficient from a computational viewpoint. However, while Cramer's rule is not usually programmed, this does not imply that one seldom wants to evaluate determinants. The evaluation of determinants is an important topic, and an efficient program for it is given in Section 2.4.

Sets of linear equations can be conveniently represented by matrices. In fact, one can often use various properties of matrices to help derive results that would otherwise require much more work. The solution to a set of linear equations can be expressed in terms of what is called the *inverse* of a matrix. A program for matrix inversion is given in Section 2.4.

The program for determinant evaluation and the program for finding the inverse of a matrix are actually the same program. In Section 2.4 it is shown that if one solves a set of equations by the Gauss elimination method, then with very little extra work one can also evaluate a determinant or invert a matrix.

It should be emphasized that solving sets of linear equations by Cramer's rule (i.e., the method of determinants) or by inverting a matrix is *not* recommended. A much more efficient and accurate approach is given in Section 2.4, which discusses the Gauss elimination method. Section 2.2 can be omitted if the reader does not wish to learn about Cramer's rule, and Section 2.3 can be skipped by those who do not need a review of matrices.

2.2 CRAMER'S RULE

Before introducing the general notation, a specific example of a set of simultaneous linear equations might be helpful. Consider

$$
\begin{aligned}
x_1 + x_2 + x_3 + x_4 &= 3 \\
2x_1 - x_2 + x_3 - x_4 &= 4 \\
x_2 - x_3 + x_4 &= -2 \\
-x_1 + x_2 + x_3 - 2x_4 &= -2.
\end{aligned} \tag{2.1}
$$

This is a set of four equations in terms of four unknowns: x_1, x_2, x_3, x_4. In general, it is not necessary to have the same number of equations as unknowns,[1] but we will restrict our attention to this case.

A set of n equations can be written in terms of n unknowns as

$$
\begin{aligned}
a_{11}x_1 + a_{12}x_2 + \cdots + a_{1n}x_n &= c_1 \\
a_{21}x_1 + a_{22}x_2 + \cdots + a_{2n}x_n &= c_2 \\
&\vdots \\
a_{n1}x_1 + a_{n2}x_2 + \cdots + a_{nn}x_n &= c_n.
\end{aligned} \tag{2.2}
$$

In these equations it is assumed that the coefficients a_{ij} are known, as are the constants c_i. For example, for the equations in (2.1) we would have $a_{11}=1$, $a_{12}=1$, $a_{13}=1$, $a_{14}=1$, $c_1=3$, etc.

Cramer's rule gives the solution of (2.2) in terms of determinants. Instead of stating the rule for this general equation and risking a confusing notation, we will see how the example in (2.1) can be solved. This example is general enough so we will then know how to solve any set of equations by Cramer's rule.

The first unknown, x_1, can be found from the following equation:

$$
x_1 = \begin{vmatrix} 3 & 1 & 1 & 1 \\ 4 & -1 & 1 & -1 \\ -2 & 1 & -1 & 1 \\ -2 & 1 & 1 & -2 \end{vmatrix} \div \begin{vmatrix} 1 & 1 & 1 & 1 \\ 2 & -1 & 1 & -1 \\ 0 & 1 & -1 & 1 \\ -1 & 1 & 1 & -2 \end{vmatrix}. \tag{2.3}
$$

The denominator in the above equation is the determinant of the coefficients a_{ij}. The numerator is that same determinant except that the first column has been replaced by the constants c_i.

---

[1] If there are more equations than unknowns, usually no solution exists; if there are fewer equations than unknowns, usually an infinite family of solutions exists.

In the process of finding the parameter x_1, the first column in a determinant was replaced by the column of constants. To find any other parameter we would replace the corresponding column by the column of constants. Thus Cramer's rule can be applied to find all the unknown parameters.

There is only one circumstance for which we cannot use Cramer's rule: if the determinant of the coefficients a_{ij} is zero, (2.3) is meaningless. But if the determinant of the coefficients is nonzero, then there is a unique solution—the one given by Cramer's rule. Of course, one might choose to obtain it by another method; but the result must be the same.

2.3 THE MATRIX SOLUTION

Sets of linear equations can be conveniently represented by matrices. Because of this one encounters matrices in many different mathematical applications. There are many properties of matrices which can be used to facilitate the solution of problems; this brief discussion will present just a few of the elementary ones.

A matrix is an ordered array of numbers such as

$$\mathbf{A} = \begin{bmatrix} 2 & 4 & 3 \\ 1 & 0 & 4 \end{bmatrix}. \tag{2.4}$$

This matrix $\mathbf{A}$ has two rows and three columns. A general 2×3 matrix can be written as

$$\mathbf{A} = \begin{bmatrix} a_{11} & a_{12} & a_{13} \\ a_{21} & a_{22} & a_{23} \end{bmatrix}. \tag{2.5}$$

A typical element of this matrix is written as a_{ij}, where i denotes the row and j denotes the column. Two matrices $\mathbf{A}$, $\mathbf{B}$ are said to be equal if and only if all corresponding elements are equal; that is, $a_{ij} = b_{ij}$ for every i and j.

A very special matrix is the *identity* matrix $\mathbf{I}$. This is a square matrix $(n \times n)$ which has all elements equal to zero except those on the diagonal, which are equal to unity. For example, for $n = 3$

$$\mathbf{I} = \begin{bmatrix} 1 & 0 & 0 \\ 0 & 1 & 0 \\ 0 & 0 & 1 \end{bmatrix}. \tag{2.6}$$

The *transpose* of a matrix is formed by interchanging the rows and columns; for example, the transpose of the matrix in (2.4) is

$$\mathbf{A}' = \begin{bmatrix} 2 & 1 \\ 4 & 0 \\ 3 & 4 \end{bmatrix}. \tag{2.7}$$

Because rows and columns are interchanged to form the transpose, it follows that $a_{ij}^t = a_{ji}$. An illustration of this for the matrix in (2.7) is $a_{12}^t = 1 = a_{21}$. By definition, a *symmetric* matrix is one for which the matrix and its transpose are identical; that is, $a_{ij} = a_{ji}$ for every i and j. Only square matrices can be symmetric (but not all square matrices are symmetric).

A matrix that has only one column is called a *vector*[2] and is usually denoted by a lower case letter such as **x**. The transpose notation can be used to provide a convenient representation for a vector. For example, a vector **x** with three components x_1, x_2, and x_3 can be represented as

$$\mathbf{x} = [\, x_1 \; x_2 \; x_3 \,]^t. \tag{2.8}$$

Often, instead of using matrix notation, a vector will be defined just by listing its components. For example, the vector in (2.8) could also be expressed as

$$\mathbf{x} = (x_1, x_2, x_3).$$

If two matrices are of the same order (e.g., both are 2×3), their sum is defined as

$$\mathbf{A} + \mathbf{B} = \mathbf{C}, \qquad \text{where} \quad a_{ij} + b_{ij} = c_{ij}. \tag{2.9}$$

That is, the corresponding elements are added together to produce the sum. For example,

$$\begin{bmatrix} 2 & 0 & 3 \\ 1 & -2 & 4 \end{bmatrix} + \begin{bmatrix} 1 & -1 & -2 \\ 4 & 6 & 0 \end{bmatrix} = \begin{bmatrix} 3 & -1 & 1 \\ 5 & 4 & 4 \end{bmatrix}.$$

A matrix can be multiplied by a scalar or another matrix. If a matrix is multiplied by a scalar, then every element of the matrix is multiplied by that scalar; e.g.,

$$2 \begin{bmatrix} 1 & 2 \\ 3 & 4 \end{bmatrix} = \begin{bmatrix} 2 & 4 \\ 6 & 8 \end{bmatrix}.$$

The product of an $m \times n$ matrix **A** and an $n \times r$ matrix **B** yields an $m \times r$ **C** whose elements are defined by

$$\mathbf{AB} = \mathbf{C}, \qquad \text{where} \quad c_{ij} = \sum_{k=1}^{n} a_{ik} b_{kj}. \tag{2.10}$$

That is, c_{ij} is formed by multiplying corresponding terms of the ith row of **A** and the jth column of **B**, then adding together these products. For

---

[2]Some texts also refer to a matrix of only one row as a (row) vector.

example,

$$\begin{bmatrix} 2 & 0 & 3 \\ 1 & -2 & 4 \end{bmatrix} \begin{bmatrix} 2 & 1 \\ 4 & 0 \\ 3 & 4 \end{bmatrix} = \begin{bmatrix} 4+0+9 & 2+0+12 \\ 2-8+12 & 1+0+16 \end{bmatrix} = \begin{bmatrix} 13 & 14 \\ 6 & 17 \end{bmatrix}.$$

This definition of matrix multiplication allows us to obtain a convenient representation of the set of n linear equations which in Section 2.2 was written as

$$a_{11}x_1 + a_{12}x_2 + \cdots + a_{1n}x_n = c_1$$
$$a_{21}x_1 + a_{22}x_2 + \cdots + a_{2n}x_n = c_2$$

$$\vdots \qquad\qquad (2.11)$$

$$a_{n1}x_1 + a_{n2}x_2 + \cdots + a_{nn}x_n = c_n.$$

If for this set of equations we define the matrices

$$\mathbf{A} = \begin{bmatrix} a_{11} & a_{12} & \cdots & a_{1n} \\ a_{21} & a_{22} & \cdots & a_{2n} \\ \vdots & \vdots & & \vdots \\ a_{n1} & a_{n2} & \cdots & a_{nn} \end{bmatrix}, \qquad \mathbf{x} = \begin{bmatrix} x_1 \\ x_2 \\ \vdots \\ x_n \end{bmatrix}, \qquad \mathbf{c} = \begin{bmatrix} c_1 \\ c_2 \\ \vdots \\ c_n \end{bmatrix}, \qquad (2.12)$$

then (2.11) can be written as $\mathbf{Ax} = \mathbf{c}$. The solution to this matrix equation is usually written as $\mathbf{x} = \mathbf{A}^{-1}\mathbf{c}$, where $\mathbf{A}^{-1}$ is called the *inverse* of the matrix $\mathbf{A}$. The inverse is a matrix with the following properties:

$$\mathbf{A}^{-1}\mathbf{A} = \mathbf{A}\mathbf{A}^{-1} = \mathbf{I}, \qquad (2.13)$$

where $\mathbf{I}$ is the identity matrix. The inverse of a square matrix can be evaluated in terms of "cofactors," but a knowledge of that process is not essential to the methods in this text.

In the next section we will learn how to find the inverse of a matrix by performing *elementary row operations*. This method is more efficient than the method of cofactors, and thus it is this method which will be programmed for use in the following chapters.

2.4 GAUSS ELIMINATION

The Gauss elimination technique will be introduced first for the specific example

$$2x_1 + x_2 - x_3 = 7$$
$$-3x_1 + 2x_2 - x_3 = -6 \qquad (2.14)$$
$$4x_1 + x_2 - 4x_3 = 10.$$

Associated with this set of equations is the coefficient matrix

$$A = \begin{bmatrix} 2 & 1 & -1 \\ -3 & 2 & -1 \\ 4 & 1 & -4 \end{bmatrix}. \tag{2.15}$$

The Gauss elimination method can simultaneously solve the set of equations in (2.14), find the determinant of the matrix of coefficients, and find the inverse of A.

To simultaneously do all of the above three tasks, we must augment (2.14) and form

$$2x_1 + x_2 - x_3 + x_4 + 0x_5 + 0x_6 = 7 + x_4$$
$$-3x_1 + 2x_2 - x_3 + 0x_4 + x_5 + 0x_6 = - + x_5 \tag{2.16}$$
$$4x_1 + x_2 - 4x_6 + 0x_4 + 0x_5 + x_6 = 10 + x_6.$$

This set of equations can be written concisely with matrices as

$$A x_a + I x_b = c + x_b,$$

where x_a is a vector having components x_1, x_2, x_3 and x_b is a vector having components x_4, x_5, x_6.

The solution to (2.16) will be obtained by using two processes, which are termed *forward elimination* and *back substitution*. As a first step in the forward elimination process we will divide the first equation by 2 so that the coefficient of x_1 becomes unity:

$$x_1 + 0.5x_2 - 0.5x_3 + 0.5x_4 + 0x_5 + 0x_6 = 3.5 + 0.5x_4.$$

This equation can be used to eliminate x_1 from the following equations. For example, multiplying by 3 and adding to the second equation eliminates x_1 there. Similarly, multiplying by 4 and subtracting from the third row will eliminate x_1 there. This result can be expressed as[3]

$$\begin{bmatrix} 1 & 0.5 & -0.5 \\ 0 & 3.5 & -2.5 \\ 0 & -1 & -2 \end{bmatrix} \begin{bmatrix} x_1 \\ x_2 \\ x_3 \end{bmatrix} + \begin{bmatrix} 0.5 & 0 & 0 \\ 1.5 & 1 & 0 \\ -2 & 0 & 1 \end{bmatrix} x_b = \begin{bmatrix} 3.5 \\ 4.5 \\ -4 \end{bmatrix} + B x_b. \tag{2.17}$$

This equation was obtained by making the coefficient of x_1 in the first equation be unity and then using this equation to eliminate x_1 from the remaining equations. The next step in this process is to make the coefficient of x_2 in (2.17) be unity and then use this equation to eliminate

---

[3]The matrix B in this equation is equal to the coefficient matrix of x_b on the left side of the equation.

x_2 in the next equation to yield

$$\begin{bmatrix} 1 & 0.5 & -0.5 \\ 0 & 1 & -\frac{5}{7} \\ 0 & 0 & -\frac{19}{7} \end{bmatrix} \begin{bmatrix} x_1 \\ x_2 \\ x_3 \end{bmatrix} + \begin{bmatrix} 0.5 & 0 & 0 \\ \frac{3}{7} & \frac{2}{7} & 0 \\ -\frac{11}{7} & \frac{2}{7} & 1 \end{bmatrix} \mathbf{x}_b = \begin{bmatrix} 3.5 \\ \frac{9}{7} \\ -\frac{19}{7} \end{bmatrix} + \mathbf{B}_1 \mathbf{x}_b. \qquad (2.18)$$

If the last row is divided by $-\frac{19}{7}$, the above matrix relation becomes

$$\begin{bmatrix} 1 & 0.5 & -0.5 \\ 0 & 1 & -\frac{5}{7} \\ 0 & 0 & 1 \end{bmatrix} \begin{bmatrix} x_1 \\ x_2 \\ x_3 \end{bmatrix} + \begin{bmatrix} 0.5 & 0 & 0 \\ \frac{3}{7} & \frac{2}{7} & 0 \\ \frac{11}{19} & -\frac{2}{19} & -\frac{7}{19} \end{bmatrix} \mathbf{x}_b = \begin{bmatrix} 3.5 \\ \frac{9}{7} \\ 1 \end{bmatrix} + \mathbf{B}_2 \mathbf{x}_b.$$

$$(2.19)$$

As a result of the steps thus far we have modified the coefficient matrix of $\mathbf{x}_a$ so that all diagonal terms are unity and all terms below the diagonal are zero. These steps constitute the *forward elimination* part of Gauss's procedure.

Forward elimination produced all zeros below the diagonal; *back substitution* can be used to produce all zeros above the diagonal. For example, from the third row in the matrix equation of (2.19) one can see by inspection that x_3 is equal to unity. This can be substituted back into the two preceeding equations to eliminate x_3.[4] Next x_2 can be found and substituted back into the first equation to yield x_1. A detailed description of back substition for equation (2.19) is given next.

Multiplying the third row by $\frac{5}{7}$ and adding it to the second row produces a zero coefficient of x_2. Similarly, multiplying the third row by 0.5 and adding it to the first row produces a zero coefficient of x_1, which changes (2.19) to

$$\begin{bmatrix} 1 & 0.5 & 0 \\ 0 & 1 & 0 \\ 0 & 0 & 1 \end{bmatrix} \begin{bmatrix} x_1 \\ x_2 \\ x_3 \end{bmatrix} + \begin{bmatrix} \frac{15}{19} & -\frac{1}{19} & -\frac{7}{38} \\ \frac{16}{19} & \frac{4}{19} & -\frac{5}{19} \\ \frac{11}{19} & -\frac{2}{19} & -\frac{7}{19} \end{bmatrix} \mathbf{x}_b = \begin{bmatrix} 4 \\ 2 \\ 1 \end{bmatrix} + \mathbf{B}_3 \mathbf{x}_b. \qquad (2.20)$$

Finally, multiplying the second row by 0.5 and subtracting from the first

---

[4]If one does not wish to find the inverse, x_3 need not be eliminated from the preceeding equations. Rather, its value can be substituted into the previous equation, which can then be solved for x_2. Finally, substituting the values for x_2, x_3 into the first equation would yield x_1. If zeros are produced above the diagonal (as in this text), then the procedure is usually referred to as Gauss-Jordan elimination; this book will simply call it Gauss elimination.

row yields

$$\begin{bmatrix} 1 & 0 & 0 \\ 0 & 1 & 0 \\ 0 & 0 & 1 \end{bmatrix} \mathbf{x}_a + \frac{1}{19} \begin{bmatrix} 7 & -3 & -1 \\ 16 & 4 & -15 \\ 11 & -2 & -7 \end{bmatrix} \mathbf{x}_b = \begin{bmatrix} 3 \\ 2 \\ 1 \end{bmatrix} + \mathbf{B}_4 \mathbf{x}_b. \quad (2.21)$$

The above equation is of the form

$$\mathbf{I}\mathbf{x}_a + \mathbf{B}_4 \mathbf{x}_b = \mathbf{d} + \mathbf{B}_4 \mathbf{x}_b; \quad (2.22)$$

thus it follows that $\mathbf{x}_a = \mathbf{d}$. That is, $x_1 = 3$, $x_2 = 2$, and $x_3 = 1$ is the solution to the set of equations in (2.14).

It can be shown that the matrix $\mathbf{B}_4$ in (2.22) is really the inverse of $\mathbf{A}$. This follows from the fact that we started with the matrix equation

$$\mathbf{A}\mathbf{x}_a = \mathbf{c} \quad (2.23)$$

and then modified the equation by doing *elementary row operations*. The elementary row operations were:

(a) Multiplying (or dividing) a row by a constant.

(b) Adding (or subtracting) one row to another.

It can be shown that[5] elementary row operations are equivalent to premultiplication by a matrix. In this case the matrix that must be used is $\mathbf{B}_4$; that is, the row operations on (2.23) are equivalent to

$$\mathbf{B}_4 \mathbf{A} \mathbf{x}_a = \mathbf{B}_4 \mathbf{c} = \mathbf{d}. \quad (2.24)$$

But we have previously stated that $\mathbf{x}_a$ is equal to $\mathbf{d}$, thus it follows from (2.24) that

$$\mathbf{B}_4 \mathbf{A} = \mathbf{I}. \quad (2.25)$$

This equation implies that $\mathbf{B}_4$ is the inverse of $\mathbf{A}$ as previously stated.

We have seen how the elementary row operations not only solved the original set of equations, but also produced the inverse of the matrix $\mathbf{A}$. We can even find the determinant of $\mathbf{A}$, $|\mathbf{A}|$, if we use the following facts from the theory of determinants:

(a) Multiplying any row of a matrix by a constant multiplies the determinant of that matrix by the same constant.

(b) Adding one row of a determinant to another row does not change the value of the determinant.

---

[5]See Problem 2.12 for a demonstration of the fact that elementary row operations can be accomplished by premultiplying $\mathbf{A}$ by a suitable matrix.

The original matrix was **A**, and it has an unknown determinant $|\mathbf{A}|$. The final coefficient matrix was **I**, and it has a determinant $|\mathbf{I}| = 1$. In producing **I**, various rows of **A** were divided by 2, $\frac{7}{2}$, and $-\frac{19}{7}$; thus

$$|\mathbf{A}| = 2 \times \tfrac{7}{2} \times \left(-\tfrac{19}{7}\right) = -19.$$

The previous example will now be generalized so that a computer program can be developed. For the general case we will assume we have a set of n linear equations which can be written as

$$a_{11}x_1 + a_{12}x_2 + \cdots + a_{1n}x_n = c_1$$

$$a_{21}x_1 \quad a_{22}x_2 + \cdots + a_{2n}x_n = c_2$$

$$\vdots \qquad\qquad\qquad\qquad\qquad (2.26)$$

$$a_{n1}x_1 + a_{n2}x_2 + \cdots + a_{nn}x_n = c_n$$

which is equivalent to

$$\mathbf{A}\mathbf{x} = \mathbf{c}. \qquad\qquad (2.27)$$

In some applications we may want to solve a set of equations which have the form in (2.26). In other applications we may wish to find the inverse of a matrix **A**; or we may simply want to evaluate a determinant $|\mathbf{A}|$. Any (or all) of these tasks can be accomplished by augmenting the **A** matrix in (2.27) to obtain

$$\mathcal{C} = \begin{bmatrix} a_{11} & a_{12} & \cdots & a_{1n} & 1 & 0 & \cdots & 0 & c_1 \\ a_{21} & a_{22} & \cdots & a_{2n} & 0 & 1 & \cdots & 0 & c_2 \\ \vdots & \vdots & & \vdots & \vdots & \vdots & & \vdots & \vdots \\ a_{n1} & a_{n2} & \cdots & a_{nn} & 0 & 0 & \cdots & 1 & c_n \end{bmatrix}. \qquad (2.28)$$

As a first step in the solution of (2.27) we normalize coefficients by dividing row_1 of the augmented matrix $\mathcal{C}$ by a_{11}. If a_{11} is zero this of course presents a problem, but not an insurmountable one. We can simply search for another row (call it row_j) which has $a_{j1} \neq 0$. Row_1 and row_j can be interchanged, and then we can normalize the new row_1.

If two rows are interchanged,[6] the new matrix is no longer $\mathcal{C}$, but the interchange affects neither the solution $(x_1, x_2, \ldots, x_n)$ nor the inverse $\mathbf{A}^{-1}$. The reason the solution $(x_1, x_2, \ldots, x_n)$ is not affected is that interchanging rows does not change the vector **x**; it just affects the coefficient matrix. Because **x** is not affected by an interchange of rows, if elementary row

---

[6]The interchanging of rows of a matrix is another elementary row operation. It changes the sign of the determinant, as demonstrated in Problem 2.11.

operations transform the coefficient matrix of $x_1, x_2, \ldots, x_n$ into the identity matrix, then the rest of the augmented matrix must be the inverse $\mathbf{A}^{-1}$. Finally, it has been stated previously in this section that interchanging rows does not change the value of the determinant, except for its sign.

Assuming a_{11} is unequal to zero, the result of normalizing the first row of the augmented matrix $\mathscr{Q}$ can be written as

$$
\mathscr{Q}' =
\begin{bmatrix}
1 & a'_{12} & \cdots & a'_{1n} & a'_{u,n+1} & 0 & \cdots & 0 & c'_1 \\
a_{21} & a_{22} & \cdots & a_{2n} & 0 & 1 & \cdots & 0 & c_2 \\
\vdots & \vdots & & \vdots & \vdots & \vdots & & \vdots & \vdots \\
a_{n1} & a_{n2} & \cdots & a_{nn} & 0 & 0 & \cdots & 1 & c_n
\end{bmatrix},
\quad (2.29)
$$

where $a'_{1j} = a_{1j}/a_{11}$. In the material that follows, the prime will be dropped; that is, even though each row operation will modify the augmented matrix $\mathscr{Q}$, we will identify the modified matrix by the same name. This implies that (in the computer program we write) only one array will be reserved for the augmented matrix: any modification of the matrix will be stored in the same location. This is a common trick used in computer programming to save storage area in a computer. In the notation commonly used, $A' \rightarrow A$.

Normalizing the first row of the matrix $\mathscr{Q}$ is equivalent to normalizing the first equation in (2.26), which implies the coefficient c_1 must also be normalized; that is,

$$
c'_1 = c_1/a_{11} \rightarrow c_1. \quad (2.30)
$$

This equation indicates that in row_1, the constant c_1 is treated just the same as any coefficient a_{1j}. In general, in row_i the constant c_i will undergo the same elementary row operations as the constants a_{ij}. Use of this fact is made in the computer program by defining $c_i = a_{i,2n+1}$ and then treating it as a regular member of the augmented matrix.

If row_1 is multiplied by a_{21} and subtracted from row_2, then the 2, 1 entry in the new matrix will be zero. Generalizing, if row_1 is multiplied by a_{i1} and subtracted from row_i, then the $i, 1$ entry in the new matrix will be zero. Applying this procedure to all the rows produces

$$
\mathscr{Q} =
\begin{bmatrix}
1 & a_{12} & \cdots & a_{1n} & a_{1,n+1} & 0 & \cdots & 0 & c_1 \\
0 & a_{22} & \cdots & a_{2n} & a_{2,n+1} & 1 & \cdots & 0 & c_2 \\
\vdots & \vdots & & \vdots & \vdots & \vdots & & \vdots & \vdots \\
0 & a_{n2} & \cdots & a_{nn} & a_{n,n+1} & 0 & \cdots & 1 & c_n
\end{bmatrix}.
\quad (2.31)
$$

We can next use row_2 as the pivot. Again assuming a_{22} is unequal to zero, the coefficients of row_2 can be normalized by dividing by a_{22}. Then multiplying row_2 by a_{32} and subtracting from row_3 produces zero in the 3, 2 entry in the new matrix. Similarly, zeros can be produced in the remaining rows.

Generalizing, when row_i is used as the pivot it should be normalized by dividing[7] by a_{ii}. Then multiplying row_i by a_{ji} and subtracting from row_j produces zero in the a_{ji} entry. This can be summarized by

$$\begin{aligned} \text{row}_i / a_{ii} &\to \text{row}_i, \\ \text{row}_j - a_{ji}\,\text{row}_i &\to \text{row}_j, \end{aligned} \qquad (2.32)$$

where

$$\begin{array}{lll} \text{first} & i=1, & j=2,3,\ldots,n, \\ \text{next} & i=2, & j=3,4,\ldots,n, \\ & \vdots & \\ \text{finally} & i=n-1, & j=n. \end{array}$$

The result of the above generalized process is

$$\mathcal{C} = \begin{bmatrix} 1 & a_{12} & a_{13} & a_{14} & \cdots & a_{1n} & a_{1,n+1} & \cdots \\ 0 & 1 & a_{23} & a_{24} & \cdots & a_{2n} & a_{2,n+1} & \cdots \\ \vdots & \vdots & \vdots & \vdots & & \vdots & \vdots & \\ 0 & 0 & 0 & 0 & \cdots & 1 & a_{n,n+1} & \cdots \end{bmatrix}. \qquad (2.33)$$

The steps described thus far complete the *forward elimination* part of Gauss's procedure for solving a linear set of equations. *Back substitution* can be used to produce zeros above the unity diagonal in (2.33). The general back substitution process is

$$\text{row}_j - a_{ji}\,\text{row}_i \to \text{row}_j, \qquad (2.34)$$

where

$$\begin{array}{lll} \text{first} & i=n, & j=1,2,\ldots,n-1, \\ \text{next} & i=n-1, & j=1,2,\ldots,n-2, \\ & \vdots & \\ \text{finally} & i=2, & j=1. \end{array}$$

The back substitution procedure modifies the augmented matrix of

---

[7]If a_{ii} is zero, then the rows should be rearranged to produce a nonzero a_{ii}. If rearrangement cannot produce a nonzero a_{ii}, then $|\mathbf{A}|=0$, so that $\mathbf{A}^{-1}$ does not exist and there is no unique solution to (2.26).

(2.33) so that it becomes

$$
\mathcal{Q} = \begin{bmatrix}
1 & 0 & \cdots & 0 & a_{11}^{-1} & a_{12}^{-1} & \cdots & a_{1n}^{-1} & x_1 \\
0 & 1 & \cdots & 0 & a_{21}^{-1} & a_{22}^{-1} & \cdots & a_{2n}^{-1} & x_2 \\
\vdots & \vdots & & \vdots & \vdots & \vdots & & \vdots & \vdots \\
0 & 0 & \cdots & 1 & a_{n1}^{-1} & a_{n2}^{-1} & \cdots & a_{nn}^{-1} & x_n
\end{bmatrix}. \quad (2.35)
$$

From this result, the components[8] a_{ij}^{-1} of the inverse matrix A^{-1} can be readily obtained, as can the components of the solution vector $x_1 x_2, \ldots, x_n$. The determinant of A can also be easily found by keeping track of the various normalization steps and row interchanges that were used in the forward elimination process.

A program for the Gauss elimination method is given in Fig. 2.1. This is the first program to be given in this text, and before it is discussed the programming philosophy that was mentioned in Section 1.4 will be re-iterated. The programs that have been included in this text are written with the emphasis on clarity and not necessarily practicality. As an example of a practical program that stresses numerical accuracy, one may consult the IBM Scientific Subroutine Package for the Gauss elimination subroutine.

Most of the steps that are shown in Fig. 2.1 are obvious from the previous discussion, but perhaps a few comments should be made about the calculation of the determinant of A, which is identified as DET in the program. Initially, DET is set equal to unity; then it is multiplied by a_{ii} whenever row_i is normalized. As previously explained, the justification for this is that multiplication of a row by a constant multiplies the determinant of the matrix by the same constant. Also, whenever two rows are inter-changed, DET is multiplied by minus one.

As mentioned previously in this section, if the pivot element is zero, then the rows should be interchanged until a nonzero element is found. If the program in Fig. 2.1 cannot find any row which has a nonzero pivot, then the determinant of A is equal to zero, so that DET$=0$ is printed and the program is stopped.

EXAMPLE 2.1

As an example of the application of the program, consider the following set of equations:

$$
\begin{aligned}
x_1 + x_2 + x_3 &= 2 \\
2x_1 - x_2 - x_3 &= 1 \\
x_1 + 2x_2 - x_3 &= -3.
\end{aligned}
$$

---

[8]This notation is meant to indicate the components of the inverse matrix; it does not imply that a_{ij}^{-1} is the reciprocal of a_{ij}.

```
01C     GAUSS ELIMINATION
02      PROGRAM G(INPUT,OUTPUT)
03 03   FORMAT(1P,5E14.5)
06      DIMENSION A(10,21),C(10)
10C
11C     INPUT,N,A,C
12      PRINT,*N*, $READ,N
14      PRINT,/,*A(I,J)*
17      READ,((A(I,J),J=1,N),I=1,N)
18      PRINT,/,*C(I)*
19      READ,(C(I),I=1,N)
22      N1=N+1 $N2=2*N+1 $N3=2*N
30C
31C     DEFINE AUGMENTED MATRIX   (EQ. 2.28)
32      DO 35 I=1,N
34      A(I,N+I)=1.
35 35   A(I,N2)=C(I)
40      DET=1.
42      DO 75 I=1,N
44      IF(A(I,I).NE.0) GO TO 61
45C
46C     INTERCHANGE ROWS I,J
47      DET=-DET
48      J=I
49 49   J=J+1
51      IF(J.GT.N) GO TO 98
52      IF(A(J,I).EQ.0) GO TO 49
53      DO 57 K=1,N2
55      SAVE=A(I,K)
56      A(I,K)=A(J,K)
57 57   A(J,K)=SAVE
59C
60C     CALCULATE DETERMINANT
61 61   DET=DET*A(I,I)
62C
63C     NORMALIZE ROW I   (EQ. 2.32)
64      X=A(I,I)
65      DO 66 K=I,N2
66 66   A(I,K)=A(I,K)/X
```

FIGURE 2.1. A program for the Gauss elimination method.

```
70C      FORWARD ELIMINATION   (EQ. 4.19)
71       I1=I+1
72       DO 75 J=I1,N
74       DO 75 K=I1,N2
75 75 A(J,K)=A(J,K)-A(J,I)*A(I,K)
77C
78C      BACK SUBSTITUTION   (EQ. 4.21)
79       DO 84 L=2,N
80       I=N+2-L  $I1=I-1  $I2=I+1
81       DO 84 J=1,I1
82       DO 84 K=I2,N2
84 84 A(J,K)=A(J,K)-A(J,I)*A(I,K)
86C
87       PRINT,/,*DETERMINANT*
88       PRINT 3,DET
89       PRINT,/,/,*X(I)*
90       PRINT 3,(A(I,N2),I=1,N)
92       PRINT,/,/,*INVERSE*
93       DO 95 I=1,N
95 95 PRINT 3,(A(I,J),J=N1,N3)
96       STOP
98 98 PRINT,*DET=0*
999      END
```

FIGURE 2.1. (Continued.)

This is equivalent to the matrix equation $Ax = c$, where

$$A = \begin{bmatrix} 1 & 1 & 1 \\ 2 & -1 & -1 \\ 1 & 2 & -1 \end{bmatrix}, \qquad x = \begin{bmatrix} x_1 \\ x_2 \\ x_3 \end{bmatrix}, \qquad c = \begin{bmatrix} 2 \\ 1 \\ -3 \end{bmatrix}.$$

If instead just the matrix A were given, then the program in Fig. 2.1 could still be used to determine A^{-1} and $|A|$, because these are independent of the constant vector c. That is, any value for c (e.g. $c_1 = c_2 = c_3 = 0$) could be used for input data, and the program would find the correct values for A^{-1} and $|A|$.

The solution from the computer program is given in Fig. 2.2.

The problems at the end of the chapter help illustrate the application of the Gauss elimination method. Problems 2.14, 2.15, 2.16 have the student apply the process (without using a program) to solve some sets of equations. Problem 2.16 could be solved by inspection without ever using the Gauss elimination method, but it is a good illustration of the necessity of interchanging rows. Problems 2.17, 2.18, 2.19 require the application of the

```
N ? 3

A(I,J)
? 1        1       1
? 2       -1      -1
? 1        2      -1

C(I)
? 2        1      -3

DETERMINANT
    9.00000E+00


X(I)
    1.00000E+00   -1.00000E+00    2.00000E+00


INVERSE
    3.33333E-01    3.33333E-01    3.55271E-15
    1.11111E-01   -2.22222E-01    3.33333E-01
    5.55556E-01   -1.11111E-01   -3.33333E-01
       STOP
```

FIGURE 2.2. An application of the Gauss elimination program.

computer program to solve some stated conditions. Finally, Problem 2.20 investigates what can be done if there are more unknowns than there are equations.

The Gauss elimination program of Fig. 2.1 can be used to solve a set of equations, find the inverse of a matrix, or evaluate a determinant. If we only want to do one of these tasks, then the program can be made more efficient. In particular, if we just want to solve a set of equations, then it is not necessary to form the augmented matrix that is shown in (2.28). Instead, the coefficient matrix can be augmented just by the column vector $(c_1, c_2, \ldots, c_n)$. A Gauss elimination program that is designed for just solving a set of equations is included in Fig. 10.1.

2.5 CROUT REDUCTION

The Gauss elimination procedure is often applied to solve a set of linear equations such as

$$\mathbf{A}\mathbf{x} = \mathbf{c}, \tag{2.36}$$

where

$$
\mathbf{A} = \begin{bmatrix} a_{11} & a_{12} & a_{13} & \cdots & a_{1n} \\ a_{21} & a_{22} & a_{23} & \cdots & a_{2n} \\ a_{31} & a_{32} & a_{33} & \cdots & a_{3n} \\ \vdots & \vdots & \vdots & & \vdots \\ a_{n1} & a_{n2} & a_{n3} & \cdots & a_{nn} \end{bmatrix}, \quad \mathbf{x} = \begin{bmatrix} x_1 \\ x_2 \\ x_3 \\ \vdots \\ x_n \end{bmatrix}, \quad \mathbf{c} = \begin{bmatrix} c_1 \\ c_2 \\ c_3 \\ \vdots \\ c_n \end{bmatrix}. \quad (2.37)
$$

In this method forward elimination is used to produce an upper triangular matrix (a matrix with all zero terms below the diagonal), and back substitution is applied to this triangular matrix to yield the solution.

Many other methods besides Gauss elimination exist for solving sets of linear equations such as (2.36). None are used as frequently as Gauss elimination, but some are encountered quite commonly nonetheless. The rest of this section will discuss one of these methods—Crout reduction—which compares favorably with Gauss elimination (storage requirements, accuracy, and speed of computation are comparable). Crout reduction is the direct[9] method of producing an **LU** decomposition. The **LU** decomposition, to be described in the next paragraph, is widely encountered in many scientific applications. An application to sparse-matrix techniques is given at the end of this section.

The Crout reduction method is quite similar to the Gauss elimination method. However, not only does it use an upper triangular matrix **U**, it also uses a lower triangular matrix **L**. It does this by decomposing the coefficient matrix **A** as

$$
\mathbf{A} = \mathbf{LU}, \quad (2.38)
$$

where

$$
\mathbf{L} = \begin{bmatrix} l_{11} & 0 & 0 & \cdots & 0 \\ l_{21} & l_{22} & 0 & \cdots & 0 \\ l_{31} & l_{32} & l_{33} & \cdots & 0 \\ \vdots & \vdots & \vdots & & \vdots \\ l_{n1} & l_{n2} & l_{n3} & \cdots & l_{nn} \end{bmatrix}, \quad \mathbf{U} = \begin{bmatrix} 1 & u_{12} & u_{13} & \cdots & u_{1n} \\ 0 & 1 & u_{23} & \cdots & u_{2n} \\ 0 & 0 & 1 & \cdots & u_{3n} \\ \vdots & \vdots & \vdots & & \vdots \\ 0 & 0 & 0 & \cdots & 1 \end{bmatrix}.
$$

$$(2.39)$$

In this section we will first learn how to find the matrices **L** and **U**; then we will express the solution $(x_1, x_2, \ldots, x_n)$ in terms of this decomposition.

The lower triangular matrix **L** and the upper triangular matrix **U** can be

---

[9]As mentioned in Tewarson, R. P. (1973), *Sparse Matrices* (New York: Academic), Gauss elimination can be used indirectly to produce an **LU** decomposition.

found by realizing that since $\mathbf{A} = \mathbf{LU}$, a typical term of $\mathbf{A}$ is given by

$$a_{ij} = \sum_{k=1}^{n} l_{ik} u_{kj} \tag{2.40}$$

But from the special form of $\mathbf{U}$ in (2.39) it follows that

$$a_{ij} = \sum_{k=1}^{j} l_{ik} u_{kj} = \sum_{k=1}^{j-1} l_{ik} u_{kj} + l_{ij}. \tag{2.41}$$

This equation can be used to give an expression for a typical term of $\mathbf{L}$:

$$l_{ij} = a_{ij} - \sum_{k=1}^{j-1} l_{ik} u_{kj}, \qquad i = j, j+1, \dots. \tag{2.42}$$

In the derivation of (2.42), attention was focused on the special form of $\mathbf{U}$ in (2.39). If instead attention is focused on the special form of $\mathbf{L}$ in (2.39), it follows that

$$u_{ij} = \frac{a_{ij} - \sum_{k=1}^{i-1} l_{ik} u_{kj}}{l_{ii}}, \qquad j = i+1, i+2, \dots. \tag{2.43}$$

Equations (2.42) and (2.43) are recursive equations: they calculate additional elements of $\mathbf{L}$ or $\mathbf{U}$ based on other elements that have already been found. This implies that the equations must be applied in a specific sequence so that all terms on the right-hand side of the equation are always known. We will presently see that the proper sequence is first a column of $\mathbf{L}$, then a row of $\mathbf{U}$, then a column of $\mathbf{L}$, etc.

From (2.38) and (2.39) it follows that the first column of $\mathbf{L}$ is

$$l_{i1} = a_{i1}, \qquad i = 1, 2, \dots. \tag{2.44}$$

This result also follows from (2.42) if one sets j equal to unity and ignores the summation[10] because it is from $k = 1$ to $k = 0$.

Similarly, from (2.38) and (2.39) [or from (2.43)] it follows that

$$u_{1j} = a_{1j} / l_{11}, \qquad j = 2, 3, \dots. \tag{2.45}$$

It should be noted that u_{11} is not calculated in (2.45); or in general, u_{ii} is not calculated in (2.43). This is because, by definition, u_{ii} is equal to unity and thus need not be calculated.

The first column of $\mathbf{L}$ can be calculated from (2.44); then since l_{11} has been determined, the first row of $\mathbf{U}$ can be calculated from (2.45). Next the second column of L can be found from (2.42), and the second row of $\mathbf{U}$

---

[10]Actually, many computer languages would yield (2.44) as a special case of (2.42) and two separate equations would not be needed.

can be found from (2.43). By alternating between (2.42) and (2.43) all elements of **L** and **U** can be found.

EXAMPLE 2.2

Let the matrix **A** be given by

$$
\mathbf{A} = \begin{bmatrix} 2 & 1 & -1 \\ -3 & 2 & -1 \\ 4 & 1 & -4 \end{bmatrix}. \tag{2.46}
$$

Equation (2.44) yields $l_{11}=2$, $l_{21}=-3$, $l_{31}=4$. Similarly applying (2.45), (2.42), and (2.43) yields $(u_{12}=\frac{1}{2}, u_{13}=-\frac{1}{2})$, $(l_{22}=\frac{7}{2}, l_{32}=-1)$, $(u_{23}=-\frac{5}{7})$, $(l_{33}=-\frac{19}{7})$. From this it follows that the **LU** decomposition of **A** is

$$
\mathbf{A} = \begin{bmatrix} 2 & 0 & 0 \\ -3 & \frac{7}{2} & 0 \\ 4 & -1 & -\frac{19}{7} \end{bmatrix} \begin{bmatrix} 1 & \frac{1}{2} & -\frac{1}{2} \\ 0 & 1 & -\frac{5}{7} \\ 0 & 0 & 1 \end{bmatrix}. \tag{2.47}
$$

The **A** matrix that was decomposed in Example 2.2 is the same one that was studied in the Gauss elimination procedure [see (2.15)]. In the Gauss elimination procedure, forward elimination produced an upper triangular matrix [see (2.19)] which is the same as the **U** matrix found in Example 2.2.

Because the **U** matrix in the Crout reduction method is the same as the upper triangular matrix produced by forward elimination in Gauss elimination, a similar approach can be used to solve for the unknown vector **x**. First, the **A** matrix is augmented by adding a column, equal to the vector **c**. Next, the **LU** decomposition is formed according to the rules given in this section. Finally, the solution vector **x** is obtained by back substitution.

The back-substitution formula that was developed for the Gauss elimination method would also work for the Crout reduction procedure, but it can be simplified because in this case the augmented matrix has only one more column than the unaugmented matrix. A simpler back-substitution formula can be obtained for the Crout reduction procedure by considering the general upper triangular matrix equation

$$
\begin{bmatrix} 1 & u_{12} & u_{13} & \cdots & u_{1n} \\ 0 & 1 & u_{23} & \cdots & u_{2n} \\ \vdots & \vdots & \vdots & & \vdots \\ 0 & 0 & 0 & \cdots & 1 \end{bmatrix} \begin{bmatrix} x_1 \\ x_2 \\ \vdots \\ x_n \end{bmatrix} = \begin{bmatrix} c_1 \\ c_2 \\ \vdots \\ c_n \end{bmatrix}. \tag{2.48}
$$

Back substitution for this can be written as

$$x_n = c_n$$

$$x_i = c_i - \sum_{j=i+1}^{n} u_{ij} x_j, \qquad i = n-1, n-2, \ldots, 1. \qquad (2.49)$$

EXAMPLE 2.3

The coefficient vector in (2.14) was $c = [7 \ -6 \ 10]'$, so that the augmented $\mathbf{A}$ matrix for Example 2.2 is

$$\mathcal{A} = \begin{bmatrix} 2 & 1 & -1 & 7 \\ -3 & 2 & -1 & -6 \\ 4 & 1 & -4 & 10 \end{bmatrix}.$$

The formulas for the $\mathbf{LU}$ decomposition yield

$$\mathcal{A} = \begin{bmatrix} 2 & 0 & 0 \\ -3 & \frac{7}{2} & 0 \\ 4 & -1 & -\frac{19}{7} \end{bmatrix} \begin{bmatrix} 1 & \frac{1}{2} & -\frac{1}{2} & \frac{7}{2} \\ 0 & 1 & -\frac{5}{7} & \frac{9}{7} \\ 0 & 0 & 1 & 1 \end{bmatrix}.$$

Back substitution applied to the augmented $\mathbf{U}$ matrix then yields the last column $[3 \ 2 \ 1]'$; thus $x_1 = 3$, $x_2 = 2$, $x_3 = 1$.

A program for the Crout reduction method is given in Fig. 2.3. This program is not as general as the Gauss elimination one of Fig. 2.1. For example, no check has been included to determine whether or not an interchange of rows is necessary to avoid division by zero. This interchange possibility could have been included, but then the $\mathbf{LU}$ decomposition would be for the interchanged $\mathbf{A}$ matrix and not the original one. If difficulty is experienced in a particular problem, then the order of the initial equations can be interchanged and the program run again.

The Crout reduction program corresponds to the description in the previous part of this section with one major exception: it uses the same memory location for a_{ij} and l_{ij} (if $i > j$) or for a_{ij} and u_{ij} (if $i < j$). This is possible because once l_{ij} (or u_{ij}) is calculated, that value of a_{ij} is no longer needed and may be destroyed. This allows conservation of memory locations and is one of the reasons for the popularity of Crout reduction.

An example of the application of the Crout reduction program is given in Fig. 2.4. This example is the same as Example 2.3; thus the output in Fig. 2.4 can be compared with the previous results.

One important use of the $\mathbf{LU}$ decomposition is in sparse-matrix techniques. A matrix is said to be sparse if it has a low proportion of nonzero

```
01C    CROUT REDUCTION
02     PROGRAM CR(INPUT,OUTPUT)
03 03  FORMAT(1P,5E14.5)
06     DIMENSION A(10,21),C(10)
10C
11C    INPUT,N,A,C
12     PRINT,*N*, $READ,N
14     PRINT,/,*A(I,J)*
17     READ,((A(I,J),J=1,N),I=1,N)
18     PRINT,/,*C(I)*
19     READ,(C(I),I=1,N)
20C
21C    DEFINE MISC. CONSTANTS
22     N1=N+1 $N2=N-1
30C
31C    DEFINE AUGMENTED MATRIX
32     DO 35 I=1,N
35 35  A(I,N1)=C(I)
39C
40C    CALCULATE A(1,J)=U(1,J)   (EQ. 2.45)
42     DO 43 J=2,N1
43 43  A(1,J)=A(1,J)/A(1,1)
47C
48C    CALCULATE A(J,I)=L(J,I)   (EQ. 2.42)
49     DO 65 I=2,N
51     DO 54 J=I,N
52     K2=I-1
53     DO 54 K=1,K2
54 54  A(J,I)=A(J,I)-A(J,K)*A(K,I)
56C
57C    CALCULATE A(I,J)=U(I,J)   (EQ. 2.43)
58     J1=I+1 $K2=I-1
60     DO 65 J=J1,N1
62     DO 63 K=1,K2
63 63  A(I,J)=A(I,J)-A(I,K)*A(K,J)
65 65  A(I,J)=A(I,J)/A(I,I)
68C
69     PRINT,/,*LU MATRIX*
70     DO 72 I=1,N
72 72  PRINT 3,(A(I,J),J=1,N1)
79C
80C    BACK SUBSTITUTION  (EQ. 2.49)
82     DO 87 K=1,N2
84     I=N-K $J1=I+1
85     DO 87 J=J1,N
87 87  A(I,N1)=A(I,N1)-A(I,J)*A(J,N1)
88C
90     PRINT,/,*X(I)*
91     PRINT 3,(A(I,N1),I=1,N)
999    END
```

FIGURE 2.3. A program for the Crout reduction method.

```
N ? 3

A(I,J)
?   2      1     -1
? -3      2     -1
?   4      1     -4

C(I)
?   7     -6     10

LU MATRIX
    2.00000E+00     5.00000E-01    -5.00000E-01     3.50000E+00
   -3.00000E+00     3.50000E+00    -7.14286E-01     1.28571E+00
    4.00000E+00    -1.00000E+00    -2.71429E+00     1.00000E+00

X(I)
    3.00000E+00     2.00000E+00     1.00000E+00
```

FIGURE 2.4. An application of the Crout reduction program.

entries. An example of a sparse matrix is

$$A = \begin{bmatrix} 2 & 5 & 0 & 0 \\ 0 & 4 & 0 & 3 \\ 0 & 0 & 3 & 7 \\ 4 & 1 & 2 & 3 \end{bmatrix}. \tag{2.50}$$

To learn how the **LU** decomposition can be applied in a sparse-matrix problem to save computation time, assume that we want to solve the problem $Ax = c$ for ten different values of the coefficient vector c. One approach would be to first apply the Gauss elimination method to find

$$A^{-1} = \begin{bmatrix} -0.238 & 0.205 & -0.246 & 0.369 \\ 0.295 & -0.082 & 0.098 & -0.148 \\ 0.918 & -1.033 & 0.639 & -0.459 \\ -0.393 & 0.443 & -0.131 & 0.197 \end{bmatrix}. \tag{2.51}$$

Once this inverse matrix has been obtained, then for any c the solution can be found from $X = A^{-1}c$. In this situation the computational time will be mainly determined by the number of multiplications (i.e., addition time will be negligible). Since (2.51) contains sixteen nonzero entries, any one particular solution for x will require sixteen multiplications. Thus for ten different values of the coefficient vector c, the computational time will be proportional to 160.

The important point to notice in the above example is that even if a matrix A is sparse, its inverse A^{-1} will usually not be sparse. For example, (2.50) had six zero terms while (2.51) had none. However, if the **LU** decomposition is used, then advantages due to sparsity may occur.

As an illustration of the application of the **LU** decomposition to a sparse matrix, again consider (2.50), which has the **LU** decomposition

$$\mathbf{A} = \mathbf{LU} = \begin{bmatrix} 2 & 0 & 0 & 0 \\ 0 & 4 & 0 & 0 \\ 0 & 0 & 3 & 0 \\ 4 & -9 & 2 & 5.083 \end{bmatrix} \begin{bmatrix} 1 & 2.5 & 0 & 0 \\ 0 & 1 & 0 & 0.75 \\ 0 & 0 & 1 & 2.333 \\ 0 & 0 & 0 & 1 \end{bmatrix}. \quad (2.52)$$

The inverse of this is

$$\begin{aligned} A^{-1} &= \mathbf{U}^{-1}\mathbf{L}^{-1} \\ &= \begin{bmatrix} 1 & -2.5 & 0 & 1.875 \\ 0 & 1 & 0 & -0.75 \\ 0 & 0 & 1 & -2.333 \\ 0 & 0 & 0 & 1 \end{bmatrix} \begin{bmatrix} 0.5 & 0 & 0 & 0 \\ 0 & 0.25 & 0 & 0 \\ 0 & 0 & 0.333 & 0 \\ -0.393 & 0.443 & -0.131 & 0.197 \end{bmatrix}. \end{aligned}$$

$$(2.53)$$

The equation $\mathbf{Ax} = \mathbf{c}$ can now be solved via $\mathbf{x} = \mathbf{A}^{-1}\mathbf{c} = \mathbf{U}^{-1}\mathbf{L}^{-1}\mathbf{c} = \mathbf{U}^{-1}\mathbf{d}$, where $\mathbf{d} = \mathbf{L}^{-1}\mathbf{c}$. Because of the zero entries of $\mathbf{L}^{-1}$, the solution for $\mathbf{d}$ requires only seven multiplications. Because of the zero entries of $\mathbf{U}^{-1}$, the solution of $\mathbf{x}$ from $\mathbf{U}^{-1}\mathbf{d}$ requires only four further multiplications, for a total of eleven multiplications. Thus for ten different values of the coefficient vector $\mathbf{c}$, 110 multiplications will be required.

In the previous discussion, the **LU** decomposition required fifty less multiplications than the $\mathbf{A}^{-1}$ solution. The savings in larger-dimension problems (e.g., $n = 50$ instead of $n = 4$) may be much more dramatic. For a further introduction to sparse-matrix techniques, the interested reader is referred to Chua and Lin.[11]

2.6 SUGGESTED READING IN RELATED TOPICS

Only some elementary properties of matrices were used in this chapter. Any good technical library contains many books about matrices or their applications. Examples of good introductory texts are Gunston (1970) and Stewart (1973).

There are quite a few modifications of the Gauss elimination method. For example, the Gauss-Jordan method eliminates terms above and below the diagonal at essentially the same time and does not require back substitution. However, the normal Gauss elimination procedure requires a smaller total number of steps and is thus more popular.

As described in this chapter, interchanging rows was done to avoid division by zero. The technique of interchanging rows can be extended to

---

[11]Chua, L. O., and Lin, P. (1975), *Computer-Aided Analysis of Electronic Circuits: Algorithms & Computational Techniques*, (Englewood Cliffs, N.J.: Prentice-Hall).

improve numerical accuracy. When large sets of equations are solved, roundoff errors may cause numerical inaccuracies. Because many of the formulas in this chapter are recursive, the inaccuracies get progressively worse as the solution advances. An approach that has been used to reduce these numerical inaccuracies is to interchange rows so that the magnitude of the pivot coefficient is always as large as possible.

If roundoff errors do tend to cause large numerical inaccuracies in the solution of a set of equations, the equations are said to be ill conditioned. Condition numbers have been introduced to give a measure of the amount of ill-conditioning. One condition number (Conte and de Boor 1972) is $\|\mathbf{A}\| \|\mathbf{A}^{-1}\|$, where $\mathbf{A}$ is the matrix of coefficients and

$$\|\mathbf{A}\| = \max_{\text{all rows}} \sum_{j=1}^{n} |a_{ij}|.$$

The equations are ill conditioned with respect to the precision used in the computations if the condition number is of the order of 2^n, where n is the number of bits used by the computer.

If matrices are of a special form, often a special program will be more efficient than a general-purpose one. For example, special programs can be written to find the inverse of a triangular matrix, or to find the LU decomposition of symmetric matrices. So also for special sets of equations: for example, if the coefficient matrix for the equations is positive definite, the square-root method[12] is widely used.

The methods discussed in this chapter for solving sets of linear equations were *direct methods*—they followed a set of rules which (after a specific number of steps) yielded a theoretically perfect answer.[13] Contrasted with direct methods are the *iterative methods*. For an iterative method, one guesses an initial solution vector $(x_1, x_2, \ldots)$, and then an application of a set of rules adjusts the initial guess so it is closer to the correct solution. This is termed one *cycle of iteration*. With a convergent procedure, by applying a sufficient number of iteration cycles one can get arbitrarily close to the solution.

Iterative procedures can be used to reduce numerical inaccuracies that arise in the solution of a large set of linear equations, but this is not their most important application. There are many cases for which an analytical solution cannot be found, and then iterative solutions are indispensable. The next chapter introduces some iterative techniques.

---

[12]Faddeeva, V. N. (1959), *Computational Methods of Linear Algebra* (New York: Dover).

[13]Only "theoretically perfect," because roundoff errors can be introduced in computer solutions.

PROBLEMS

2.1 Solve the following set of equations by using Cramer's rule:
$$x_1 + x_3 = 5, \qquad x_1 - x_2 = 6, \qquad x_1 + x_2 + x_3 = 1.$$

2.2 Does the following set of equations have a unique solution? If so, what is it?
$$x_1 + x_3 = 0, \qquad x_1 - x_2 = 0, \qquad x_1 + x_2 + x_3 = 0.$$

2.3 A group of equations that does not have a unique solution is $x_1 + x_3 = 0$, $x_1 - x_2 + x_3 = 0$, $x_1 + x_2 + x_3 = 0$.
   (a) Show that the determinant of coefficients is equal to zero.
   (b) If $x_1 = 2$, find x_2 and x_3.
   (c) If $x_1 = 1$, find x_2 and x_3.

2.4 In this problem the matrices **A**, **B** are defined as
$$\mathbf{A} = \begin{bmatrix} 1 & 2 & 3 \\ 0 & -1 & 4 \end{bmatrix}, \qquad \mathbf{B} = \begin{bmatrix} 1 & 0 & 1 \\ 2 & -1 & 4 \end{bmatrix}.$$
If the sum is defined, find (a) $\mathbf{A} + \mathbf{B}$, (b) $\mathbf{A}' + \mathbf{B}$, (c) $\mathbf{A}' + \mathbf{B}'$.

2.5 This problem demonstrates that in general $\mathbf{AB} \neq \mathbf{BA}$. Let
$$\mathbf{A} = \begin{bmatrix} 1 & 2 \\ 3 & 4 \end{bmatrix}, \qquad \mathbf{B} = \begin{bmatrix} 1 & 1 \\ 0 & 2 \end{bmatrix}.$$
   (a) Find $\mathbf{AB}$.
   (b) Find $\mathbf{BA}$.
   (c) Find $|\mathbf{AB}|$ and $|\mathbf{BA}|$.

2.6 It can be shown that $(\mathbf{AB})' = \mathbf{B}'\mathbf{A}'$. As a specific application of this let
$$\mathbf{A} = \begin{bmatrix} 1 & 2 & 3 \\ 0 & -1 & 4 \end{bmatrix}, \qquad \mathbf{B} = \begin{bmatrix} 1 & 2 \\ 0 & -1 \\ 1 & 4 \end{bmatrix}.$$
   (a) Find $\mathbf{AB}$ and then form $(\mathbf{AB})'$.
   (b) Find $\mathbf{B}'$ and also $\mathbf{A}'$, then form $\mathbf{B}'\mathbf{A}'$.
   (c) If it is defined, find $\mathbf{A}'\mathbf{B}$.

2.7 For most matrices, the order of multiplication is important; that is, $\mathbf{AB} \neq \mathbf{BA}$. However, this is not true for a matrix and its inverse; that is, $\mathbf{AA}^{-1} = \mathbf{A}^{-1}\mathbf{A}$. As a specific application of this, evaluate $\mathbf{AA}^{-1}$ and $\mathbf{A}^{-1}\mathbf{A}$ for
$$\mathbf{A} = \begin{bmatrix} 1 & 2 \\ 3 & 4 \end{bmatrix}, \qquad \mathbf{A}^{-1} = \frac{1}{2}\begin{bmatrix} -4 & 2 \\ 3 & -1 \end{bmatrix}.$$

2.8 Solve the following set of equations by using matrix techniques:
$$x_1 + 2x_2 = 8$$
$$3x_1 + 4x_2 = 20.$$

Hint: Problem 2.7 contains the necessary inverse matrix.

2.9 If one row of a determinant is added to another row, the value of the determinant is unchanged. As an example of this, evaluate the following two determinants (note that **B** was obtained from **A** by adding the first row to the third):

$$\mathbf{A} = \begin{vmatrix} 1 & 2 & 1 \\ 0 & 1 & 2 \\ -1 & 2 & 1 \end{vmatrix}, \qquad \mathbf{B} = \begin{vmatrix} 1 & 2 & 1 \\ 0 & 1 & 2 \\ 0 & 4 & 2 \end{vmatrix}.$$

2.10 If one row of a determinant is multiplied by a constant, then the value of the determinant is multiplied by that constant. As an example of this, evaluate the following two determinants (note that **B** was obtained from **A** by multiplying the second row by 3):

$$\mathbf{A} = \begin{vmatrix} 1 & 2 & 1 \\ 0 & 1 & 2 \\ -1 & 2 & 1 \end{vmatrix}, \qquad \mathbf{B} = \begin{vmatrix} 1 & 2 & 1 \\ 0 & 3 & 6 \\ -1 & 2 & 1 \end{vmatrix}.$$

2.11 If two rows or columns of a determinant are interchanged, then the value of the determinant is multiplied by minus one. As an example of this, evaluate the following two determinants:

$$\mathbf{A} = \begin{vmatrix} 1 & 2 & 1 \\ 0 & 1 & 2 \\ -1 & 2 & 1 \end{vmatrix}, \qquad \mathbf{B} = \begin{vmatrix} 0 & 1 & 2 \\ 1 & 2 & 1 \\ -1 & 2 & 1 \end{vmatrix}.$$

2.12 Any of the elementary row operations on a matrix **A** may be accomplished by premultiplying **A** by a suitable matrix **P**. Parts (a), (b), (c) of this problem give various special forms for **P**. Assuming **A** is a 3×3 matrix, how is **PA** related to **A**?

$$\text{(a)} \begin{bmatrix} 0 & 0 & 1 \\ 0 & 1 & 0 \\ 1 & 0 & 0 \end{bmatrix}, \qquad \text{(b)} \begin{bmatrix} 1 & 0 & 0 \\ 0 & k & 0 \\ 0 & 0 & 1 \end{bmatrix}, \qquad \text{(c)} \begin{bmatrix} 1 & 0 & -1 \\ 0 & 1 & 0 \\ 0 & 0 & 1 \end{bmatrix}.$$

2.13 Problems 2.9, 2.10, 2.11 investigated the effect of various elementary row operations on the value of a determinant. Problem 2.12 demonstrated that any elementary row operation on a matrix **A** may be accomplished by premultiplying **A** by a suitable matrix *P*. Outline how the results of Problem 2.12 could be applied to prove the statements made in Problems 2.9, 2.10, 2.11.

2.14 Use the Gauss elimination method to solve the following set of equations, find the inverse of the coefficient matrix and the determinant of the coefficient matrix:

$$2x_1 - 3x_2 = 8$$
$$4x_1 + x_2 = 2.$$

2.15 Find the inverse of the following matrix by using the Gauss elimination method; also find its determinant:

$$\mathbf{A} = \begin{bmatrix} 1 & 0 & 1 \\ 1 & 1 & 1 \\ 0 & 2 & -3 \end{bmatrix}.$$

2.16 Use the Gauss elimination method to solve the following set of equations and to find the inverse and the determinant of the coefficient matrix (note that an interchange of rows is necessary):

$$0x_1 + x_2 = 2$$
$$x_1 + x_2 = 3.$$

2.17 Use the Gauss elimination program to evaluate the following determinant:

$$\begin{vmatrix} 1 & 2 & 3 & 4 & 5 \\ 1 & 2 & 1 & 4 & 1 \\ 6 & 8 & 7 & 2 & 1 \\ 9 & -4 & 0 & 0 & 1 \\ -8 & -6 & 4 & 1 & 7 \end{vmatrix}.$$

Check your answer by interchanging rows 1 and 5.

2.18 Find the inverse of the following matrix by using the Gauss elimination program; then find the inverse of your answer to determine whether or not the original matrix is obtained:

$$\begin{bmatrix} 1 & 2 & 8 \\ 6 & 1 & 2 \\ -1 & 0 & -8 \end{bmatrix}.$$

What is the relation between $|A|$ and $|A^{-1}|$?

2.19 Solve the following set of equations by using the Gauss elimination program:

$$2x_1 + x_3 - 2x_4 = 9$$
$$x_2 + x_3 - x_4 = 5$$
$$3x_1 + 2x_2 - x_4 = 0$$
$$x_2 + x_3 - 4x_4 = -7.$$

2.20 The three equations in this problem contain four unknowns; thus there is no unique solution—that is, one of the parameters can be selected arbitrarily. Initially choose $x_4=2$ and obtain a solution for x_1, x_2, x_3; then choose $x_4=-3$ and obtain a new solution, given the equations

$$x_1+2x_2-x_3+ x_4=7$$
$$2x_1+3x_2+x_3-2x_4=0$$
$$3x_2-x_3+ x_4=10.$$

2.21 Decompose the following matrix into a lower triangular matrix **L** and an upper triangular matrix **U**:

$$\mathbf{A}=\begin{bmatrix} 2 & 1 \\ 8 & 6 \end{bmatrix}.$$

2.22 Find the **LU** decomposition for

$$\mathbf{A}=\begin{bmatrix} 2 & 4 & 8 \\ 0 & 1 & 2 \\ 1 & 1 & 2 \end{bmatrix}.$$

2.23 A matrix equation is relatively easy to solve if it is an upper triangular matrix. Solve for x_1, x_2, x_3 in the following matrix equation:

$$\begin{bmatrix} 1 & -4 & 2 \\ 0 & 1 & 6 \\ 0 & 0 & 1 \end{bmatrix}\begin{bmatrix} x_1 \\ x_2 \\ x_3 \end{bmatrix}=\begin{bmatrix} 9 \\ 40 \\ 5 \end{bmatrix}.$$

2.24 It follows from (2.43) that if the lower triangular matrix **A** has any diagonal terms that are equal to zero, then an **LU** decomposition does not exist for the original matrix **A**. However, sometimes rows can be interchanged and an **LU** decomposition can be found for the new matrix. Interchange row_1 and row_2 in the following relation, and then use an **LU** decomposition to solve for x_1, x_2, x_3:

$$\begin{bmatrix} 0 & 8 & 9 \\ 2 & 4 & 3 \\ 4 & 2 & -2 \end{bmatrix}\begin{bmatrix} x_1 \\ x_2 \\ x_3 \end{bmatrix}=\begin{bmatrix} 9 \\ 5 \\ 2 \end{bmatrix}.$$

2.25 Solve the following set of equations by the **LU** decomposition and then use the fact that the determinant of a product is equal to the product of the determinants to evaluate the determinant of the coefficient matrix:

$$2x_1+4x_2-2x_3=8$$
$$x_1+ x_2+ x_3=-2$$
$$x_1-2x_2-3x_3=14.$$

2.26 Modify the **LU** decomposition program so that it calculates the determinant of **A**.

Chapter Three

Solutions for a Nonlinear Equation

3.1 INTRODUCTION

The previous chapter discussed how to solve a linear set of equations. Because the equations were linear, the solution did not require an iterative approach. In this chapter we will no longer restrict attention to linear equations; as a result we will not be able to obtain an analytical answer.

The fact that we cannot obtain an analytical answer does not imply we cannot obtain an accurate answer. We will discover that by following a set of computation rules over and over again (that is, by an iterative process) we will be able to obtain any desired accuracy. The more accuracy we desire, the more computation time is required.

The nonlinear equations that we consider in this chapter will be a function of just one variable. An example of such an equation is

$$\tan x = x + 2. \tag{3.1}$$

In this chapter we will *not* consider sets of nonlinear equations that contain more than one variable. This topic must wait until we study optimization techniques later in the book.

The nonlinear equations will be solved by finding roots of the equations. For example, (3.1) can be rewritten as

$$f(x) = \tan x - x - 2. \tag{3.2}$$

Any x that makes $f(x)$ zero is called a root of that equation.

In Chapter 1 we briefly discussed one numerical method that can be used to obtain roots of an equation: the interval-halving method. That method, also known as the bisection method, is very popular because it almost always converges to a root. By continually halving the area of uncertainty a computer can quite rapidly find a zero to sufficient accuracy. This would obviously be a tedious method if hand calculations were used, but the use of a computer can make it practical. It has the advantage of being guaranteed to converge to a root. For example, in ten iterations the interval of uncertainty is reduced by 2^{-10} or more than a factor of a thousand; in twenty iterations, by more than a million.

43

The bisection method requires that an interval be found in which there is a sign change. In this chapter we will study Newton's method, which does not have that restriction. Like the interval-halving method, Newton's method is simple and widely used.

Newton's method iteratively finds roots of an equation by using a straight-line approximation of a function. Muller's method uses a second-order approximation, a parabola, and thus usually converges faster than Newton's method. A second-order function can also be used to find the minimum of a function, as is demonstrated by the quadratic interpolation method. Considerable time will be spent studying quadratic interpolation because it is an important part of some of the optimization programs that are included in this book.

The procedures that were just mentioned were designed for general functions; they are not limited to polynomials. Bairstow's method is restricted to polynomials, but it has the attraction of easily being able to yield complex roots.

3.2 ITERATIVE PROCEDURES

"Iterative procedures" is a fancy way of saying, "if at first you don't succeed, try, try again". Almost any repetitous task can become tedious, and the same is true for an iterative procedure. Fortunately, computers are now widely available and we can assign the repetitive calculations to them. It is the speed of digital computers that have really made iterative procedures practical.

An iterative procedure will require an initial guess. For example, if we are trying to find a root of

$$f(x) = \tan x - x - 2, \tag{3.3}$$

we may make the initial guess $x = 3$. This yields $f(x) = -3.14$, which is certainly not zero. However, a good iterative procedure should be able to improve on the initial guess and eventually make $f(x)$ negligible. For example, four iterations of Newton's method (to be described in the next section) yield $f(10.9183) = 9.7 \times 10^{-7}$.

The selection of the initial value should be done with care—the closer it is to an actual root, the faster will be the convergence of the iterative procedure. In fact, for a poor guess the iterative procedure may diverge instead of converge. Also, if a nonlinear equation has more than one root, the one that is found will be determined by the initial guess. Often, some practical knowledge about the problem being studied can yield a good initial value. Another approach is to do a series of computer runs and thus obtain some insight into the solution.

An iterative procedure will keep trying to improve previous solutions until instructed to stop. In computer programming there are two different approaches that can be used to terminate an iterative process. If a program is run in the interactive mode, a person can observe the results and stop the calculations when the result is deemed to be accurate enough. If a program is instead run in the batch mode, there must be instructions in the program that will cause the program to stop when a particular criterion is satisfied. Of course, an interactive program can also have stop criteria included in it.

It is often convenient to have the termination of the iterative procedure be under the control of the computer user (as is possible in the interactive mode), because the accuracy that is desired may depend on the particular application. For example, if the roots of an equation correspond to the average daily temperature, then two-digit accuracy might be sufficient. On the other hand, if the roots of an equation correspond to the resistance of an electrical component, then four-digit accuracy might be necessary.

In this book it will be assumed that the programs will be run in the interactive mode. Most of the programs will not stop automatically, but will require intervention by the computer user. Of course, these programs can be modified to include stop criteria if it is necessary to use the batch mode.

3.3 NEWTON'S METHOD[1]

As in any iterative procedure, an initial guess must be made for Newton's method. Assume that x_0 is the initial guess for a root of $f(x)$. The function $f(x)$ can be expanded in a Taylor series about this initial value:

$$f(x) = f(x_0) + f'(x_0)(x - x_0) + \frac{f''(x_0)(x - x_0)^2}{2} + \cdots . \tag{3.4}$$

Unless the guess was very lucky, x_0 will not be a root, but we can obtain a better value by assuming that x_0 is very close to a root r, so that $(r - x_0)^2$ is a small quantity and (3.4) can be approximated as

$$f(r) \cong f(x_0) + f'(x_0)(r - x_0). \tag{3.5}$$

But $f(r)$ is equal to zero, since by assumption r is a root. Therefore solving (3.5) yields

$$r \cong x_0 - \frac{f(x_0)}{f'(x_0)} . \tag{3.6}$$

---

[1]Also called the Newton-Raphson method.

This relation is the basis of Newton's method. A graphical interpretation of the method can be obtained from Fig. 3.1. This figure indicates that if a line is drawn tangent to $f(x)$ at x_0, then the line intercepts the x-axis a distance $x_0 - f(x_0)/f'(x_0)$ away from x. This new point can next be used as an "initial value" and Newton's method applied again. Repeating the process enough times will bring the solution arbitrarily close to the root r.

Instead of the notation in (3.6) we will find it more convenient to write

$$x - \frac{f(x)}{f'(x)} \to x. \tag{3.7}$$

This implies that the operation on the left side produces a new value for x which replaces the old one.

EXAMPLE 3.1

The function $f(x) = x^3 - x^2 - 2x + 1$ has a root near $x = 0.6$. In this example we apply two iterations of Newton's method to improve upon this initial value.

Since $f(0.6) = -0.344$ and $f'(0.6) = -2.12$, using (3.7) yields $x = 0.4377$.

The next iteration uses $f(0.4377) = 0.01687$ and $f'(0.4377) = -2.3$, so that (3.7) yields $x = 0.445$. After two iterations we now have $f(0.445) = 9.6 \times 10^{-5}$, which has a much smaller magnitude than the initial value $f(0.6) = -0.344$.

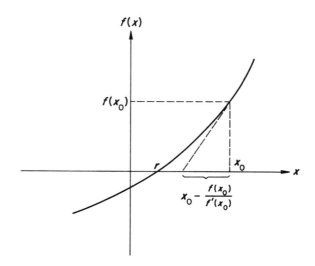

FIGURE 3.1. A graphical interpretation of Newton's method.

Although the calculations in Newton's method are relatively simple, they are time consuming if many iterations are required; it is thus worthwhile to write a program. Before this can be done we should note that (3.7) requires the evaluation of a derivative.

There are two methods that could be used to evaluate the derivative in a computer program. One is to include a subroutine that evaluates an analytical expression for the derivative. For Example 3.1 this subroutine would evaluate $f'(x) = 3x^2 - 2x - 2$. This has the disadvantage of requiring a different subroutine for every new function. The other possibility is to use an approximate (but accurate) formula for the derivative. This is the approach that will be used in this text.

By definition, the derivative of $f(x)$ is given by

$$\frac{df}{dx} = \lim_{\delta x \to 0} \frac{f(x + \delta x) - f(x)}{\delta x}. \tag{3.8}$$

It is of course not possible to let δx approach zero in a computer program; instead we must settle for some very small number. The question is "How small?" The best solution is to let the size of δx be proportional to the size of x: if x is a large number, then the change in x will be large; if x is a small number, then the change in x will be small. That is, δx will be given as

$$\delta x = \varepsilon x, \tag{3.9}$$

where ε is the constant of proportionality.

The constant of proportionality ε should be made small enough so that (3.9) is a good approximation to (3.8). However, if ε is made too small then roundoff errors can cause the numerator of (3.8) to be very inaccurate. The amount of roundoff error will depend on the function $f(x)$ that is evaluated, and it will also depend on the computer that is used. For the fourteen-digit Cyber 70, a reasonable value for ε is 10^{-6}. A less accurate computer might require that ε be 10^{-4} or even larger.

It should be noted that if x were zero, then $\delta x = \varepsilon x$ would also be zero, which would cause an attempt at division by zero in (3.8). The computer program that is discussed in this section will check to see if x is equal to zero; if it is, then δx will instead be set equal to ε.

A program for Newton's method is shown in Fig. 3.2. As indicated in the figure, the program is based on (3.7) and (3.8). It is important to note that (3.7) is based on the assumption that the parameter change $f(x)/f'(x)$ is small. Occasionally, it may happen (especially if the initial guess for a root location is poor) that the parameter change is quite large. In this case, applying (3.7) may actually move one farther from the root. To protect against this possibility, line 58 checks whether or not $|f(x_{\text{new}})| < |f(x_{\text{old}})|$.

```
01C     NEWTON'S METHOD
02      PROGRAM NM(INPUT,OUTPUT)
03  03  FORMAT(1P,2E14.5)
09C
10C     INITIAL VALUE
14      PRINT,*X*, $READ,X
15      PRINT,/,*       X                    F(X)*
18      FX=F(X)
19      PRINT 3,X,FX
20C
21C     FIND DERIVATIVE   (EQ. 3.8)
22  22  DELTA=.000001*X
24      IF(ABS(X).LT.1E-12) DELTA=.000001
27      DERIV=(F(X+DELTA)-FX)/DELTA
50C
51C     FIND NEW X   (EQ. 3.7)
52      DO 59 J=1,6
54      SF=.5**(J-1)
55      X1=X-SF*FX/DERIV
56      FX1=F(X1)
58      IF(ABS(FX1).LT.ABS(FX)) GO TO 81
59  59  CONTINUE
80C
81  81  X=X1 $FX=FX1
84      PRINT 3,X,FX
89      GO TO 22
890     END
898C
899     FUNCTION F(X)
900     F=X*X-7.*X+10.
950     RETURN
999     END
```

FIGURE 3.2. A program for Newton's method.

If not, then line 54 causes the parameter change δx to be reduced until it is. Many of the programs that are included in this text have similar checks. In fact, another one will be mentioned in this chapter.

At the bottom of the program for Newton's method is a function statement that is used to define the function $f(x)$. This function statement must be rewritten whenever the function $f(x)$ is changed (that is, whenever a new problem must be solved). The function that is shown in Fig. 3.2 is $f(x) = x^2 - 7x + 10$. This equation has two roots; the one that is found by a particular computer run depends on the initial value that is used for x. For example, Fig. 3.3 indicates that an initial guess of $x = 1$ yielded $r \approx 2$, while a value of $x = 10$ yielded $r \approx 5$.

```
X ? 1
```

X	F(X)
1.00000E+00	4.00000E+00
1.80000E+00	6.39999E-01
1.98824E+00	3.54322E-02
1.99995E+00	1.37308E-04
2.00000E+00	2.00316E-09
2.00000E+00	0.

(a)

```
X ? 10
```

X	F(X)
1.00000E+01	4.00000E+01
6.92308E+00	9.46747E+00
5.54019E+00	1.91239E+00
5.07152E+00	2.19661E-01
5.00163E+00	4.88470E-03
5.00000E+00	2.65352E-06

(b)

FIGURE 3.3. An application of the Newton-method program.

This is a good opportunity to repeat one of the programming philosophies that has been used in this text. To keep the programs simple (and flexible), STOP criteria usually have not been included. In this specific example, when it was observed that the computations had converged to a root, the "Break" key on the teletypewriter was pressed.

In the above example we knew that one root was approximately 5 because $f(x)$ was quite small for that value. If the program had been allowed to run longer, then $f(x)$ would have become even smaller, indicating that the root was more accurate. By examining the behavior of x we can obtain a good idea about the number of digits that are significant. For example, near the end of the first column in Fig. 3.3(b), the first three digits of x did not change, so the answer is probably accurate to at least three significant figures.

Insight into the rate of convergence of Newton's method may be obtained by considering the Taylor series

$$f(x) = f(x_0) + f'(x_0)(x - x_0) + \frac{f''(x_0)(x - x_0)^2}{2} + \cdots . \qquad (3.10)$$

Given an initial value x_0, Newton's method approximates the root by ignoring all terms after the first derivative. That is, (3.10) is approximated as

$$f(x) \approx f(x_0) + f'(x - x_0).$$ (3.11)

Comparing (3.10) and (3.11), we can see that the function error is of the order of $(x - x_0)^2$.

The Taylor series can also be used to investigate the root error, which is defined as $e_n = x_n - r$, where r is the root and x_n is the estimate of the root at the nth iteration. Newton's method uses

$$x_{n+1} = x_n - f(x_n)/f'(x_n).$$ (3.12)

Subtracting r from both sides of the equation yields

$$e_{n+1} = e_n - f(x_n)/f'(x_n).$$ (3.13)

This can be approximated by expanding $f(x_n)$ in a Taylor series about the root r:

$$f(x_n) = f(r) + f'(r)(x_n - r) + \frac{f''(r)(x_n - r)^2}{2} + \cdots.$$ (3.14)

Using $f(r) = 0$ and ignoring higher-order terms because we are near a root, we have

$$f(x_n) \approx f'(r)e_n + f''(r)e_n^2/2.$$ (3.15)

Differentiating (3.14) then produces

$$f'(x_n) \approx f'(r) + f''(r)e_n.$$ (3.16)

Substituting (3.15) and (3.16) and using $(1 + \varepsilon/2)/(1 + \varepsilon) \approx 1 - \varepsilon/2$, where $\varepsilon = f''(r)e_n/f'(r)$, we have

$$e_{n+1} \approx \frac{f''(r)}{2f'(r)} e_n^2.$$ (3.17)

This equation indicates that (sufficiently close to a root) the current error e_{n+1} is a quadratic function of the previous error e_n—thus Newton's method is said to be quadratically convergent or to be of second order.

3.4. QUADRATIC INTERPOLATION AND MULLER'S METHOD

In this section we will assume that in a sufficiently small region a function can be approximated by a second-degree polynomial. This is equivalent to assuming that the third- and higher-order terms in the following Taylor series can be ignored:

$$f(x) = f(x_a) + f'(x_a)(x - x_a) + \frac{f''(x - x_a)^2}{2} + \cdots.$$ (3.18)

For quadratic interpolation, the point x will be made to iteratively approach the minimum of a function. For Muller's method, the point x will be made to iteratively approach the root of a function. If the initial guess in the iterative procedure is poor, then x will not be near x_a and the high-order terms in (3.18) will not be negligible. However, as x_a is approached the approximation of the function by a second-degree polynomial will become valid, and convergence will be faster than for a method such as Newton's, which uses a linear approximation.

Because quadratic interpolation and Muller's method both approximate a function by a second-degree polynomial (i.e., a parabola), they are both presented in this section. However, they are being presented for different reasons. Quadratic interpolation is used to minimize a function and will be very important in the optimization programs that are developed in some of the following chapters. Muller's method is a relatively new numerical method that is now widely used for finding roots of functions. Since this chapter is concerned with finding solutions for a nonlinear equation, it is appropriate that Muller's method be studied.

Since quadratic interpolation will find substantial application in later chapters, it will be explained more thoroughly than Muller's method. Quadratic interpolation will be used to find a minimum; thus the approximating parabola should be concave upward as shown in Fig. 3.4. In that figure, the initial point is located at x_0, f_0 where f_0 is the notation that will be used for $f(x_0)$. The program in Fig. 3.5 describes how points x_1, f_1, and x_2, f_2 can be selected so that a parabola passed through these three points is concave upward as desired.

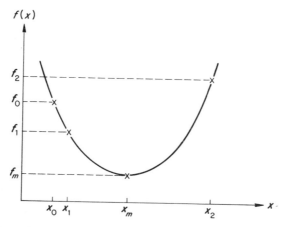

FIGURE 3.4. Illustration of the notation used for quadratic interpolation.

```
01C     QUADRATIC INTERPOLATION
02      PROGRAM QUAD(INPUT,OUTPUT)
03 03 FORMAT(1P,2E14.5)
09C
10C     INITIAL VALUE
14      PRINT,*X*, $READ,X
15      PRINT,/,*         X                F(X)*
18 18 F0=F(X)
19 19 PRINT 3,X,F0
20C
21C     FIND ALPHA 1
22      A1=.01
24 24 F1=F((1.+A1)*X)
26      IF(F1.LT.F0) GO TO 32
27      A1=-.5*A1
28      IF(ABS(A1) .LT. 1E-10) STOP
29      GO TO 24
30C
31C     FIND ALPHA 2
32 32 A2=A1
33 33 A2=2.*A2
35      F2=F((1.+A2)*X)
36      IF(F2.GT.F1) GO TO 42
38      A1=A2 $F1=F2
39      GO TO 33
40C
41C     FIND ALPHA    (EQ. 3.24)
42 42 A=(A1*A1-A2*A2)*F0+A2*A2*F1-A1*A1*F2
43      A=.5*A/((A1-A2)*F0+A2*F1-A1*F2)
50C
51C     FIND NEW X
52      X=(1.+A)*X
54      F0=F(X)
56      IF(F0.LT.F1) GO TO 19
58      X=(1.+A1)*X/(1.+A)
60      GO TO 18
890     END
898C
899     FUNCTION F(X)
900     F=X**4+X**3+3*X*X+X+2.
950     RETURN
999     END
```

FIGURE 3.5. A program for quadratic interpolation.

The first part of the program in Fig. 3.5 indicates how the point x_1, f_1 can be picked so that $f_1 < f_0$. The computer first tries a value

$$x_1 = (1 + \alpha_1)x_0, \tag{3.19}$$

where $\alpha_1 = 0.01$. That is, x_1 is 1% greater than x_0. If at this point the value f_1 is not less than f_0, then the computer next tries a point that is 0.5% less than x_0. If this again fails, it tries a point that is 0.25% greater than x_0. Eventually, by looking sufficiently close to x_0, the computer must find a point x_1 such that $f_1 < f_0$ unless x_0 is the minimum.[2]

Next the computer searches for a point

$$x_2 = (1 + \alpha_2)x_0 \tag{3.20}$$

such that $f(x_2) = f_2 > f_1$. This is done by first giving α_2 twice the last value of α_1. If this does not work, then α_2 is doubled until the function increases sufficiently that f_2 becomes greater than f_1.

It should be noted that in the program of Fig. 3.5, if f_2 is not greater than f_1, then in step 38 the present value of f_2 is redefined to be f_1. This reduces the value of f_1, thus putting it closer to the minimum, which will make the quadratic interpolation procedure converge faster.

We have seen how it is possible to pick three points $(x_0, f_0), (x_1, f_1), (x_2, f_2)$ so as to yield a parabola that is concave upward. The equation of this parabola can be easily written if we use a result that will be proven in the next chapter. A second-degree function that goes through three points can be expressed as

$$f(x) = \frac{(x - x_1)(x - x_2)}{(x_0 - x_1)(x_0 - x_2)} f_0 + \frac{(x - x_0)(x - x_2)}{(x_1 - x_0)(x_1 - x_2)} f_1 + \frac{(x - x_0)(x - x_1)}{(x_2 - x_0)(x_2 - x_1)} f_2.$$

$$\tag{3.21}$$

The minimum of this parabola can be found by differentiating and then setting the derivative equal to zero. This yields

$$x = 0.5 \frac{(x_1^2 - x_2^2)f_0 + (x_2^2 - x_0^2)f_1 + (x_0^2 - x_1^2)f_2}{(x_1 - x_2)f_0 + (x_2 - x_0)f_1 + (x_0 - x_1)f_2}. \tag{3.22}$$

This equation can be simplified if we express x relative to x_0 as we previously expressed x_1 relative to x_0 in (3.19), and similarly for x_2 in (3.20). That is, we will write x as

$$x = (1 + \alpha)x_0. \tag{3.23}$$

---

[2]Statement 28 causes the calculations to stop if x_0 is sufficiently close to the minimum.

Substituting (3.19), (3.20), and (3.23) into (3.22) yields

$$\alpha = 0.5 \frac{(\alpha_1^2 - \alpha_2^2) f_0 + \alpha_2^2 f_1 - \alpha_1^2 f_2}{(\alpha_1 - \alpha_2) f_0 + \alpha_2 f_1 - \alpha_1 f_2}. \tag{3.24}$$

Once α has been calculated by this equation, x can be calculated from (3.23).

The quadratic interpolation program of Figure 3.5 is based on using (3.24) to calculate the minimum of a parabola. However, the function $f(x)$ will usually not behave quadratically except close to a minimum. Thus, far from a minimum it may happen that the value of x calculated from $x = (1 + \alpha) x_0$ may yield $f(x) > f(x_0)$. If this happens, then line number 58 causes the new point to be $x = (1 + \alpha_1) x_0$. This point is used because the selection of α_1 guarantees that $f(x_1) < f(x_0)$.

EXAMPLE 3.2

The function at the bottom of the quadratic interpolation program in Fig. 3.5 is $f(x) = x^4 + x^3 + 3x^2 + x + 2$. As illustrated in Fig. 3.6, choosing an initial value of $x_0 = 1$ yields a minimum of -0.178846.

```
        X ? 1

              X                    F(X)
        1.00000E+00           8.00000E+00
       -1.94588E-01           1.91307E+00
       -1.78859E-01           1.91241E+00
       -1.78846E-01           1.91241E+00
            STOP
```

FIGURE 3.6. An application of the quadratic interpolation program.

As mentioned previously, Muller's method is similar to quadratic interpolation: it uses a parabolic approximation to find a root instead of a minimum. If the parabola

$$f(x) = ax^2 + bx + c \tag{3.25}$$

is equated to the parabola of (3.21), namely

$$f(x) = \frac{(x - x_1)(x - x_2)}{(x_0 - x_1)(x_0 - x_2)} f_0 + \frac{(x - x_0)(x - x_2)}{(x_1 - x_0)(x_1 - x_2)} f_1 + \frac{(x - x_0)(x - x_1)}{(x_2 - x_0)(x_2 - x_1)} f_2,$$

```
01C    MULLER'S METHOD
02        PROGRAM MM(INPUT,OUTPUT)
03 03  FORMAT(1P,2E14.5)
09C
10C    INITIAL VALUE
14 14  PRINT ,*X*, $READ,X0
15        PRINT,/,*         X              F(X)*
18        F0=F(X0)
19        PRINT 3,X0,F0
20C
21C    ARBITRARILY PICK X1,X2
22        X1=1.1*X0
23        F1=F(X1)
25        X2=.9*X0
26        F2=F(X2)
40C
41C    FIND B0,B1,B2   (EQ. 3.26)
42 42  B0=F0/(X0-X1)/(X0-X2)
43        B1=F1/(X1-X0)/(X1-X2)
44        B2=F2/(X2-X0)/(X2-X1)
50C
51C    FIND A,B,C   (EQ. 3.26)
52        A=B0+B1+B2
53        B=-((X1+X2)*B0+(X0+X2)*B1+(X0+X1)*B2)
54        C=X1*X2*B0+X0*X2*B1+X0*X1*B2
56        IF(A .EQ. 0) X3=-C/B
57        IF(A .EQ. 0) GO TO 68
60C
61C    FIND THE ROOT CLOSEST TO X2 (EQ. 3.27)
62        DSC=B*B-4.*A*C
63        IF(DSC .LT. 0.) DSC=0.
64        X3=(-B+SQRT(DSC))/(2.*A)
65        X4=(-B-SQRT(DSC))/(2.*A)
67        IF(ABS(X4-X2) .LT. ABS(X3-X2)) X3=X4
68 68  F3=F(X3)
69        PRINT 3,X3,F3
70C
71C    DISCARD THE OLDEST POINT
72        X0=X1 $X1=X2 $X2=X3
73        F0=F1 $F1=F2 $F2=F3
76        GO TO 42
890      END
891C
899      FUNCTION F(X)
900      F=X*X-7.*X+10.
950      RETURN
999      END
```

FIGURE 3.7. A program for Muller's method.

```
X ? 1

        X                    F(X)
  1.00000E+00         4.00000E+00
  2.00000E+00        -1.09139E-11
```

(a)

```
X ? 4

        X                    F(X)
  4.00000E+00        -2.00000E+00
  5.00000E+00           0.
```

(b)

```
X ? 1

        X                    F(X)
  1.00000E+00        -2.80000E+01
  2.06986E+00         1.21385E+00
  1.99598E+00        -7.25479E-02
  1.99998E+00        -3.07846E-04
  2.00000E+00        -4.80895E-09
```

(c)

FIGURE 3.8. An application of the Muller program.

it follows that[3]

$$a = b_0 + b_1 + b_2$$
$$b = -\left[(x_1 + x_2)b_0 + (x_0 + x_2)b_1 + (x_0 + x_1)b_2\right] \tag{3.26}$$
$$c = x_1 x_2 b_0 + x_0 x_2 b_1 + x_0 x_1 b_2,$$

where

$$b_0 = \frac{f_0}{(x_0 - x_1)(x_0 - x_2)}$$

$$b_1 = \frac{f_1}{(x_1 - x_0)(x_1 - x_2)} \qquad b_2 = \frac{f_2}{(x_2 - x_0)(x_2 - x_1)}.$$

Once a, b, c have been calculated from (3.26), the roots of the parabola can

---

[3]To demonstrate this use $f(0) = c$, $f'(0) = b$, $f''(0) = 2a$.

be found from

$$x_r = \frac{-b \pm (b^2 - 4ac)^{\frac{1}{2}}}{2a}.$$ (3.27)

A program implementing these equations is given in Fig. 3.7, and some applications are given in Fig. 3.8. Figures 3.8(a, b) shows an application to finding the roots of $x^2 - 7x + 10$. Since this is a second-degree equation, Muller's method was able to determine the roots (except for numerical inaccuracies) in one iteration. Figure 3.8(c) shows an application of Muller's method to $(x^2 - 7x + 10)(x - 8)$. This time more than one iteration was required because the polynomial was third-degree.

The description of Muller's method that was just given emphasized clarity and not numerical accuracy. In particular, calculating b_0, b_1, b_2, as given in (3.26) can cause inaccuracies because the denominator terms will become small as the minimum is approached. As described by Conte and DeBoor (1972), Muller used different equations to solve for the roots. If one needs to find roots very accurately, then it is recommended that the program in Fig. 3.7 be so modified.

As described in this chapter, the Newton program and the Muller program only find *real* roots.[4] The method in the next section was developed specifically to solve for complex roots of polynomials.

3.5 BAIRSTOW'S METHOD

In this section we will learn how to find the roots of the following nth-degree equation:

$$f(x) = x^n + A_1 x^{n-1} + A_2 x^{n-2} + \cdots + A_{n-1}x + A_n = 0.$$ (3.28)

It should be noted that the first coefficient is unity (that is, $A_0 = 1$). If the leading coefficient is not equal to one, then the equation can be divided by A_0, as that will not affect the roots; thus there is no loss in generality if we assume the normalized form shown in (3.28).

Bairstow's method removes a quadratic factor, $x^2 + Px + Q$, from (3.28). The remainder is thus two degrees lower, and Bairstow's method can be applied again, so that eventually all quadratic factors can be found.[5]

In order to remove the quadratic factor $x^2 + Px + Q$, an iterative procedure will be used. First, as an initial guess, it will be assumed that

---

[4]Problem 3.30 requests the reader to modify the program of Fig. 3.7 so that it will find complex roots.

[5]If n is odd, then the final remainder will be a linear term.

$x^2 + P_0x + Q_0$ is a factor of (3.28); thus the equation can be rewritten as

$$f(x) = (x^2 + P_0x + Q_0)(B_0x^{n-2} + B_1x^{n-3} + \cdots + B_{n-2}) + Rx + S. \quad (3.29)$$

If $x^2 + P_0x + Q_0$ is really a factor, then the remainders R, S should be zero. However, usually the initial guess will not be so successful; but P_0 and Q_0 can be iteratively adjusted until the remainders R, S are negligibly small.

Equations for the remainders R and S can be obtained by equating coefficients of like powers in (3.28) and (3.29). Problem 3.17 establishes that these remainders can be written as

$$R = B_{n-1}$$
$$S = B_n + P_0B_{n-1}, \quad (3.30)$$

where the coefficients B_n, B_{n-1} can be found from the following recursive relations:

$$B_0 = 1$$
$$B_1 = A_1 - P_0$$
$$B_i = A_i - P_0B_{i-1} - Q_0B_{i-2}, \quad i = 2, 3, \ldots, n. \quad (3.31)$$

EXAMPLE 3.3

For the function $f(x) = x^3 + 2x^2 + 3x + 2$, find the remainder if it is assumed that a factor is $x^2 + P_0x + Q_0 = x^2 + 2x + 3$.

SOLUTION

Applying (3.31) with $P_0 = 2$ and $Q_0 = 3$, we have

$$B_0 = 1$$
$$B_1 = 2 - 2 = 0$$
$$B_2 = 3 - 2(0) - 3(1) = 0$$
$$B_3 = 2 - 2(0) - 3(0) = 2.$$

Thus (3.30) yields $R = 0$, $S = 2 + 2(0) = 2$. This implies that

$$x^3 + 2x^2 + 3x + 2 = (x^2 + 2x + 3)(x + 0) + 0x + 2.$$

The remainder terms, R and S, are of course a function of the initial guess P_0, Q_0. Given an initial guess P_0, Q_0, we want to choose a better pair P_1, Q_1 so that R, S is made smaller. This will be done by using the Taylor series approximation:[6]

$$R(P_1, Q_1) \cong R(P_0, Q_0) + \frac{\partial R}{\partial P} \delta P + \frac{\partial P}{\partial Q} \delta Q$$

$$S(P_1, Q_1) \cong S(P_0, Q_0) + \frac{\partial S}{\partial P} \delta P + \frac{\partial P}{\partial Q} \delta Q,$$

(3.32)

where δP and δQ are defined by

$$P_1 = P_0 + \delta P, \qquad Q_1 = Q_0 + \delta Q.$$

(3.33)

Summarizing Bairstow's method to this point: We made an initial guess that $x^2 + P_0 x + Q_0$ is a quadratic factor of $f(x)$. This yielded remainders which can be calculated by (3.30). We now want to choose increments, $\delta P, \delta Q$ so that the remainders become zero. That is, we want $R(P_1, Q_1)$ and $S(P_1, Q_1)$ to equal zero; thus (3.32) yields

$$\frac{\partial R}{\partial P} \delta P + \frac{\partial R}{\partial Q} \delta Q \cong -R(P_0, Q_0)$$

(3.34a)

$$\frac{\partial S}{\partial P} \delta P + \frac{\partial S}{\partial Q} \delta Q \cong -S(P_0, Q_0).$$

(3.34b)

In these two equations we are assuming we know the quantities $R(P_0, Q_0)$ and $S(P_0, Q_0)$. The partial derivatives can be calculated by differentiating (3.30); thus we have two equations and just two unknowns: $\delta P, \delta Q$. It is shown in Problems 3.20 to 3.23 that the solution to (3.34) can be expressed as

$$\delta P = \frac{B_{n-1} C_{n-2} - B_n C_{n-3}}{K}$$

(3.35)

$$\delta Q = \frac{B_n C_{n-2} - B_{n-1}(C_{n-1} - B_{n-1})}{K},$$

(3.36)

where[7]

$$C_0 = 1$$
$$C_1 = B_1 - P_0$$
$$C_i = B_i - P_0 C_{i-1} - Q_0 C_{i-2}, \qquad i = 2, 3, \ldots n,$$

(3.37)

and the constant K is defined as

$$K = C_{n-2}^2 + C_{n-3}(B_{n-1} - C_{n-1}).$$

(3.38)

---

[6]This is a two-dimensional generalization of (3.5) which was used in Newton's method, so Bairstow's method can be considered to be a generalization of Newton's method.

[7]Note the similarity between (3.31) and (3.37). If the B's in (3.31) are replaced by C's and the A's by B's, then one obtains (3.37).

EXAMPLE 3.4

Example 3.3 assumed $x^2 + 2x + 3$ was a factor of $x^3 + 2x^2 + 3x + 2$ and found that the remainder was $Rx + S = 0x + 2$. This example will apply (3.35) and (3.36) to yield changes $\delta P, \delta Q$ which will produce a better quadratic factor $x^2 + P_1 x + Q_1$.

In Example 3.3, for $P_0 = 2$ and $Q_0 = 3$ it was found $B_0 = 1$, $B_1 = 0 = B_2$, $B_3 = 2$. Thus applying (3.37) yields

$$C_0 = 1$$
$$C_1 = 0 - 2 = -2$$
$$C_2 = 0 - 2(-2) - 3(1) = 1$$
$$C_3 = 2 - 2(1) - 3(-2) = 6.$$

Next, applying (3.38) produces $K = 3$. Finally, applying (3.35) and (3.36) gives the desired changes

$$\delta P = -\tfrac{2}{3}, \qquad \delta Q = -\tfrac{4}{3},$$

so that

$$P_1 = P_0 + \delta P = \tfrac{4}{3}, \qquad Q_1 = Q_0 + \delta Q = \tfrac{5}{3}.$$

Usually, the increments $\delta P, \delta Q$ will not be perfect: they will not result in remainders R, S which are both exactly zero. This is because the Taylor series in (3.32) were only approximations. However, this can be the basis of an iterative procedure. As the procedure progresses, the increments $\delta P, \delta Q$ will become smaller, the Taylor series will become more exact, and the solution will converge.

Thus by using Bairstow's iterative procedure it is possible to find a quadratic factor of

$$f(x) = x^n + A_1 x^{n-1} + A_2 x^{n-2} + \cdots + A_{n-1} x + A_n. \tag{3.39}$$

Denoting this quadratic factor as $x^2 + Px + Q$, it follows from (3.29) that $f(x)$ can be expressed as

$$f(x) = (x^2 + Px + Q)(B_0 x^{n-2} + B_1 x^{n-3} + \cdots + B_{n-2}), \tag{3.40}$$

where

$$B_0 = 1$$
$$B_1 = A_1 - P \tag{3.41}$$
$$B_i = A_i - P B_{i-1} - Q B_{i-2}, \qquad i = 2, 3, \ldots, n.$$

```
01C     BAIRSTOW'S METHOD
02C     THIS PROGRAM FINDS THE FACTORS OF
03C     X**N+A2*X**(N-1)+A3*X**(N-2)+...
04C     QUADRATIC FACTORS: X**2+P*X+Q
05C     LINEAR FACTOR:     X+X0
06C
07      PROGRAM B(INPUT,OUTPUT)
08  08  FORMAT(1P,2E14.5)
09      DIMENSION A(10),B(10),C(10)
10      REAL K
11C
12      PRINT,*N*, $READ,N
14      PRINT,/,*A(I) I=2,3,...N+1*
16      N1=N+1 $A(1)=1.
17      READ,(A(I),I=2,N1)
20  20  PRINT,/,*INITIAL P,Q*, $READ,P,Q
23C
24C     CALCULATE B,C   (EQS. 3.31,3.37)
25      B(1)=1.      $C(1)=1.
27  27  B(2)=A(2)-P $C(2)=B(2)-P
29      DO 32 I=3,N1
31      B(I)=A(I)-P*B(I-1)-Q*B(I-2)
32  32  C(I)=B(I)-P*C(I-1)-Q*C(I-2)
35C
36C     CALCULATE K   (EQ. 3.38)
37      K=C(N-1)**2+C(N-2)*(B(N)-C(N))
38      IF(K.EQ.0) K=.001
40C
41C     CALCULATE DP,DQ   (EQS. 3.35,3.36)
42      DP=(B(N)*C(N-1)-B(N1)*C(N-2))/K
43      DQ=(B(N1)*C(N-1)-B(N)*(C(N)-B(N)))/K
45C
46C     CALCULATE P,Q   (EQ. 3.33)
47      P=P+DP   $Q=Q+DQ
49C
50C     ACCURACY CONTROL
51      IF(ABS(DP)+ABS(DQ).GT.1E-6) GO TO 27
53C
54      PRINT,*  FINAL P,Q*, $PRINT 8,P,Q
59C
60C     REDUCE DEGREE BY 2   (EQ. 3.42)
61      N=N-2 $N1=N1-2
62      A(2)=A(2)-P
63      IF(N.EQ.1) GO TO 92
64      DO 65 I=3,N1
65  65  A(I)=A(I)-P*A(I-1)-Q*A(I-2)
67      IF(N.GT.2) GO TO 20
80C
82C     LAST QUADRATIC FACTOR
83      PRINT,/,*  FINAL P,Q*, $PRINT 8,A(2),A(3)
84      STOP
90C
92  92  PRINT,/,*LINEAR TERM X0=*, $PRINT 8,A(2)
999     END
```

FIGURE 3.9. A program for Bairstow's method.

Once the quadratic factor has been removed as indicated in (3.40), the other factor can be again analyzed by Bairstow's method. Before this can be done, two minor items need to be taken care of. First, the degree of the second factor in (3.40) is $n-2$, so the substitution $n-2 \rightarrow n$ must be performed. Second, the coefficients are identified as B_i in (3.40), while the program is written in terms of A_i. This can be taken care of by using the following instead of (3.41):

$$A_1 - P \rightarrow A,$$
$$A_i - PA_{i-1} - QA_{i-2} \rightarrow A_i, \qquad i = 2, 3, \ldots, n. \tag{3.42}$$

A program for Bairstow's method is given in Fig. 3.9. This will automatically remove quadratic factors $x^2 + Px + Q$ from an nth-degree polynomial $f(x)$ until no more quadratic factors remain. If the degree is odd there will be a linear factor, which is denoted as $x + x_0$.

Most of the steps in the program are obvious from the discussion on the previous pages, but a couple may need clarifying. At line 38 a check is made to see whether or not $K = 0$, so that division by zero will not result when δP and δQ are calculated. If K does equal zero it is redefined to be 0.001; the effects of this will disappear after a few iterations. Note that the iterations continue until $|\delta P| + |\delta Q| \leq 10^{-6}$. Reducing the δP and δQ even more would produce a more accurate quadratic factor, but this would of course require more iterations (and thus more computation time).

EXAMPLE 3.5

Example 3.4 started analyzing the third-degree function $f(x) = x^3 + 2x^2 + 3x + 2$. After one iteration it was found that the initial guess of $P_0 = 2$, $Q_0 = 3$ was modified to $P_1 = \frac{4}{3}$, $Q_1 = \frac{5}{3}$.

The Bairstow program can be used to factor this function. The output in Fig. 3.10 was obtained by choosing as the initial guess $P_0 = 0$, $Q_0 = 0$. The

```
N ? 3

A(I)  I=2,3,...N+1
? 2   3   2

INITIAL P,Q ? 0,0
    FINAL P,Q   1.00000E+00      2.00000E+00

LINEAR TERM X0=   1.00000E+00
    END.
```

FIGURE 3.10. An application of the Bairstow program.

output indicates that $f(x)$ can be factored as

$$f(x)=(x^2+x+2)(x+1).$$

The program in Fig. 3.9 indicates that initial values for P, Q are required as input data. The values that are used are not very critical. In fact, if the initial values are always chosen as zero, the algorithm will work fine. Thus the initial values could have been set internally and not left as input data; however, this was not done, in order to provide more flexibility.

```
N ? 7

A(I)  I=2,3,...N+1
? 13   65   172   277   293   177   42

INITIAL P,Q ? 0,0
   FINAL P,Q    1.55051E+00      5.50510E-01

INITIAL P,Q ? 0,0
   FINAL P,Q    1.00000E+00      2.00000E+00

INITIAL P,Q ? 0,0
   FINAL P,Q    5.00000E+00      7.00000E+00

LINEAR TERM X0=     5.44949E+00
   END.
```

(a)

```
N ? 7

A(I)  I=2,3,...N+1
? 13   65   172   277   293   177   42

INITIAL P,Q ? 4.9,6.9
   FINAL P,Q    5.00000E+00      7.00000E+00

INITIAL P,Q ? 1.5,.5
   FINAL P,Q    1.55051E+00      5.50510E-01

INITIAL P,Q ? .9,1.9
   FINAL P,Q    1.00000E+00      2.00000E+00

LINEAR TERM X0=     5.44949E+00
   END.
```

(b)

FIGURE 3.11. The values chosen for P, Q can influence the order of root removal.

By choosing different initial values for P, Q one can change the order in which the roots are removed. This property can be used to check the accuracy of the roots. Because Bairstow's method proceeds by successively removing factors, the roots removed first will be the most accurate: roundoff errors can accumulate and make the last roots relatively inaccurate. Thus using Bairstow's method again with a different order of factorization can serve as a check on accuracy. If accuracy is a problem, then the root with the smallest magnitude should be removed first, because this reduces the effect of roundoff error.

EXAMPLE 3.6

Figure 3.11 shows output for the function

$$f(x) = x^7 + 13x^6 + 65x^5 + 172x^4 + 277x^3 + 293x^2 + 177x + 42.$$

The results in Fig. 3.11(a) were obtained by always using as initial values $P = 0$, $Q = 0$. Notice that the last quadratic factor removed was $x^2 + 5x + 7$.

Figure 3.11(b) shows the result of a second computer run for the same problem. This time, we chose as initial values $P = 4.9$ and $Q = 6.9$, and the first factor to be removed was $x^2 + 5x + 7$. The initial values were chosen to be different from $P = 5$ and $Q = 7$ in order to verify that the original answer was accurate.

From the output in Fig. 3.11, it follows that $f(x)$ can be factored as

$$f(x) = (x^2 + 1.55x + 0.55)(x^2 + x + 2)(x^2 + 5x + 7)(x + 5.45).$$

It should be noted that the output in Fig. 3.11 is more accurate than this; the answer here was simplified for ease of presentation.

3.6 SUGGESTED READING IN RELATED TOPICS

In this chapter we considered three algorithms that can be used to find the roots of equations. The three methods were very different in their approach to the problem. Newton's method used the derivative to help predict the location of a root; Muller's method used a second-degree curve-fitting approach; and Bairstow's method successively removed quadratic factors.

Newton's method had simplicity as its main virtue; thus it served as a good introduction to iterative techniques. However, as indicated by Hamming (1973), Newton's method may encounter difficulty in some special cases. For example, if $f(x)$ has a multiple zero at a root, then the derivative will also be zero at that root, which causes division by zero in the algorithm. Newton's method can also encounter difficulty if the root is at an inflection point (second derivative equals zero), in which case the procedure may never converge.

It is possible to modify Newton's method and eliminate the problems mentioned above. One modification was mentioned in Section 3.3. It was based on the observation, illustrated in Fig. 3.1, that Newton's method predicts the parameter change δx by using the negative of the slope. If this parameter change is too large and results in an $f(x)$ which has a magnitude greater than the previous $f(x)$, then the modified Newton's method halves the parameter change until $f(x)$ finally has a smaller magnitude. An approach similar to this is used in the steepest-descent method of Section 9.4.

There are many other methods which are as simple as Newton's method. Some of the more popular ones are the secant method and the bisection method. The secant method can be considered to be a simplification of Newton's method which solves iteratively for a root via

$$x_{n+1} = x_n - f(x_n)/f'(x_n).$$

In the secant method the derivative is approximated by

$$f'(x_n) = \frac{f(x_n) - f(x_{n-1})}{x_n - x_{n-1}}.$$

Newton's method was second-order; further approximating the derivative as above makes the secant method of lower order. However, since the secant method does not require the evaluation of a derivative it uses fewer function evaluations than Newton's methods and may require less computation time.

Recall that Newton's method was exact for any linear function, and quadratic interpolation was exact for any second-degree function. Continuing this approach, cubic interpolation would be exact for any third-degree function. Thus in theory cubic interpolation may sound even better than quadratic interpolation; but in practice it is not. By the time one is close enough to the minimum so that $f(x)$ can be approximated by a third-degree function, quadratic interpolation will also do a good job. Any saving that cubic interpolation would produce because of increased accuracy is usually more than offset by the necessity of fitting a curve to four points instead of the three required by quadratic interpolation.

The golden section method[8] is an algorithm that can be used to find the minimum of a function $f(x)$ and is simpler than quadratic interpolation. First it is assumed that we have found a region in which $f(x)$ is unimodal —i.e., $f(x)$ has one and only one minimum in that region. Let x_1 and x_4 be points which bracket the unimodal region. Interior points $x_2 = 0.618x_1 + 0.382x_4$ and $x_3 = 0.382x_1 + 0.618x_4$ are next examined. If $f(x_2)$ is greater than $f(x_3)$ then point x_1 is discarded and x_2, x_4 are now known to bracket a

---

[8]This is analogous to the bisection method which was used for finding roots of a function.

```
01C     GOLDEN SECTIONS
02      PROGRAM GS(INPUT,OUTPUT)
03 03   FORMAT(1P 2E14.5)
09C
10C     INITIAL VALUES
11      PRINT ,*        UNIMODAL POINTS*
12      READ ,X1,X4
13C
20C     FIND INTERIOR POINTS
21      X2=.618*X1+.382*X4
22      F2=F(X2)
24      X3=.382*X1+.618*X4
25      F3=F(X3)
29C
30 30   PRINT 3,X1,X4
39C
40C     IF F2>F3 THE NEW UNIMODAL POINTS ARE X2,X4
41      IF(F3 .GT. F2) GO TO 63
43      X1=X2
44      X2=X3    $F2=F3
46      X3=.382*X1+.618*X4
47      F3=F(X3)
48      GO TO 30
59C
60C     IF F3>F2 THE NEW UNIMODAL POINTS ARE X1,X3
63 63   X4=X3
64      X3=X2    $F3=F2
66      X2=.618*X1+.382*X4
67      F2=F(X2)
68      GO TO 30
69      END
88C
89      FUNCTION F(X)
90      F=(X*X*X+6.*X*X+11.*X+6.)**2
98      RETURN
99      END
```

FIGURE 3.12. A program for the golden section method.

unimodal region. Point x_3 is still used as an interior point and another one is found from $0.382x_2 + 0.618x_4$. On the other hand, if $f(x_3)$ is greater than $f(x_2)$ then point x_4 is discarded and a new interior point is found from $0.618x_1 + 0.382x_3$. The numbers 0.382 and 0.618 are related to the golden ratio (Forsythe 1977). They were used in the above equations because they allow the bounds of the unimodal region to be reduced by the same amount if f_2 is greater than f_3 or vice versa. A program for the golden section method is given in Fig. 3.12. This program will not be used in the following chapters because we will prefer the more involved but more accurate quadratic interpolation method.

As described in this chapter, Bairstow's method usually works very well for finding the quadratic factors of a polynomial. However, the method sometimes fails to converge if there are multiple roots. Hamming (1973) discusses a modification of Bairstow's method that can cure this problem. As just noted, Bairstow's method can only be applied to find roots of a polynomial. Muller's method does not have this restriction—it can find real or complex roots of a polynomial or an arbitrary function.

PROBLEMS

3.1 The function $f(x) = x^2 + 0.9x - 2.2$ has a root near $x = 1$. Use one iteration of Newton's method to approximate this root. Check the answer by using the quadratic formula to find both roots of the equation.

3.2 The function $f(x) = x^3 + 4.4x^2 + 6.2x + 2.8$ has three roots, one of which is near $x = -1.6$.

(a) Use this as an initial value and apply one iteration of Newton's method to find a better answer.

(b) If the answer in (a) is rounded to two significant figures, it is exact; thus one factor of the cubic equation is now known. Remove this factor so as to obtain a quadratic remainder. Find the roots of the quadratic term.

3.3 The equation $e^x = 3x^2$ has a solution near $x = 4$. Use two iterations of Newton's method to improve this initial value.

3.4 Apply the relation in (3.9) with $\varepsilon = 0.1$ to estimate the derivative of $f(x) = x^2 + 2$ at $x = 2$.

3.5 Use the program in Fig. 3.2 to check the answer obtained in Problem 3.3. Stop the computer when the answer is accurate to four significant figures.

3.6 Modify the program in Fig. 3.2 so that data are only printed if $|f(x)| < 10^{-6}$; once these data are printed, have the program automatically stop. Use this modified program on Problem 3.3.

3.7 Using the modified program of Problem 3.6, find the four roots of

$$x^4 + x^3 - 4x^2 - 3x + 3 = 0.$$

3.8   Use $x_0=2$ as an initial guess for the root of $f(x)=ax+b$. Apply one iteration of Newton's method to find the exact solution (the answer will be exact because Newton's method is exact for linear equations).

3.9   Show that Newton's method is not exact for every second-degree equation by considering the function $f(x)=x^2-4$. Choose as an initial value $x=3$ and show that one iteration does not yield the exact answer.

3.10 In Chapter 1 the square root of two was approximated by using the binomial series. A more efficient approximation uses Newton's method to find a root of $f(x)=x^2-2$. Choose the initial value as x equal to 1 and apply two iterations of Newton's method.

3.11 For the function $f(x)=x^3-2x^2-x+2$, choose as the initial value $x_0=1.5$. Follow the process described by the program in Fig. 3.5 to find α_1 and α_2. Also find x_1 and x_2.

3.12 For the function $f(x)=x^2-5x+3$ let $x_0=1$, $x_1=2$, $x_2=4$. Find f_0, f_1, f_2.

3.13 (a) Find the minimum x_m of the parabola that goes through the three points $(1,-1)$, $(2,-3)$, $(4,-1)$.

       (b) Find the minimum of $f(x)=x^2-5x+3$, and compare the answer with the result found in (a).

3.14 For the function $f(x)=x^3-2x^2-x+2$ let $x_0=1.2$, $x_1=1.4$, $x_2=1.8$.

       (a) Find f_0, f_1, f_2.

       (b) Find the minimum x_m of a parabola that goes through the three points (x_0,f_0), (x_1,f_1), (x_2,f_2).

       (c) Find the minimum of $f(x)$ and compare it with the answer in (b).

3.15 Check the answer in Problem 3.13(b) by using the quadratic interpolation program.

3.16 Solve the following nonlinear equation by using the quadratic interpolation program:

$$2e^x=x^2.$$

3.17 This problem establishes the relations in (3.30) and (3.31).

       (a) Compare the coefficient of x^n in (3.28) with the coefficient in (3.29) to yield one of the relations in (3.31).

       (b) Repeat (a) for the coefficients of x^{n-1}.

       (c) Equate the coefficients of x^i for $i=2,3,\ldots,n-2$ to obtain the relation $B_i=A_i-P_0B_{i-1}-Q_0B_{i-2}$.

       (d) Define $B_{n-1}=A_{n-1}-P_0B_{n-2}-Q_0B_{n-3}$, and show that $R=B_{n-1}$.

(e) Define $B_n = A_n - P_0 B_{n-1} - Q_0 B_{n-2}$, and show that $S = B_n + P B_{n-1}$.

3.18 Example 3.3 assumed that a factor of $f(x) = x^3 + 2x^2 + 3x + 2$ was $x^2 + 2x + 3$ and found the remainders. Generalize this result and find the remainders for $f(x) = x^3 + A_1 x^2 + A_2 x + A_3$, assuming that $x^2 + A_1 x + A_2$ is a factor.

3.19 If x^2 is assumed to be a factor of $f(x) = x^3 + A_1 x^2 + A_2 x + A_3$, what is the remainder?

3.20 (a) Show that (3.34a) is equivalent to

$$\frac{\partial B_{n-1}}{\partial P} \delta P + \frac{\partial B_{n-1}}{\partial Q} \delta Q = - B_{n-1}.$$

(b) Show that (3.34b) is equivalent to

$$\left(\frac{\partial B_n}{\partial P} + P_0 \frac{\partial B_{n-1}}{\partial P} + B_{n-1} \right) \delta P + \left(\frac{\partial B_n}{\partial Q} + P_0 \frac{\partial B_{n-1}}{\partial Q} \right) \delta Q$$

$$= - B_n - P_0 B_{n-1}.$$

(c) Use the results in (a) and (b) to show that

$$\left(\frac{\partial B_n}{\partial P} + B_{n-1} \right) \delta P + \frac{\partial B_n}{\partial Q} \delta Q = - B_n.$$

3.21 Show that

$$- \frac{\partial B_i}{\partial P} = B_{i-1} + P_0 \frac{\partial B_{i-1}}{\partial P} + Q_0 \frac{\partial B_{i-2}}{\partial P},$$

$$- \frac{\partial B_i}{\partial Q} = B_{i-2} + P_0 \frac{\partial B_{i-1}}{\partial Q} + Q_0 \frac{\partial B_{i-2}}{\partial Q}.$$

3.22 Show that if the definitions

$$\frac{\partial B_i}{\partial P} = - C_{i-1} \quad \text{and} \quad \frac{\partial B_i}{\partial Q} = - C_{i-2}$$

are substituted into the results of Problem 3.21, then (3.37) is produced.

3.23 Substitute the expressions from Problem 3.22 into Problem 3.20(a, c); then solve the resulting equations to yield (3.35) and (3.36).

3.24 Use two iterations of Bairstow's method to find a quadratic factor of $x^3 + 2x^2 + 3x + 2$. Let the initial guesses be $P = 0$ and $Q = 0$.

3.25 If the output of the Bairstow program indicates $P=2$, $Q=5$, $x_0=4$.

   (a) What was the original function $f(x)$?

   (b) What are the roots of $f(x)$?

3.26 Use the Bairstow program to factor $f(x)=2x^3+4x^2+16x+14$.

3.27 If one quadratic factor of $f(x)=x^4+8x^3+20x^2+23x+4$ is x^2+5x+1, then what is the other quadratic factor?

3.28 (a) Factor $f(x)=x^4+3x^3+15x^2+17x+36$ by using the Bairstow program with initial values $P=0$ and $Q=0$.

   (b) Use the Bairstow program again, but this time choose initial values that will change the order of factorization.

3.29 (a) Factor $f(x)=x^3+6x^2+11x+6$ by using the Bairstow program with initial values $P=0$ and $Q=0$.

   (b) Repeat (a) with $P=5$ and $Q=5$. Compare the answers in (a) and (b).

3.30 Muller's method can also be used to find complex roots. Modify the program of Fig. 3.7 so that it will find complex roots. *Hint*: define certain parameters as complex, modify statement 14, and delete statement 63.

Chapter Four

Interpolation

4.1 INTRODUCTION

The title of this chapter may be somewhat misleading; perhaps a better title would be "Interpolation and Extrapolation". Interpolation is usually meant to imply that a function is to be estimated at a point *interior* to some data. For example, given the values of $\sin 37°$ and $\sin 38°$, one can interpolate for the value of $\sin 37.2°$. On the other hand, extrapolation implies that a function is to be estimated at a point *exterior* to some data. For example, given the values for $\sin 37°$ and $\sin 38°$, one can extrapolate for the value of $\sin 38.3°$.

In this text, the word interpolation will be used to indicate an estimation of a function value based on some given (or calculated) values. It will not imply whether the point is interior or exterior to the given data. The reason for this is that we will learn how to calculate a polynomial which represents the given data. Once we have this polynomial, we will be able to estimate the value of the function at any interior or exterior point. Even though this polynomial can be used for extrapolation as well as interpolation, it is customarily referred to as an *interpolating polynomial*.

A student is usually first introduced to the subject of interpolation in an elementary mathematics course that requires the use of tables: for example, tables of trigonometric functions or of logarithms. By interpolating one is able to estimate the value of a function at points that are not tabulated. This use of interpolation has decreased with the proliferation of calculators that contain subroutines for calculating trigonometric functions as well as many other functions. However, interpolation has many additional uses and is still important.

Interpolation can be useful when one is analyzing experimental data. For example, after an experiment has been concluded and the apparatus dismantled, one may discover an additional measurement would have been beneficial. Instead of doing the experiment again, it may be possible to use the experimental data that are already available to estimate the desired measurement. Or one of the data points might be incorrect; interpolation techniques can be used to replace it with a better value.

Another use of interpolating polynomials is to aid in plotting smooth curves to represent experimental data. One can find an interpolating polynomial which exactly matches the measured values. This polynomial can then be evaluated at enough additional points so that a smooth curve can be plotted. In fact, a computer can be programmed to evaluate the interpolating polynomial and then plot the results.

It is not always best to use an interpolating polynomial which exactly matches the measured values. In any practical experiment there will be sources of error. One way of compensating for the errors is to take more data than should be theoretically necessary and then smooth the data by using a least-squares fitting approach. Another method that will also be studied in this chapter is the use of a cubic spline function to produce a smooth curve.

Interpolating polynomials will be very useful to us in many of the chapters that follow. They will enable us to derive many different formulas. For example, consider numerical integration. It may happen that we wish to integrate a function $f(x)$, but can neither find it in a table of integrals nor discover a way to integrate it analytically. The function $f(x)$ may be evaluated at various points and then approximated by an interpolating polynomial $P(x)$. This polynomial $P(x)$ can be integrated to estimate the integral of $f(x)$. By evaluating $f(x)$ at a sufficient number of points, the numerical integration can be made arbitrarily accurate.

4.2 A UNIQUE SOLUTION

In order to become familiar with notation that will be used throughout this text, consider the following hypothetical experiment. The speed of a race car is measured at different distances from a starting line. The independent variable (distance of the car) will be denoted by x, and the dependent variable (speed of the car) by $f(x)$.

The initial value of the independent variable will be written as x_0, the next will be x_1, etc. Thus the value of the dependent variable at these locations can be written as $f(x_0), f(x_1), f(x_2), \ldots, f(x_n)$. We will prove in this section that there is a unique nth-degree interpolating polynomial that passes through the $n+1$ data values.

In order to demonstrate that it is a *unique* polynomial, assume the opposite. That is, assume that $P(x)$ and $Q(x)$ are two *different* nth-degree polynomials that match the $n+1$ values. Because these polynomials give the same values as the data at points $x_0, x_1, \ldots, x_n$, we have

$$P(x_0) = Q(x_0), \qquad P(x_1) = Q(x_1), \ldots, \qquad P(x_n) = Q(x_n). \quad (4.1)$$

The difference of the two polynomials can be written as $D(x) = P(x) - Q(x)$. It follows from (4.1) that $D(x)$ is zero at $x = x_0, x_1, x_2, \ldots, x_n$. Since

$D(x)$ has at least $n+1$ zeros, its degree must be at least equal to $n+1$. But by assumption $P(x)$ and $Q(x)$ were nth-degree functions, so their difference must be no greater than an nth-degree function. Since the assumption that $P(x)$ and $Q(x)$ were *different* functions led to a contradiction, we must conclude they are really the same function.

The fact that there is a unique nth-degree polynomial that matches $n+1$ data values will be extremely important to us. If one refers to other books for additional information about interpolation, one will find many different interpolating polynomials. However, we know they must all yield the same answer. That is, their form may be different, but we know they could all eventually be manipulated to have the same form, since there is a unique polynomial.

The reader must now be wondering, "If there is a unique polynomial, why do people like to have so many different expressions for it?" The answer is that, depending on the specific application, one form may be easier to evaluate than another. However, the fact that a special form may save a few milliseconds of computer time is of little consequence to most of us. The majority of the readers of this book will not want to invest hours of study to save milliseconds of computer time, so we will limit attention to just two important forms.

4.3 THE NORMALIZED VARIABLE

As mentioned in the previous section, we will want to pass an nth-degree polynomial through $n+1$ values

$$f(x_0), \ f(x_1), \ f(x_2), \ldots, \ f(x_n). \tag{4.2}$$

In most applications we will be able to choose the locations of the independent variable x. It will simplify the calculations if the points are equally spaced, that is, if

$$x_1 - x_0 = x_2 - x_1 = x_3 - x_2 = \cdots = h. \tag{4.3}$$

Because we will encounter equally spaced data so frequently, it will be useful to define a normalized variable s. For this important special case the normalized variable is defined as

$$s = (x - x_0)/h, \tag{4.4}$$

where x_0 is the initial point and h is the spacing between the equidistant points. The parameter h is often called the step size or the increment.

For evenly spaced data we will often use the notation f_s instead of $f(x)$. It should be noted from the definition of s in (4.4) that s is not restricted to integer values.

EXAMPLE 4.1

At 4 P.M., 6 P.M., and 8 P.M. the temperature was measured as 60°, 70°, and 65°. Let x represent the time and $f(x)$ the temperature.

(a) $s = 1.5$ corresponds to what time?
(b) If $x = 2$ P.M., what is s?
(c) What is the value of f_2?

SOLUTION

The initial measurement was at 4 P.M., so that $x_0 = 4$. The measurements were made at increments of two hours; therefore $h = 2$.

(a) Substituting into (4.4),

$$1.5 = (x - 4)/2.$$

Solving for x yields 7 P.M.

(b) $s = (2 - 4)/2 = -1$.

(c) If $s = 2$ then $x = 8$ P.M., so that

$$f_2 = f(x = 8 \text{ P.M.}) = 65°.$$

4.4 SOME USEFUL OPERATORS, Δ AND E

In this section we will study some operators that can be used to derive an especially convenient form for the interpolating polynomial. It must be emphasized that these operators assume evenly spaced data. That is, we are considering the data

$$f_0, f_1, f_2, \ldots, f_n, \tag{4.5}$$

where the x-values $x_0, x_1, x_2, \ldots, x_n$ are uniformly spaced with distance h between adjacent points.

The *difference operator* Δ is defined by the following equation

$$\Delta f_s = f_{s+1} - f_s. \tag{4.6}$$

In this equation s is not necessarily an integer, but in our applications it usually will be. From (4.6) it can be seen that when Δ operates on a function we first replace s by $s + 1$ and then subtract the original function from this shifted function. This produces the *difference function* Δf_s.

Higher-order difference operators are defined analogously to the Δ-operator. For example

$$\Delta^2 f_s = \Delta(\Delta f_s) = \Delta(f_{s+1} - f_s)$$
$$= \Delta f_{s+1} - \Delta f_s$$
$$= (f_{s+2} - f_{s+1}) - (f_{s+1} - f_s).$$

Combining terms yields

$$\Delta^2 f_s = f_{s+2} - 2f_{s+1} + f_s. \tag{4.7}$$

Similarly, by extending this process it can be shown that the third-order and fourth-order difference functions are given by

$$\Delta^3 f_s = f_{s+3} - 3f_{s+2} + 3f_{s+1} - f_s, \tag{4.8}$$
$$\Delta^4 f_s = f_{s+4} - 4f_{s+3} + 6f_{s+2} - 4f_{s+1} + f_s. \tag{4.9}$$

EXAMPLE 4.2

For the function values $f_0 = 2$, $f_1 = 3$, $f_2 = 3$, $f_3 = 1$ we will calculate $\Delta^3 f_0$ two different ways to illustrate the above formulas.

(a) $\Delta^3 f_0 = \Delta^2 f_1 - \Delta^2 f_0$. From (4.7), $\Delta^2 f_1 = f_3 - 2f_2 + f_1 = -2$. Similarly $\Delta^2 f_0 = f_2 - 2f_1 + f_0 = -1$, so that $\Delta^3 f_0 = -1$.
(b) From (4.8), $\Delta^3 f_0 = f_3 - 3f_2 + 3f_1 - f_0 = -1$.

The coefficients in (4.6) to (4.9) are the same as would be encountered if we expanded the binomial $(a-b)^n$ where, for example, $n=4$ for (4.9). We can easily prove that they are the binomial coefficients by introducing the *shift operator* E defined by

$$Ef_s = f_{s+1}. \tag{4.10}$$

Just as we were able to define higher-order difference operators, so can we also define higher-order shift operators. For example, $E^2 f_s = E(Ef_s) = E(f_{s+1}) = f_{s+2}$. Generalizing,

$$E^i f_s = f_{s+i}. \tag{4.11}$$

The difference operator can be expressed in terms of the shift operator:

$$\Delta f_s = f_{s+1} - f_s = Ef_s - f_s. \tag{4.12}$$

This suggests that we write

$$\Delta = E - 1. \tag{4.13}$$

In interpreting this expression we would keep in mind that Δ and E are operators: they cannot really stand alone, but must operate on a function such as f_s.

The relation in (4.13) is very useful because it allows us to easily evaluate higher-order difference functions such as $\Delta^3 f_s$. It follows from (4.13) that

$$\Delta^3 = (E-1)^3 = E^3 - 3E^2 + 3E - 1,$$

so that

$$\Delta^3 f_s = E^3 f_s - 3E^2 f_s + 3E f_s - f_s$$
$$= f_{s+3} - 3f_{s+2} + 3f_{s+1} - f_s,$$

which is the same as (4.8).

This process is easily generalized, as is demonstrated next for the special case of s equal to zero:[1]

$$\Delta^r = (E-1)^r = E^r - rE^{r-1} + \frac{r(r-1)}{2} E^{r-2} - \frac{r(r-1)(r-2)}{3!} E^{r-3} + \cdots,$$

so that

$$\Delta^r f_0 = f_r - r f_{r-1} + \frac{r(r-1)}{2} f_{r-2} - \frac{r(r-1)(r-2)}{3!} f_{r-3} + \cdots. \quad (4.14)$$

The process indicated continues until the last function is f_0.

The expression in (4.14) verifies the observation made earlier that the coefficients of the various functions are the binomial coefficients. As an application of (4.14), consider the case when $r = 4$:

$$\Delta^4 f_0 = f_4 - 4f_3 + 6f_2 - 4f_1 + f_0.$$

This equation agrees with (4.9).

After we study difference tables in the next section, we will develop a program that can find an interpolating polynomial. Part of the program will have to calcuate difference functions. Anticipating this need, we will conclude this section on difference functions by putting (4.14) in a form that is suitable for a computer program. The form we will choose is

$$\Delta^r f_0 = \sum_{i=0}^{r} a_i f_{r-i}, \quad (4.15)$$

where

$$a_0 = 1,$$

$$a_i = -a_{i-1} \frac{r+1-i}{i}, \qquad i = 1, 2, \ldots, r. \quad (4.16)$$

---

[1]The expression for $\Delta^r f_s$ can be obtained from (4.14) by simply increasing each subscript by s.

4.5 DIFFERENCE TABLES

Assume that an experiment has been done and measurements were recorded at many different points. If one then wants to estimate what would have been measured at an additional point, this can be done by interpolation. In the next section we will learn how to construct a polynomial that goes through all data pairs. This polynomial could then be used to interpolate at any other point.

The above process may appear to require an unreasonable amount of work, but this is not true. We will be able to use very high-order interpolating polynomials, because we will develop a program that will delegate the work to a computer. However, we may wish to avoid high-order interpolating polynomials for a reason other than excessive computations.[2]

Very often an understanding of the mathematical relations that describe an experiment can let the experimenter know that a certain degree equation should exactly describe his results. For example, if a car undergoes constant acceleration, then the distance (as a function of time) should be described by a second-degree equation. In this case a second-degree function should be used as an interpolating polynomial.

If in a particular problem one has not obtained any insight into what degree polynomial may describe the situation, the knowledge about the difference functions may help. It is shown in Chapter 5 that the nth-order difference function is related to the nth-order derivative. It thus follows that if a process can be represented by an nth-degree function, then the $(n+1)$th-order difference function should be zero.

A difference table provides a convenient means for examining the various difference functions. An illustration is given in Table 4.1. In order to construct a difference table one must first know the value of the function at the various data points. Thus in order to construct Table 4.1 the values of $f(1), f(1.5), \ldots, f(3.5)$ were used.

Table 4.1
A difference table

x	f	Δf	$\Delta^2 f$	$\Delta^3 f$	$\Delta^4 f$
1.0	3.0	5.5	4.0	1.5	0
1.5	8.5	9.5	5.5	1.5	0
2.0	18.0	15.0	7.0	1.5	
2.5	33.0	22.0	8.5		
3.0	55.0	30.5			
3.5	85.5				

[2]See Section 4.12.

The values for the column labeled Δf were found by applying the formula $\Delta f_s = f_{s+1} - f_s$. Similarly, the entries in the $\Delta^2 f$ column were found by applying $\Delta^2 f_s = \Delta f_{s+1} - \Delta f_s$. Of course, the general formula (4.14) could be used to find any particular difference function, but a difference table lets one see at a glance how a particular function behaves.

An examination of Table 4.1 indicates that all the third-order difference functions are constant and thus the fourth-order difference functions are zero. We can conclude that this particular function is third-order, and we should be able to find the value of the function at any point by constructing a third-order interpolating polynomial.

In most problems the proper degree for the interpolating polynomial will not be as obvious as for the hypothetical case in Table 4.1. Usually there will be some experimental error in the data, and thus the difference functions will also contain errors. However, examining a difference table can help one detect such errors. If a particular datum is thought to be incorrect, a different value can be assumed and then one can observe how this change propagates throughout the difference table.

4.6 THE NEWTON-GREGORY POLYNOMIAL

In this section we will derive a formula for an nth-degree polynomial that exactly matches $n + 1$ equally spaced data. These data will be written as

$$f_0, f_1, f_2, \ldots, f_n. \tag{4.17}$$

Once we have this interpolating polynomial, we will be able to calculate $f(x)$ at any value of x.

The Newton-Gregory polynomial may be obtained by utilizing two simple relations from the previous material about the operators Δ and E. First, it follows from (4.11) that

$$f_s = E^s f_0. \tag{4.18}$$

Second, it follows from (4.13) that

$$E = 1 + \Delta. \tag{4.19}$$

Combining these relations yields $f_s = (1 + \Delta)^s f_0$; thus it follows that

$$f_s = f_0 + s\Delta f_0 + \frac{s(s-1)}{2} \Delta^2 f_0 + \frac{s(s-1)(s-2)}{3!} \Delta^3 f_0 + \cdots. \tag{4.20}$$

The process continues until the last term $\Delta^n f_0$ is reached. The coefficient of this term will contain s^n; thus f_s will be nth-degree as desired.

EXAMPLE 4.3

Use a second-degree polynomial to interpolate the following data:

$$f(-1)=2, \qquad f(1)=6, \qquad f(3)=34.$$

In particular, find $f(0)$.

SOLUTION

For a second-degree polynomial (4.20) becomes

$$f_s = f_0 + s\Delta f_0 + \frac{s(s-1)}{2}\Delta^2 f_0.$$

For this problem

$$f_0 = 2, \qquad \Delta f_0 = 6 - 2 = 4,$$
$$\Delta^2 f_0 = 34 - 2(6) + 2 = 24,$$

so that

$$f_s = 2 + 4s + 12s(s-1) = 12s^2 - 8s + 2.$$

The point $x=0$ corresponds to $s = [0-(-1)]/2 = 0.5$. Substituting $s=0.5$ into f_s yields $f_{0.5} = 1$.

In the above example the second-degree interpolating polynomial was expressed as $f_s = 12s^2 - 8s + 2$. It will usually be sufficient to express the polynomial in terms of s, but if necessary it can be written in terms of x by substituting $s = (x - x_0)/h$. For this problem $x_0 = -1$ and $h = 2$, so that the function becomes $f(x) = 3x^2 + 2x + 1$. Note that $f(0) = 1$, which agrees with the result from Example 4.3, $f_{0.5} = 1$.

It is relatively easy to develop a program that uses a Newton-Gregory polynomial to interpolate data. For this purpose, (4.20) will be rewritten as[3]

$$f_s = \sum_{r=0}^{n} b_r \Delta^r f_0, \tag{4.21}$$

where

$$b_0 = 1, \tag{4.22}$$

$$b_r = b_{r-1}\frac{s+1-r}{r}, \qquad r = 1, 2, \ldots, n.$$

A program for Newton-Gregory interpolation is shown in Fig. 4.1. First, a few words should be said about the comment "subscript translation". An

---

[3]Note the similarity to (4.15) and (4.16).

```
01C     NEWTON-GREGORY INTERPOLATION
02      PROGRAM NG(INPUT,OUTPUT)
06      DIMENSION DEL(50),FT(50)
08      INTEGER R
10C
11C     SUBSCRIPT TRANSLATION: FT(I+1)=F(I)
12C
15      PRINT,*N,X0,H*
16      READ,N,X0,H
17      PRINT,/,*F0,F1,F2,...FN*
18      N1=N+1
19      READ,(FT(I),I=1,N1)
20C
21C     CALCULATE DEL(R)   (EQS. 4.15,4.16)
22      DO 32 R=1,N
24      A=1.
26      DEL(R)=FT(R+1)
28      DO 32 I=1,R
30      A=-A*(R+1-I)/I
32  32  DEL(R)=DEL(R)+A*FT(R-I+1)
34C
35  35  PRINT,/,*X*, $READ,X
37      S=(X-X0)/H
39C
40C     CALCULATE F(X)   (EQS. 4.21,4.22)
44      B=1. $FX=FT(1)
46      DO 50 R=1,N
48      B=B*(S+1-R)/R
50  50  FX=FX+B*DEL(R)
52C
54      PRINT,*F(X)*,FX
56      GO TO 35
999     END
```

FIGURE 4.1. A program for Newton-Gregory interpolation.

unfortunate fact about FORTRAN is that it does not allow for a subscript to be zero. That is, F(0) is not an allowable representation for f_0. In this program this deficiency of FORTRAN was overcome by translating all subscripts by one; for example, FT(1)=f_0 or similarly FT(2)=f_1. Similar substitutions will be made in some of the other programs in this text.

In the Newton-Gregory program, the difference functions $\Delta^r f_0$ are identified as DEL(R) and are calculated as described in Eqs. (4.15), (4.16). An important observation should be made: the calculations of the various difference functions do not need a value for x (the point at which we wish

```
N,X0,H
? 9,0,10

F0,F1,F2,...FN
? 0.0000  .1736  .3420  .5000  .6428
?  .7660  .8660  .9397  .9848 1.0000

X ? -10
F(X)           -.16490E+00

X ? 45
F(X)            .70709E+00

X ? 100
F(X)            .97800E+00
```

FIGURE 4.2. Interpolation by using a ninth-degree Newton-Gregory polynomial to approximate the sine function.

to interpolate). That is, the difference functions are evaluated before a value of x is input into the computer. Because the difference functions do not have to be evaluated for every new x, the interpolation process in Fig. 4.1 is fast. Notice that the calculations are done in terms of the normalized variable s and not in terms of the input variable.

An application of the Newton-Gregory program is shown in Fig. 4.2. The data shown there represent the function

$$f(x) = \sin x$$

evaluated at $x = 0°, 10°, 20°, \ldots, 90°$. The program thus matched a ninth-degree polynomial to these ten data pairs. Once it had calculated the nine different difference functions, it was then able to interpolate for any desired value of x. The interpolated values that are shown in Fig. 4.2 are

$$\sin(-10°) = -0.1649, \quad \sin 45° = 0.7071, \quad \sin 100° = 0.9780.$$

The value for $\sin 45°$ is more accurate than either of the others because $45°$ was in the middle of the interpolation range, while $-10°$ and $100°$ were both beyond the interpolation range—they required extrapolation. In general, a result produced by interpolation will be much more accurate than one produced by extrapolation.

The Newton-Gregory polynomial is very similar to a Taylor series expansion. The similarity can be emphasized by rewriting (4.21) as

$$f_s = \sum_{r=0}^{n} \frac{\Delta^r f_0}{r!} s^{(r)}, \tag{4.23}$$

where

$$s^{(0)} = 1,$$
$$s^{(r)} = s(s-1)(s-2)\cdots(s-r+1). \tag{4.24}$$

The polynomial in (4.23) was derived for discrete function values: $f_0, f_1, \ldots, f_n$. If we were instead given a continuous function, we could expand $f(x)$ in the Taylor series

$$f(x) = \sum_{r=0}^{\infty} \frac{d^r f / dx^r}{r!} (x - x_0)^r. \tag{4.25}$$

Comparing (4.23) and (4.25), we see that the Newton-Gregory polynomial is to discrete functions as the Taylor series is to continuous functions.

4.7 THE LAGRANGE POLYNOMIAL

The Newton-Gregory polynomial is an interpolating polynomial that can be used for evenly spaced data; however, sometimes data will not be evenly spaced. In fact, in the very next section we will discuss inverse interpolation which does not have evenly spaced values. Also, when we study boundary-value differential equations we will need to interpolate data that are not evenly spaced.

The Lagrange polynomial is an interpolating polynomial that can be used for unevenly spaced data, and, of course, for evenly spaced data as a special case. Since there is a unique nth-degree interpolating polynomial, the Newton-Gregory polynomial and the Lagrange polynomial must give the same interpolation results for evenly spaced data. However, the Newton-Gregory polynomial is easier to evaluate, so it should be used if the points are evenly spaced.

Lagrange interpolation expresses the polynomial $f(x)$ as

$$f(x) = \sum_{i=0}^{n} P_i(x) f_i, \tag{4.26}$$

where the polynomials $P_i(x)$ have the following properties:

(a) $P_i(x)$ is an nth-degree polynomial.
(b) $P_i(x_i) = 1$.
(c) $P_i(x_k) = 0$ for $i \neq k$.

For example, if we want to match a second-degree polynomial to three data, then (4.26) becomes

$$f(x) = P_0(x)f_0 + P_1(x)f_1 + P_2(x)f_2, \qquad (4.27)$$

where the polynomials $P_0(x)$, $P_1(x)$, and $P_2(x)$ are all second degree. Also, from property (b) we have

$$P_0(x_0) = P_1(x_1) = P_2(x_2) = 1,$$

and from (c) we have

$$P_0(x_1) = P_0(x_2) = P_1(x_0) = P_1(x_2) = P_2(x_0) = P_2(x_1) = 0.$$

Because of these properties of $P_i(x)$ it follows that $f(x_k) = f_k$ for $k = 0, 1, 2$. That is, the second-degree polynomial in (4.27) matches the three points x_0, x_1, x_2 and is thus another way the *unique* interpolating polynomial can be written.

Generalizing the results from the above discussion, the interpolating polynomial can be expressed as in (4.26)—provided we can find functions $P_i(x)$ that have properties (a), (b), (c). Polynomials that have these properties are

$$P_i(x) = \prod_{\substack{j=0 \\ j \neq i}}^{n} \frac{x - x_j}{x_i - x_j}, \qquad (4.28)$$

where the π symbol indicates that the product of terms should be formed. For example, for $n = 2$

$$P_0(x) = \frac{x - x_1}{x_0 - x_1} \frac{x - x_2}{x_0 - x_2},$$

$$P_1(x) = \frac{x - x_0}{x_1 - x_0} \frac{x - x_2}{x_1 - x_2},$$

$$P_2(x) = \frac{x - x_0}{x_2 - x_0} \frac{x - x_1}{x_2 - x_1}.$$

The Lagrange polynomial is obtained by substituting (4.28) into (4.26), which yields

$$f(x) = \sum_{i=0}^{n} \left[\prod_{\substack{j=0 \\ j \neq i}}^{n} \frac{x - x_j}{x_i - x_j} f_i \right]. \qquad (4.29)$$

In order to illustrate the meaning of this notation we will consider first the case $n = 2$ and then the case $n = 3$. For $n = 2$,

$$f(x) = \frac{x - x_1}{x_0 - x_1} \frac{x - x_2}{x_0 - x_2} f_0 + \frac{x - x_0}{x_1 - x_0} \frac{x - x_2}{x_1 - x_2} f_1 + \frac{x - x_0}{x_2 - x_0} \frac{x - x_1}{x_2 - x_1} f_2. \qquad (4.30)$$

Similarly for $n = 3$,

$$f(x) = \frac{x-x_1}{x_0-x_1}\frac{x-x_2}{x_0-x_2}\frac{x-x_3}{x_0-x_3}f_0 + \frac{x-x_0}{x_1-x_0}\frac{x-x_2}{x_1-x_2}\frac{x-x_3}{x_1-x_3}f_1$$

$$+ \frac{x-x_0}{x_2-x_0}\frac{x-x_1}{x_2-x_1}\frac{x-x_3}{x_2-x_3}f_2 + \frac{x-x_0}{x_3-x_0}\frac{x-x_1}{x_3-x_1}\frac{x-x_2}{x_3-x_2}f_3. \quad (4.31)$$

EXAMPLE 4.4

Example 4.3 found the second-degree Newton-Gregory polynomial that passes through the following data: $f(-1) = 2$, $f(1) = 6$, and $f(3) = 34$. The problem then continued and interpolated to find $f(0)$. In this problem we will use the second-degree Lagrange polynomial to interpolate for $f(0)$.

Applying (4.30) for the data in this problem,

$$f(x) = \frac{x-1}{-1-1}\frac{x-3}{-1-3}2 + \frac{x+1}{1+1}\frac{x-3}{1-3}6 + \frac{x+1}{3+1}\frac{x-1}{3-1}34$$

$$= 3x^2 + 2x + 1.$$

```
01C     LAGRANGE INTERPOLATION
02      PROGRAM L(INPUT,OUTPUT)
06      DIMENSION XT(50),FT(50)
10C
11C     SUBSCRIPT TRANSLATION
12C     FT(I+1)=FT(I)   XT(I+1)=XT(I)
13C
15      PRINT,*N*, $READ,N
18      N1=N+1
20      PRINT,*    X(I)      F(I)*
22      READ,(XT(I),FT(I),I=1,N1)
34C
35 35   PRINT,/,*X*, $READ,X
39C
40C     CALCULATE F(X)    (EQ. 4.29)
41      FX=0.
43      DO 55 I=1,N1
44      P=1.
46      DO 50 J=1,N1
50 50   IF(J.NE.I) P=P*(X-XT(J))/(XT(I)-XT(J))
55 55   FX=FX+P*FT(I)
60C
64      PRINT,*FX*,FX
66      GO TO 35
999     END
```

FIGURE 4.3. A program for Lagrange interpolation.

This polynomial can be evaluated at any value of x; in particular, $f(0)=1$, which agrees with the answer in Example 4.3.

A program for Lagrange interpolation is given in Fig. 4.3. In this program the letter P represents the polynomials $P_i(x)$ that are described in (4.28). These polynomials are multiplied by the functions f_i and then added together to form the summation in (4.26). An illustration of the use of this program is given in the next section.

4.8 INVERSE INTERPOLATION

The following data are plotted in Fig. 4.4:

$$f(0.2)=0.45, \quad f(0.4)=0.5, \quad f(0.6)=0.6, \quad f(0.8)=0.75, \quad f(1)=1.$$

The function $y=f(x)$ is a single-valued function of x. That is, for any value of x there is only one value of y; thus we can interpolate and for any x find y. For example, using the Newton-Gregory program to fit a fourth-degree polynomial to the data and then interpolating for the function at $x=0.5$ yields $y(0.5)=0.54$.

For the above function we can also consider x to be a single-valued function of y. That is, for any value of y there is only one value of x; thus we can interpolate and for any y find x. This process of finding what x produced $y=f(x)$ is called inverse interpolation.

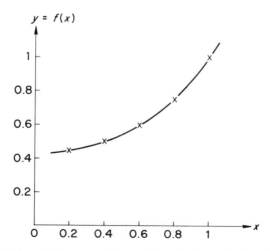

FIGURE 4.4. For these data, y can be considered to be a single-valued function of x or vice versa.

The interpolation problem can be stated as: given the points $x_0, x_1, \ldots, x_n$ and the function values $f_0, f_1, \ldots, f_n$ at these points, estimate the value of the function at the point x. The points $x_0, x_1, \ldots, x_n$ are usually chosen to be equally spaced so as to simplify the calculations.

The inverse interpolation problem can be stated as: given the function values $f_0, f_1, \ldots, f_n$ at the points $x_0, x_1, \ldots, x_n$, estimate the location of the point x at which the function has a certain value f.

Notice that the inverse interpolation problem is just like the interpolation problem—except the roles of the points $x_0, x_1, \ldots, x_n$ and the function values $f_0, f_1, \ldots, f_n$ have been interchanged. If one is doing an experiment, or using a table of data, one usually does not have total control over the function values; thus for inverse interpolation the function values will probably not be evenly spaced. For inverse interpolation there is not a choice between Newton-Gregory interpolation and Lagrange interpolation; Lagrange interpolation must be used because of the unevenly spaced data.

EXAMPLE 4.5

Figure 4.5 illustrates inverse interpolation for the sine function. The Lagrange interpolation program of the previous section was used to fit a

```
N ? 3
      X(I)        F(I)
?  .1736        10
?  .3420        20
?  .6428        40
?  .7660        50

X ?  .5
FX              29.92
```

FIGURE 4.5. Inverse interpolation by using the Lagrange program.

third-degree polynomial to the four data values

$$0.1736 = \sin^{-1} 10°, \quad 0.342 = \sin^{-1} 20°,$$
$$0.6428 = \sin^{-1} 40°, \quad 0.766 = \sin^{-1} 50°.$$

The computer was then asked to determine what angle has a sine equal to 0.5. The output indicates $0.5 = \sin^{-1} 29.92°$.

4.9 INTRODUCTION TO LEAST-SQUARES DATA FITTING

In the curve fitting we have done so far we have assumed we want to match the data exactly. However, this may not be the case if the data contain errors. In any practical experiment there will be sources of error and thus the data will not be totally reliable. In order to compensate for errors one can take more data than should theoretically be necessary in the hope that some of the errors will cancel.

Figure 4.6 illustrates a hypothetical situation. The ×'s represent experimental data, and the curve that goes through all these points represents a high-order interpolation polynomial. Because it is high-order, it need not be very smooth. On the other hand, a lower-order interpolating polynomial may not go through all the experimental points, but it may yield more realistic results when used for interpolation. Often a plot such as this is very useful in alerting one to possible trouble.

Suppose from our knowledge of the system we know that an nth-degree polynomial should describe the experimental results. If the results were error free we would be content to take $n+1$ measurements, because this determines a unique nth-degree polynomial. However, we will instead take $m+1$ measurements (where $m>n$) to determine the nth-degree polynomial.

In this section we will assume we have taken measurements at $m+1$ points $x_0, x_1, x_2, \ldots, x_m$ and recorded the data $y_0, y_1, y_2, \ldots, y_m$. We want to fit the following nth-degree polynomial to the data:

$$f(x) = \sum_{j=0}^{n} a_j x^j. \tag{4.32}$$

The error (difference between the experimental data and the polynomial) at point x_i is

$$e_i = y_i - f(x_i), \qquad i = 0, 1, 2, \ldots, m. \tag{4.33}$$

We would like to choose the coefficients a_j in (4.32) so as to minimize the errors at each of the data points. We know it is not possible to make the error zero at every point, because an nth-degree polynomial cannot exactly

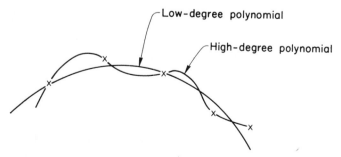

FIGURE 4.6. A low-degree polynomial may yield better results.

match $m+1$ points. Realizing that it is not possible to obtain zero error, the least-squares error criteria seeks to minimize the sum of the squared errors. That is, it minimizes[4]

$$E = \sum_{i=0}^{m} e_i^2$$

$$= \sum_{i=0}^{m} \left[y_i - \left(a_0 + a_1 x_i + a_2 x_i^2 + \cdots a_n x_i^n \right) \right]^2. \tag{4.34}$$

Minimization requires that

$$\frac{\partial E}{\partial a_0} = 0, \qquad \frac{\partial E}{\partial a_1} = 0, \ldots, \qquad \frac{\partial E}{\partial a_n} = 0. \tag{4.35}$$

This is a set of $n+1$ equations in terms of the $n+1$ unknowns $a_0, a_1, \ldots, a_n$, and thus we can solve for these unknown coefficients. The details of this solution can be obtained by differentiating (4.34):

$$\frac{\partial E}{\partial a_0} = 0 = \sum_{i=0}^{m} 2 \left[y_i - \left(a_0 + a_1 x_i + a_2 x_i^2 + \cdots + a_n x_i^n \right) \right] (-1)$$

$$\frac{\partial E}{\partial a_1} = 0 = \sum_{i=0}^{m} 2 \left[y_i - \left(a_0 + a_1 x_i + a_2 x_i^2 + \cdots + a_n x_i^n \right) \right] (-x_i) \quad (4.36)$$

$$\vdots$$

$$\frac{\partial E}{\partial a_n} = 0 = \sum_{i=0}^{m} 2 \left[y_i - \left(a_0 + a_1 x_i + a_2 x_i^2 + \cdots + a_n x_i^n \right) \right] (-x_i^n).$$

The above set of equations is equivalent to

$$C_{00} a_0 + C_{01} a_1 + C_{02} a_2 + \cdots + C_{0n} a_n = \sum_{i=0}^{m} y_i,$$

$$C_{10} a_0 + C_{11} a_1 + C_{12} a_2 + \cdots + C_{1n} a_n = \sum_{i=0}^{m} x_i y_i, \tag{4.37}$$

$$\vdots$$

$$C_{n0} a_0 + C_{n1} a_1 + C_{n2} a_2 + \cdots + C_{nn} a_n = \sum_{i=0}^{m} x_i^n y_i,$$

where

$$C_{ij} = \sum_{k=0}^{m} x_k^{i+j}. \tag{4.38}$$

[4]The individual errors e_i are squared so that negative errors will not be canceled by positive errors.

EXAMPLE 4.6

In this example we will choose a second-degree function $f(x) = a_0 + a_1 x + a_2 x^2$ to minimize the mean-square error E for the following data:

x:	0	0.5	1	1.5	2
y:	-2.9	-1.8	0.2	2.0	5.2

The coefficients a_0, a_1, and a_2 can be obtained by solving (4.37), which for this example is

$$5a_0 + 5a_1 + 7.5a_2 = 2.7$$
$$5a_0 + 7.5a_1 + 12.5a_2 = 12.7$$
$$7.5a_0 + 12.5a_1 + 22.125a_2 = 25.05.$$

This set of linear equations can be solved by applying any of the techniques described in Chapter 2. For example, the Gauss elimination program of Fig. 2.1 yields

$$a_0 = -2.889, \qquad a_1 = 1.714, \qquad a_2 = 1.143,$$

so that the second-degree polynomial is

$$f(x) = -2.889 + 1.714x + 1.143x^2.$$

This section has served as an *introduction* to least-squares data fitting. Least-squares data fitting is a practical method of reducing the effects of experimental errors, but solving the set of equations in (4.37) is not the most practical means of obtaining the least-squares solution. The coefficients in (4.37) may differ greatly in size, and thus the set of equations may be ill conditioned.

In Chapter 10 we will develop a general purpose program that can be used to minimize error functions. In particular, we will be able to apply the program to adjust iteratively the polynomial coefficients $a_0, a_1, \dots, a_n$ so as to minimize the mean-square error. This will be a practical means of doing least-squares data fitting.

4.10 SPLINE FUNCTIONS

It is not always wise to use a high-degree interpolating polynomial to match a larger number of data values. The previous section described how data can be fitted by using a least-squares approach. Another possibility is to use spline functions. The spline function that is most commonly used is the cubic one, and that will be discussed in this section.

A spline function can be considered to be an analytical French curve. A French curve is a graphical tool that is used as an aid in drawing curves (plots). If the draftsperson is skilled, the resulting curve will go through the data points and be smooth—the first derivative will be continuous. A cubic polynomial can be used to do an even better job, since it has four parameters that can be selected. The parameters can be selected so that the curve goes through two adjacent points and also so that the first and second derivatives are continuous. A cubic polynomial that has these properties is said to be a cubic spline function; it can be found by using equations as outlined below.

We will assume that we have taken measurements at $x_0, x_1, x_2, \ldots, x_n$ and obtained the values $f_0, f_1, f_2, \ldots, f_n$. For ease of presentation the x-values will be assumed to be uniformly spaced with distance h between the adjacent points, but this restriction is not necessary.

The cubic spline function $f(x)$ is a set of third-degree polynomials that goes through each of the data points and has continuous first and second derivatives. It can be shown[5] that it is given by

$$
f(x) = \frac{(x_i - x)^3}{6h} M_{i-1} + \frac{(x - x_{i-1})^3}{6h} M_i + (x - x_{i-1}) \left(\frac{f_i}{h} - \frac{hM_i}{6} \right)
$$

$$
+ (x_i - x) \left(\frac{f_{i-1}}{h} - \frac{hM_{i-1}}{6} \right), \tag{4.39}
$$

where x is between x_{i-1} and x_i.

M_i represents the second derivative of $f(x)$ evaluated at x_i. These derivatives can be found by solving

$$
M_{i-1} + 4M_i + M_{i+1} = \frac{6}{h^2}(f_{i-1} - 2f_i + f_{i+1}), \qquad i = 1, 2, \ldots, n-1. \tag{4.40}
$$

This is a set of $n-1$ linear equations in terms of $n+1$ unknowns $(M_0, M_1, \ldots, M_n)$. Two other equations can be obtained by putting constraints on the derivatives at the end points. The actual constraints that are used depend on the problem that is being solved. One approach is to require that near the end points the curves should be as smooth as possible, which is accomplished by requiring that the third derivatives be continuous at x_1 and x_{n-1}. This yields[6]

$$
M_0 - 2M_1 + M_2 = 0
$$

$$
M_{n-2} - 2M_{n-1} + M_n = 0. \tag{4.41}
$$

[5]Liou, M. L. (May 1976), "Spline Fit Made Easy", *IEEE Trans. Computers*, pp. 522–527.
[6]Pennington, R. H. (1970), *Introductory Computer Methods and Numerical Analysis*, (London: MacMillan).

EXAMPLE 4.7

In this example we will find a third-degree cubic spline function for the following data:

$$x: \quad 0 \quad 0.5 \quad 1 \quad 1.5 \quad 2$$

$$f(x): -2.9 \quad -1.8 \quad 0.2 \quad 2.0 \quad 5.2$$

Applying (4.40) and (4.41) yields

$$M_0 + 4M_1 + M_2 = 21.6$$
$$M_1 + 4M_2 + M_3 = -4.8$$
$$M_2 + 4M_3 + M_4 = 33.6$$
$$M_0 - 2M_1 + M_2 = 0$$
$$M_2 - 2M_3 + M_4 = 0.$$

Solving these equations by the Gauss elimination program of Chapter 2 yields

$$M_0 = 10.7, \quad M_1 = 3.6, \quad M_2 = -3.5, \quad M_3 = 5.6, \quad M_4 = 14.7.$$

Now that the second derivatives M_i are known, (4.39) can be used for interpolation. For example,

$$f(0.75) = 0.5(f_1 + f_2) - 0.015625(M_1 + M_2) = -0.8016.$$

4.11 FOURIER SERIES APPLIED TO INTERPOLATION

The interpolation methods that have been discussed thus far in this chapter used polynomials to match data. This section will introduce another way that is common—the data will be interpolated by using a sum of sine and cosine functions which is termed a Fourier series. it will be shown later in this section that sines and cosines have a special property called orthogonality. There are many other orthogonal functions that are used in numerical analysis (e.g. Legendre polynomials), but they will not be discussed here.

This book will not discuss many of the general theorems that have been developed about the Fourier series, as that is too specialized for an introductory text such as this. However, it is worth mentioning that the Fourier theory is well developed and can provide powerful tools for numerical analysis. Not only is there the Fourier series of sine and cosine functions; there is also a Fourier series of complex exponentials. Furthermore, there is the Fourier transformation, which has found many applications, especially since the introduction of the fast Fourier transformation (Brigham 1974).

In order to keep the material that follows to a reasonable length, phrases such as "it can be shown that" will be resorted to. Asking the reader to take some results on faith or to derive the results will allow more time for the applicaton of Fourier series to numerical methods.

If $f(x)$ is a periodic function,[7] then it can be expressed in terms of a Fourier series. An example of a periodic function is shown in Fig. 4.7. The

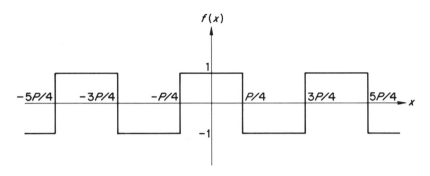

FIGURE 4.7. A square wave of unit amplitude and period P.

function shown in that figure has a period of length P; that is,

$$f(x)=f(x+P)=f(x+2P)=\cdots. \tag{4.42}$$

While most functions that we want to interpolate will not be periodic, they can usually be "truncated" and then treated as periodic. More will be said about this later.

If a function $f(x)$ is periodic with period P, then it can be shown that it can be expressed by the Fourier series

$$f(x)=\frac{A_0}{2}+\sum_{i=1}^{\infty} A_i\cos\frac{2\pi ix}{P}+\sum_{i=1}^{\infty} B_i\sin\frac{2\pi ix}{P}. \tag{4.43}$$

Theoretically, the above summation requires an infinite number of terms; practically, the coefficients A_i and B_i usually become so small as i increases that eventually they can be ignored.

The coefficients A_i can be found by multiplying both sides of (4.43) by

[7]It must also satisfy some rather nonrestrictive requirements known as the Dirichlet conditions.

$\cos(2\pi kx/P)$ and then integrating over the period. That is,[8]

$$\int_0^P f(x)\cos\frac{2\pi kx}{P}\,dx = \frac{A_0}{2}\int_0^P \cos\frac{2\pi kx}{P}\,dx$$

$$+\sum_{i=1}^{\infty} A_i \int_0^P \cos\frac{2\pi ix}{P}\cos\frac{2\pi kx}{P}\,dx$$

$$+\sum_{i=1}^{\infty} B_i \int_0^P \sin\frac{2\pi ix}{P}\cos\frac{2\pi kx}{P}\,dx. \qquad (4.44)$$

This was done because the sine and cosine functions have a special property: it can be shown that

$$\int_0^P \cos\frac{2\pi ix}{P}\cos\frac{2\pi kx}{P}\,dx = \begin{cases} P & i=k=0 \\ 0.5P & i=k\neq0 \\ 0 & i\neq k \end{cases}$$

$$\int_0^P \sin\frac{2\pi ix}{P}\cos\frac{2\pi ix}{P}\,dx = 0. \qquad (4.45)$$

Functions that satisfy relations such as those in (4.45) are said to be *orthogonal*. Other functions besides sines and cosines are orthogonal and find applications in numerical methods.

It follows from (4.44) and (4.45) that

$$A_i = \frac{2}{P}\int_0^P f(x)\cos\frac{2\pi ix}{P}\,dx, \qquad i=0,1,2,\dots. \qquad (4.46)$$

Similarly, it can be shown that

$$B_i = \frac{2}{P}\int_0^P f(x)\sin\frac{2\pi ix}{P}\,dx, \qquad i=1,2,\dots. \qquad (4.47)$$

These equations indicate how to find the Fourier coefficients (A_i, B_i) for continuous $f(x)$. In order to apply the Fourier series to interpolation it is necessary to replace the continuous function $f(x)$ by a discrete function, since there can only be a finite number of data. As was assumed for Newton-Gregory interpolation, it will again be assumed that there are $n+1$ equally spaced data points $x_0, x_1, x_2, \dots, x_n$, which have function values $f_0, f_1, f_2, \dots, f_n$.

---

[8]The fact that the integral starts at $x=0$ implies that the origin is the reference point. Eventually we will let an arbitrary point x_0 be the reference.

If "discrete Fourier coefficients" A_i, B_i are chosen properly, then the function values f_k can be expressed in the following form which is very similar to (4.43):

$$f_k = \frac{A_0}{2} + \sum_{i=1}^{m-1} A_i \cos\frac{2\pi i x_k}{P} + \sum_{i=1}^{m-1} B_i \sin\frac{2\pi i x_k}{P} + \frac{A_m}{2}\cos\frac{2\pi m x_k}{P}. \quad (4.48)$$

This is a form adopted from Hamming (1973). An important point is that there should be as many unknown coefficients (A_i, B_i) as there are data (f_k). That is, $1 + 2(m-1) + 1 = n+1$, which implies

$$m = (n+1)/2.$$

The above discussion implies that for m to be an integer, n must be odd. Furthermore, the data must represent a periodic function, since it is to be approximated by a Fourier series. The case $n=5$ is illustrated in Fig. 4.8. The period P for this case is $6h$, where h is the spacing between points. In general, the period is $P = (n+1)h$. Although $f(x)$ is shown as restricted to the interval P in Fig. 4.8, the representation by a discrete Fourier series will make it repeat periodically outside of this interval.

If n is even, then we could ignore the last function value and thus cause n to become odd. That is, the substitution $n-1 \to n$ changes an even number to an odd number. However, instead of simply discarding the last function value it is better to first make the substitution $(f_0+f_n)/2 \to f_0$, which replaces the initial function value by the average of the first and last values.

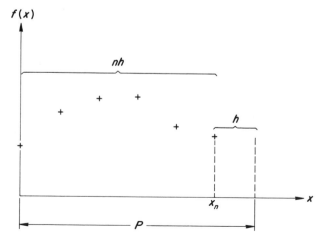

FIGURE 4.8. Representation of a function by discrete data points.

```
01C    FOURIER INTERPOLATION
02     PROGRAM FI(INPUT,OUTPUT)
03 03  FORMAT(1P,E14.5)
06     DIMENSION AT(50),BT(50),FT(50)
10C
11C    SUBSCRIPT TRANSLATION
12C    AT(I+1)=A(I)  BT(I+1)=B(I)  FT(I+1)=F(I)
13C
15     PRINT,*N,X0,H*
16     READ,N,X0,H
17     PRINT,/,*F0,F1,F2,...FN*
18     N1=N+1
19     READ,(FT(I),I=1,N1)
20C
21C    REDEFINE TERMS IF N EVEN
22     M=(N+1)/2
23     M1=M+1
24     IF(2*M.EQ.N+1) GO TO 32
28     FT(1)=.5*(FT(1)+FT(N1))
29     N=N-1 $N1=N1-1
30C
31C    CALULATE A(I ),B(I)   (EQ. 11.8)
32 32  DO 44 I=1,M1
34     AT(I)=BT(I)=0.
36     Z=6.283185308*(I-1)/N1
38     DO 41 K=1,N1
40     AT(I)=AT(I)+FT(K)*COS(K*Z-Z)
41 41  BT(I)=BT(I)+FT(K)*SIN(K*Z-Z)
43     AT(I)=2.*AT(I)/N1
44 44  BT(I)=2.*BT(I)/N1
46C
47 47  PRINT,/,*X*, $READ,X
49C
50C    CALCULATE F(X)   (EQ. 11.7)
52     FX=.5*AT(1)
54     Z=6.283185308*(X-X0)/(N1*H)
56     DO 57 I=2,M
57 57  FX=FX+AT(I)*COS(I*Z-Z)+BT(I)*SIN(I*Z-Z)
59     FX=FX+.5*AT(M1)*COS(M*Z)
64C
66     PRINT,*F(X)*, $PRINT 3,FX
68     GO TO 47
999    END
```

FIGURE 4.9. A program for Fourier interpolation.

The discrete Fourier coefficients in (4.48) can be found by analogy to the derivation of the continuous Fourier series. The result is

$$A_i = \frac{2}{n+1} \sum_{k=0}^{n} f_k \cos \frac{2\pi i k}{n+1}, \qquad i = 0, 1, 2, \ldots,$$

$$B_i = \frac{2}{n+1} \sum_{k=0}^{n} f_k \sin \frac{2\pi i k}{n+1}, \qquad i = 1, 2, \ldots, \qquad (4.49)$$

which is very similar to (4.46) and (4.47). In (4.49) it is assumed that $x_k = kh/P$; that is, x_0 is located at the origin. This is analogous to the zero lower limit of integration in (4.46).

A program for the calculation of the discrete Fourier series is given in Fig. 4.9. This program does not restrict the reference point x_0 to be located at the origin. The origin is shifted by using $x - x_0$ instead of x in the right-hand side of (4.48).

An application of the Fourier interpolation program is given in Fig. 4.10. The data in that figure represent the function $f(x) = e^x$ evaluated at $x = 0.6, 0.7, 0.8, 0.9, 1.0$. Since there are an odd number of points, the initial value was automatically changed by the computer to $(e^{0.6} + e^1)/2 = 2.2702$. This explains why $f(0.6) = 2.2702$ and $f(1) = 2.2702$ was found by the

```
N,X0,H
? 4,.6,.1

F0,F1,F2,...FN
? 1.8221    2.0138    2.2255    2.4596    2.7183

X ? .6
F(X)      2.27020E+00

X ? .7
F(X)      2.01380E+00

X ? .75
F(X)      2.06886E+00

X ? 1
F(X)      2.27020E+00

X ? 1.1
F(X)      2.01380E+00
```

FIGURE 4.10. An application of the Fourier interpolation program.

computer. The fact that the discrete Fourier series matches the data exactly is demonstrated by $f(0.7) = 2.0138$. An application of the program to interpolation is illustrated by $f(0.75) = 2.06886$. This is quite close to the value $e^{0.75} = 2.117$. The fact that the evaluation is periodic is illustrated by $f(1.1) = 2.0138 = f(0.7)$. It should be noted that this value is not close to $e^{1.1} = 3.004$. This demonstrates that the Fourier interpolation program should be used only to interpolate—because of the periodicity property it should not be used for extrapolation.

4.12 SUGGESTED READING IN RELATED TOPICS

It should be emphasized that there is a unique nth-degree polynomial that exactly matches $n + 1$ data values. However, there is not a unique way of writing this polynomial. Some forms of the interpolating polynomial are easier to evaluate than others. For example, in this chapter we studied the Newton-Gregory polynomial and the Lagrange polynomial. Either representation of the interpolating polynomial can be used for evenly spaced data.[9]

The Newton-Gregory polynomial will be used in future chapters to help derive numerical integration and differentiation formulas. This material will later be extended to aid in the numerical solution of differential equations. In these applications we will be able to formulate the problem so that the data are evenly spaced; however, this is not always possible, so in some cases we are not able to apply the Newton-Gregory formula. For example, inverse interpolation requires a formula (such as Lagrange's) that is valid for unevenly spaced data.

In addition to the Newton-Gregory polynomial there are numerous other representations of the interpolating polynomial that have been used to interpolate evenly spaced data. In fact, the polynomial given in (4.20) is often called the Newton-Gregory *forward* polynomial, because there is also a Newton-Gregory *backward* polynomial. The forward polynomial is formulated in terms of the function value at an initial point x_0. The other data are used by proceeding forward from x_0 and calculating the various *forward* difference functions. The forward difference operator was defined by $\Delta f_s = f_{s+1} - f_s$. There is also a backward difference operator which is defined by $\nabla f_s = f_s - f_{s-1}$. The Newton-Gregory backward polynomial is formulated in terms of the last function value f_n. The other data are used by proceeding backward from x_n and calculating various backward difference functions.

One is not restricted to proceeding just in a forward direction or just in a backward direction; there are numerous "zigzag" paths that are possible. A

[9]The Lagrange polynomial can also be used for unevenly spaced data.

Lorenge diagram can be used to picture these different possibilities, some of which have been named after Bessel, Stirling, etc. See Hildebrand (1974) for a discussion of these forms and many others.

An nth-degree interpolating polynomial can exactly match $n+1$ data points, but that of course does not mean there will be no interpolation errors. For example, in Section 4.6 a ninth-degree polynomial was matched to the sine function at ten points, but the interpolated value of $\sin(-10°)$ was -0.1649 instead of the actual value of -0.1736.

There is a formula that can be used to predict the value of the interpolation error; however, as we shall shortly see, it is usually not very informative. Carnahan (1969) demonstrates that the error is given by

$$E(x) = \frac{f^{(n+1)}(\eta)}{(n+1)!} \prod_{i=0}^{n} (x - x_i), \tag{4.50}$$

where $f^{(n+1)}(\eta)$ is the $(n+1)$st derivative evaluated at the point η for η somewhere between the initial point x_0 and the final point x_n. There are two difficulties in using (4.50). First, the function $f(x)$ is not known (this is why we are interpolating), and thus the $(n+1)$th derivative certainly is not known. Second, the location of the point η is not known except that it is between x_0 and x_n.

While an exact error estimate cannot be obtained from (4.50), it can still provide some useful information. First we can note that the error can be minimized by minimizing $\prod_{i=0}^{n}(x - x_i)$. This fact has been applied to show that choosing the data locations x_i not to be evenly spaced, but instead to be located according to a Chebyshev criterion, will lead to smaller errors (Householder 1953).

An even more important observation has been made regarding the error formula (4.50). For many functions, the magnitude of the derivative increases as the order of the derivative increases (Hamming 1973). Thus (4.50) implies that increasing the degree n of the interpolating polynomial will not necessarily result in a smaller error; it may actually increase it.

If we know (from physical reasoning, from examining a difference table, etc.) that an nth-degree polynomial should describe a particular situation, we will not improve accuracy by fitting a higher-degree polynomial to more data. However, as described in Section 4.9, the least-squares method can be applied to reduce errors. Also, as discussed in Chapter 10, this approach can be generalized, leading to the least-pth optimization technique. In fact, the least-pth technique is very closely related to the Chebyshev theory of Section 10.6.

It is not always wise to use a high-degree interpolating polynomial to match a large number of data. One solution is to use cubic *spline functions* to connect the points. These functions were briefly introduced in this chapter, but books have been dedicated to them. An example was solved by using the Gauss elimination method to obtain the second-derivative coefficients. There exist methods of finding these coefficients that are much more efficient and accurate (Liou, 1976, note 5).

This chapter on interpolation was concluded by illustrating how the Fourier series can be applied to interpolation. This is an alternative solution which can be used instead of approximating the data with polynomials. The Fourier approach is well developed and has been applied to other facets of numerical methods—but that will not be done in this text. The interested reader is referred to Hamming (1973).

It is interesting to note that the polynomial approach to least-squares data fitting that was used in Section 4.9 can be related to the Fourier-series approach of Section 4.11. In Section 4.9 the coefficients a_j of the sum $\sum_{j=0}^{n} a_j x^j$ were picked so as to minimize the mean-square error. In Section 4.11 we used coefficients of sine or cosine functions instead of coefficients of a power series. This can be generalized so that the coefficients a_j of the sum $\sum_{j=0}^{n} a_j g_j(x)$ are picked to minimize mean square error. Thus, e.g., in Section 4.9 we studied the special case $g_j(x) = x^j$. For this special case we demonstrated that the a_j were solutions to

$$c_{i0}a_0 + c_{i1}a_1 + \cdots + c_{in}a_n = \sum_{k=0}^{m} x_k^i y_k, \qquad i = 0, 1, \ldots, n,$$

where $c_{ij} = \sum_{k=0}^{m} x_k^{i+j}$. For the more general case it can be shown (Conte and de Boor 1972) that the a_j are solutions to

$$c_{i0}a_0 + c_{i1}a_1 + \cdots + c_{in}a_n = \sum_{k=0}^{m} g_i(x_k) y_k,$$

where $c_{ij} = \sum_{k=0}^{m} g_i(x_k) g_j(x_k)$. It can also be shown that solving the above equations is equivalent to solving the following matrix equation:

$$\begin{bmatrix} a_0 \\ a_1 \\ \vdots \\ a_n \end{bmatrix} = (\mathbf{A}^T \mathbf{A})^{-1} \mathbf{A} \begin{bmatrix} y_0 \\ y_1 \\ \vdots \\ y_m \end{bmatrix},$$

where

$$\mathbf{A} = \begin{bmatrix} g_0(x_0) & g_1(x_0) & \cdots & g_n(x_0) \\ g_0(x_1) & g_1(x_1) & \cdots & g_n(x_1) \\ \vdots & \vdots & \vdots & \\ g_0(x_m) & g_1(x_m) & \cdots & g_n(x_m) \end{bmatrix}.$$

PROBLEMS

4.1 If $x_0 = -2$ and $h = 4$, what is x_5?

4.2 Given that $x_0 = 0$ and $h = 1.5$, find the x that corresponds to $s = -2.2$.

4.3 Using the fact that $\Delta^2 f_s = f_{s+2} - 2f_{s+1} + f_s$, derive the expression for $\Delta^3 f_s$.

4.4 Negative step sizes are also possible. As an illustration, assume $x_1 = 4$ and $h = -2$. Find x_3.

4.5 If $\Delta^2 f_0 = 2$, $\Delta^2 f_1 = 4$, $\Delta^2 f_2 = 5$, and $\Delta^2 f_3 = 1$,
  (a) What is $\Delta^3 f_1$?
  (b) What is $\Delta^4 f_1$?

4.6 For $f_0 = 2$, $f_1 = 3$, $f_2 = 3$, $f_3 = 1$, $f_4 = -5$,
  (a) What is $E^2 f_1$?
  (b) What is $\Delta^3 f_1$?

4.7 Apply (4.14) to find an expression for $\Delta^5 f_0$. What is $\Delta^5 f_s$?

4.8 Construct a difference table for $f(x) = 2x^2 - 3x + 4$. Use $x_0 = -1$, $x_1 = -0.5, \ldots, x_4 = 1$.

4.9 Find a new difference table for Problem 4.8 if the function at x_1 is incorrectly calculated as $f_1 = 5$.

4.10 Apply (4.8) to the data in Table 4.1 to verify that the value of $\Delta^3 f$ is equal to 1.5 at $x = 1.5$.

4.11 For the case $n = 3$, use (4.20) to determine the coefficients a_0, a_1, a_2, a_3 in the following equation:
$$f_s = a_0 + a_1 s + a_2 s^2 + a_3 s^3.$$

4.12 If $f_s = 2s^3 + s + 15$, then the function can also be expressed as $f(x) = a_3 x^3 + a_2 x^2 + a_1 x + a_0$. Find these coefficients if $x_0 = 2$ and $h = 1$.

4.13 The Newton-Gregory polynomial is supposed to be exact at the given data pairs. For the case $n = 7$, verify that (4.20) gives the exact answer at $s = 3$. That is, evaluate the right side of (4.20) at $s = 3$ and show that it is f_3.

4.14 If $f(x) = 4x^2 + 2x - 1$ passes through evenly spaced data that have $x_0 = 3$ and $h = 2$, then the function can also be expressed as $f_s = a_2 s^2 + a_1 s + a_0$. Find these coefficients.

4.15 At 1 P.M., 2 P.M., and 3 P.M. the temperature was measured as 60°, 70°, and 65°. Use a second-degree polynomial to estimate the temperature at 2:30 P.M.

4.16 Use the Newton-Gregory polynomial to find a second-degree function that fits the following data:

$$(1,1), \quad (2,2), \quad (3,3).$$

4.17 Data were taken at $x_0=1$, $x_1=3$, and $x_2=5$, and the following interpolating polynomial was obtained:

$$f_s = 8s^2 + 4s + 1.$$

The polynomial can instead be expressed as

$$f(x) = A_2 x^2 + A_1 x + A_0.$$

Find A_0, A_1, A_2.

4.18 Assume that an object accelerates at a constant rate, so that its location r can be expressed as a second-degree equation in terms of the time. If $r(1)=6$, $r(3)=34$, and $r(5)=86$, use a Newton-Gregory polynomial to discover what $r(2)$ was.

4.19 Use the Newton-Gregory program to pass a fourth-degree polynomial through the values $f(1)=2$, $f(3)=3$, $f(5)=3$, $f(7)=2$, and $f(9)=-4$. Interpolate for the following data: $f(0)$, $f(2)$, $f(4)$, $f(6)$, $f(8)$, and $f(10)$.

4.20 Use the Newton-Gregory program to pass a fourth-degree polynomial through the values $f(-1)=4$, $f(1)=2$, $f(3)=3$, $f(5)=3$, and $f(7)=2$. Interpolate for the same data as in Problem 4.19 and then compare the answers.

4.21 Use the Newton-Gregory program to pass a fifth-degree polynomial through the values $f(-1)=4$, $f(1)=2$, $f(3)=3$, $f(5)=3$, $f(7)=2$, and $f(9)=-4$. Interpolate for the same data as in Problem 4.19 and then compare the answers.

4.22 The function $s^{(r)}$ that was defined in (4.24) is called the factorial function. Discover the reason for this name by evaluating $r^{(r)}$.

4.23 Show that $\Delta s^{(n)} = n s^{(n-1)}$. This relation explains why the notation $s^{(r)}$ was used for the formula in (4.24): because it behaves similarly to x^r which has $(d/dx)x^r = rx^{r-1}$.

4.24 Use a Lagrange polynomial to interpolate the following data for $f(2)$:

$$f(-1) = -3, \quad f(0) = 1, \quad f(1) = 7.$$

4.25 Solve Problem 4.15 again, this time using a Lagrange polynomial.

4.26 The number of cans of beer sold at the Pines Speedway may be expressed as a polynomial in the temperature. Three weeks ago the temperature was $60°$ and 156 cans of beer were sold. Two weeks ago it was $50°$ and only 135 cans were sold; however, last week it was $80°$

and 204 cans were sold. If it is 70° this week, estimate how many cans of beer will be sold at the Pines Speedway.

4.27 Use the Lagrange-interpolation program to verify the answer in Problem 4.26.

4.28 Apply the Lagrange-interpolation program to the following data to determine what angle has a tangent equal to unity:

$$0.1763 = \tan^{-1}10°, \qquad 0.364 = \tan^{-1}20°, \qquad 0.5774 = \tan^{-1}30°,$$
$$0.8391 = \tan^{-1}40°, \qquad 1.1918 = \tan^{-1}50°, \qquad 1.7321 = \tan^{-1}60°.$$

4.29 Inverse interpolation can be used to approximate roots of equations. This is done by finding what value of x makes the function $f(x)$ equal to zero. As an example, consider the function $f(x) = x^3 + 4.4x^2 + 6.2x + 2.8$, which was previously analyzed by Newton's method in Problem 3.2. This time apply the Lagrange-interpolation program to $f(1.3)$, $f(1.35)$, $f(1.45)$, and $f(1.5)$ to approximate the root.

4.30 Example 4.6 matched some data with the polynomial $f(x) = 1.143x^2 + 1.714x - 2.889$. Find the mean-square error.

4.31 Match a second-degree Newton-Gregory polynomial to the following data pairs: $(0, -2.9)$, $(1, 0.2)$, $(2, 5.2)$. For this polynomial, what is the mean-square error of the data in Example 4.6? Should this answer be less than or greater than the answer found in Problem 4.30?

4.32 Find the second-degree function that minimizes the mean-square error for the following data:

$$x: \quad -1 \qquad 0 \qquad 1 \qquad 2$$
$$y: -4.5 \quad -1.9 \quad 3.2 \quad 9.1$$

4.33 The discrete Fourier coefficient A_i is given by

$$A_i = \frac{2}{n+1} \sum_{k=0}^{n} f_k \cos \frac{2\pi i k}{n+1}.$$

Show that A_i is periodic with period $n+1$. That is, show $A_i = A_{i+n+1}$.

4.34 Show that the discrete Fourier coefficients have the following properties:

$$A_{n+1-i} = A_i, \qquad B_{n+1-i} = -B_i.$$

4.35 Use the Fourier interpolation program for the following values: $f(1) = 2$, $f(3) = 3$, $f(5) = 3$, $f(7) = 2$, and $f(9) = 4$. Interpolate for the following data: $f(0)$, $f(1)$, $f(2)$.

4.36 Use the Fourier interpolation program for the following values: $f(-1) = 4$, $f(1) = 2$, $f(3) = 3$, $f(5) = 3$, and $f(7) = 2$. Interpolate for the following data: $f(0)$, $f(1)$, $f(2)$.

Chapter Five

Differentiation

5.1 INTRODUCTION

Numerical differentiation can be used to find the derivative of an analytical function or to estimate the derivative from discrete data. If one has an analytical function, the rules of differentiation could be applied to yield an analytical derivative. However, if a computer program requires the calculation of a derivative it is inconvenient to supply a different subroutine for each different derivative. As was the case in Newton's method of Chapter 3, it is often preferable to use numerical differentiation.

If one has only discrete data, there is no choice: if a derivative is to be found it must be estimated by numerical methods. This case is not emphasized in this chapter because the following chapters only require derivatives for analytical functions. For the discrete case, it is best to first fit the data with spline functions. As explained in Section 4.10, spline functions can be used to give a smooth match to discrete data. This smooth analytical curve can then be differentiated.

Two curves may appear to be quite similar, but have very different derivatives. For example, consider the two functions shown in Fig. 5.1. The function in Fig. 5.1(a) resembles part of a sine function, so the derivative would be similar to a cosine function. However, the derivative of the function in Fig. 5.1(b) is very different: it is zero everywhere except at the discontinuities where it is undefined.

This discussion implies that small changes in input data can cause large changes in the derivative. That is, differentiation is a very sensitive process —it amplifies changes in input data. This will be contrasted in the next chapter with integration, which smoothes changes in input data. Because differentiation is a sensitive process, high-order polynomials should not be used to fit the data before differentiating. As mentioned above, spline functions can be applied to smooth the data—or a least-squares fit can be used for noisy data.

Because differentiation is a sensitive process, one usually does not attempt to numerically calculate any derivative higher than the first. However, we will derive some formulas for higher-order derivatives in this chapter—not because we are anticipating practical applications, but

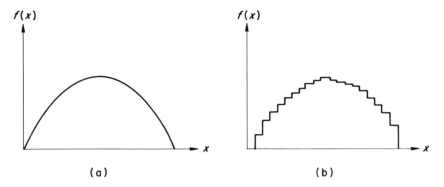

FIGURE 5.1. Two functions may be similar in appearance, but have very different derivatives.

because it will give us further insight into the meaning of difference functions and provide an opportunity for becoming more familiar with interpolating polynomials. Also, this chapter introduces the method of undetermined coefficients, which is used in later chapters.

5.2 METHOD OF INTERPOLATING POLYNOMIALS

From the previous chapter we know that an nth-degree polynomial can be passed through $n+1$ points. Thus, given some data, an interpolating polynomial can be found, and then this polynomial can be differentiated. This approach will be used in this section to derive some differentiation formulas.

Usually the data will be evenly spaced, so the following Newton-Gregory polynomial can be used:

$$f_s = f_0 + s\,\Delta f_0 + \frac{s(s-1)}{2}\Delta^2 f_0 + \frac{s(s-1)(s-2)}{3!}\Delta^3 f_0 + \cdots. \tag{5.1}$$

The derivative of $f(x)$ can be found by applying the chain rule to f_s:

$$\frac{df(x)}{dx} = \frac{df_s}{dx} = \frac{df_s}{ds}\frac{ds}{dx} = \frac{1}{h}\frac{df_s}{ds}. \tag{5.2}$$

For the general case, df_s/dx is difficult to determine from (5.1), but for $s=0$ (that is, for $x=x_0$) substituting (5.1) into (5.2) yields the following simple result:

$$f'(x_0) \approx \frac{1}{h}\left[\Delta f_0 - \frac{\Delta^2 f_0}{2} + \frac{\Delta^3 f_0}{3} - \cdots \pm \frac{\Delta^n f_0}{n}\right]. \tag{5.3}$$

The $+$ is selected for n odd, the $-$ for n even.

The approximation in (5.3) is illustrated below in (5.4) for the cases $n=1,2,3$. The result in (5.4a) is the approximation that was used to calculate the derivative for Newton's method in Chapter 3.

$$f'(x_0) \approx \frac{1}{h}(f_1 - f_0) \tag{5.4a}$$

$$f'(x_0) \approx \frac{1}{h}\left(-\tfrac{1}{2}f_2 + 2f_1 - \tfrac{3}{2}f_0\right) \tag{5.4b}$$

$$f'(x_0) \approx \frac{1}{h}\left(\frac{f_3}{3} - \tfrac{3}{2}f_2 + 3f_1 - \tfrac{11}{6}f_0\right). \tag{5.4c}$$

The approximations in (5.4b) and 5.4c) are more accurate than the one used for Newton's method; however, they require more evaluations of the function.

EXAMPLE 5.1

The following data were found by evaluating $f(x) = e^x$ at the points indicated: $f(1) = 2.7183$, $f(1.1) = 3.0042$, $f(1.2) = 3.3201$, $f(1.3) = 3.6693$. Applying (2.4a), (2.4b), and (2.4c) yields 2.859, 2.709, and 2.720. Comparing these approximations with the analytical answer 2.718, we can see that the answers became increasingly accurate as more terms were included. This is usually the case—the answer gets better as one goes to a higher-order formula.

Information about the error of the derivative estimates can be obtained from Section 1.5 by recalling that:

If sample points of separation h are used to estimate df/dx and the approximation is exact for every mth-degree function, but not every $(m+1)$th-degree function, then the error is proportional to h^m.

Thus, for example, consider (5.4c), which was derived by using a third-degree polynomial and is therefore exact for every third-degree function. Problem 5.3 demonstrates that (5.4c) is not exact for every fourth-degree function, so that the error is proportional to h^3. Similarly, for (5.4b) the error is proportional to h^2, and for (5.4a) it is proportional to h.

EXAMPLE 5.2

In Example 5.1 the approximation $f'(x_0) \approx (f_1 - f_0)/h$ yielded $f'(1) \approx 2.859$ as an approximation for the derivative of e^x at $x = 1$. This approximation was obtained for $h = 0.1$ and has an error which will be written as error(0.1) = 0.141. If h is reduced to 0.05, then the error is reduced to error(0.05) = 0.069; thus reducing h by a factor of two reduced the error by approximately a factor of two, which verifies that the error in (5.4a) is proportional to h (for small h).

Estimates for the first derivative were obtained by differentiating the Newton-Gregory polynomial that was given in (5.1). This can be differentiated again to yield the following approximation for the second derivative:

$$f''(x_0) \approx \frac{1}{h^2} \left[\Delta^2 f_0 - \Delta^3 f_0 + \tfrac{11}{12} \Delta^4 f_0 - \cdots \right]. \tag{5.5}$$

Thus the simplest estimate for the second derivative is

$$f''(x_0) \approx \Delta^2 f_0 / h^2.$$

The above process can be generalized to yield the simplest estimate for the nth derivative as

$$f^{(n)}(x_0) \approx \frac{\Delta^n f_0}{h^n}. \tag{5.6}$$

This gives us insight into the physical interpretation of the nth-order difference function $\Delta^n f_0$: except for a scale factor of h^n it is the discrete version of the nth derivative.

The work on error analysis in Chapter 1 can be extended to yield:

If sample points of separation h are used to estimate the nth derivative and the approximation is exact for every mth-degree function, but not for every $(m+1)$th-degree function, then the error is proportional to h^{m+1-n}.

Thus, for example, consider (5.6) with $n = 3$:

$$f^{(3)}(x_0) \approx \frac{\Delta^3 f}{h^3} = \frac{f_3 - 3f_2 + 3f_1 - f_0}{h^3}. \tag{5.7}$$

This was derived by using a third-degree polynomial and is therefore exact for every third-degree function. Problem 5.5 demonstrates that (5.7) is not exact for every fourth-degree function, so that the error is proportional to $h^{m+1-n} = h^{3+1-3} = h$. In fact, it can be shown in general that the error in (5.6) is proportional to h.

It should be emphasized that the main purpose of this chapter is not to derive a long list of useful formulas for numerical differentiation. The formulas that are needed in this text could be easily derived in a single section. Instead, the chapter offers a means of becoming familiar with the use of interpolating polynomials. Also, it will introduce the method of undetermined coefficients, which is a powerful tool that will be used in later chapters.

5.3 METHOD OF UNDETERMINED COEFFICIENTS[1]

In the previous section, derivative formulas were derived by using the Newton-Gregory polynomial

$$f_s = f_0 + s\Delta f_0 + \frac{s(s-1)}{2}\Delta^2 f_0 + \frac{s(s-1)(s-2)}{3!}\Delta^3 f_0 + \cdots . \qquad (5.8)$$

This polynomial was truncated to a finite number of terms and then differentiated.

In this section an alternate derivation for the previous results will be presented. This new method, the method of undetermined coefficients, is useful because it eliminates the need to differentiate (5.8), which can be a tedious task. The method of undetermined coefficients will also be applied in this section to obtain some new derivative formulas, and in the next chapter will be applied to obtain some integral formulas.

In order to obtain the method of undetermined coefficients, note that if expressions for the difference functions are substituted into (5.8), then that equation can be rewritten as

$$f_s = c_0(s)f_0 + c_1(s)f_1 + c_2(s)f_2 + c_3(s)f_3 + \cdots , \qquad (5.9)$$

where the notation $c_0(s)$ indicates that the coefficient of f_0 is a function of s. For example, if (5.8) is truncated after the second-order difference function, then it can be expressed as

$$f_s \approx (1 - 1.5s + 0.5s^2)f_0 + (2s - s^2)f_1 + 0.5s(s-1)f_2, \qquad (5.10)$$

so that $c_0 = 1 - 1.5s + 0.5s^2$, $c_1 = 2s - s^2$, $c_2 = 0.5s(s-1)$. It should be noted that if (5.8) is instead truncated after the third-order difference function, then each of the above coefficients will change.

The fact essential to the method of undetermined coefficients is that if $f(x)$ is an nth-degree polynomial, then it could be matched exactly by continuing the terms in (5.9) to $c_n(s)f_n$. Because it would then be matched exactly, any derivative calculated from it would also be exact.

To learn how this fact can be applied, assume we have an approximation for the first derivative that is expressed in terms of f_0, f_1, and f_2. Since f_s can be expressed as in (5.9), the derivative can be approximated as

$$f_s' \approx d_0(s)f_0 + d_1(s)f_1 + d_2(s)f_2, \qquad (5.11)$$

where the coefficients are the derivatives of the ones in (5.10).

---

[1]This is termed "the direct method of finding formulas" by Hamming (1973). Hamming also discusses a Taylor-series method of finding formulas which can yield similar results.

The approximation in (5.11) is valid for any value of s, but we will be particularly interested in the location $s = 0$. For this we will write

$$f_0' \approx d_0 f_0 + d_1 f_1 + d_2 f_2. \tag{5.12}$$

It should be emphasized that (5.12) is *exact* for any function which is of second degree or less. In particular, it is exact for the functions $f_s = 1$, $f_s = s$, and $f_s = s^2$, so for any of these simple functions, the approximation symbol in (5.12) will be replaced by an equality symbol.

For the function $f_s = 1$ it follows that $f_0 = f_1 = f_2 = 1$ and $f_0' = 0$, so that (5.12) becomes

$$d_0 + d_1 + d_2 = 0. \tag{5.13}$$

Similarly, for the function $f_s = s$ it follows that $f_0 = 0$, $f_1 = 1$, $f_2 = 2$, and $f_0' = 1$, so that

$$d_1 + 2d_2 = 1, \tag{5.14}$$

while the function $f_s = s^2$ yields

$$d_1 + 4d_2 = 0. \tag{5.15}$$

In summary, we picked three simple functions $f_s = 1$, $f_s = s$, and $f_s = s^2$ for which the relation in (5.12) was exact. This produced three equations for the coefficients d_0, d_1, and d_2. Solving the three equations produces the "undetermined coefficients" $d_0 = -1.5$, $d_1 = 2$, $d_2 = -0.5$.

Substituting these values into (5.12) yields

$$f_0' \approx -1.5 f_0 + 2 f_1 - 0.5 f_2. \tag{5.16}$$

If we use the fact that $f_0' = hf'(x_0)$, then it is evident that (5.16) agrees with 5.4b), which was derived by the method of interpolating polynomials instead of the method of undetermined coefficients.

The method of undetermined coefficients is very powerful because it lets us choose the form for our answer ahead of time. To illustrate this, suppose we want to express the first derivative as

$$f'(x_0) \approx a_{-1} f_{-1} + a_0 f_0 + a_1 f_1. \tag{5.17}$$

The coefficients a_{-1}, a_0, and a_1 can be easily determined by considering the related expression

$$hf'(x_0) = f_0' \approx d_{-1} f_{-1} + d_0 f_0 + d_1 f_1. \tag{5.18}$$

Utilizing the fact that this expression is exact for the functions $f_s = 1$, $f_s = s$, and $f_s = s^2$ leads to

$$\begin{aligned} d_{-1} + d_0 + d_1 &= 0 \\ -d_{-1} + 0 d_0 + d_1 &= 1 \\ d_{-1} + 0 d_0 + d_1 &= 0. \end{aligned} \tag{5.19}$$

These three equations can be conveniently rewritten using matrix notation as

$$\begin{bmatrix} 1 & 1 & 1 \\ -1 & 0 & 1 \\ 1 & 0 & 1 \end{bmatrix} \begin{bmatrix} d_{-1} \\ d_0 \\ d_1 \end{bmatrix} = \begin{bmatrix} 0 \\ 1 \\ 0 \end{bmatrix}. \tag{5.20}$$

Solving by the techniques discussed in Chapter 2 yields $d_{-1} = -0.5$, $d_0 = 0$, $d_1 = 0.5$. Substituting into (5.18), we have

$$f'(x_0) \approx \frac{f_1 - f_{-1}}{2h}. \tag{5.21}$$

In the previous section we derived another two-term approximation for the derivative, $f'(x_0) \approx (f_1 - f_0)/h$. This had an error that was proportional to h.

Instead of just looking on one side of x_0, equation (5.21) considers both sides: that is, it considers both f_{-1} and f_1. For this reason it is called the *central-difference* formula for the first derivative. Since we are using information from both sides of x_0, it seems probable that the error should be less than if just one side were considered. This intuitive feeling can be verified by recalling that the central-difference formula was derived by considering three points, and thus it is exact for any second-degree function. This implies that the error is proportional to h^2.

The method of undetermined coefficients can also be applied for higher-order derivatives. In fact, we can use it to improve on our previous result from (5.6),

$$f''(x_0) \approx (f_2 - 2f_1 + f_0)/h^2. \tag{5.22}$$

This approximation had an error which was proportional to h. Note that the expression is not centered about x_0, but only looks at one side. From the previous work on the central-difference formula we would expect that a better three-term approximation would be of the form

$$h^2 f''(x_0) = f_0'' = d_{-1} f_{-1} + d_0 f_0 + d_1 f_1. \tag{5.23}$$

Using the functions $f_s = 1$, $f_s = s$, and $f_s = s^2$ yields

$$\begin{bmatrix} 1 & 1 & 1 \\ -1 & 0 & 1 \\ 1 & 0 & 1 \end{bmatrix} \begin{bmatrix} d_{-1} \\ d_0 \\ d_1 \end{bmatrix} = \begin{bmatrix} 0 \\ 0 \\ 2 \end{bmatrix}, \tag{5.24}$$

which has as its solution $d_{-1} = 1$, $d_0 = -2$, $d_1 = 1$. Thus the central difference formula for the second derivative is

$$f''(x_0) \approx (f_{-1} - 2f_0 + f_1)/h^2. \tag{5.25}$$

This section will conclude with another example that should further emphasize the power of the method of undetermined coefficients. Assume we want to estimate the derivative at $x = x_2$ as

$$f'(x_2) \approx a_{-1} f_{-1} + c_1 f_1 + c_2 f_2. \tag{5.26}$$

There are two new aspects to this problem. First, we want to evaluate the derivative at x_2 instead of x_0. Second, we are not considering f_0; thus the data are not evenly spaced.

If for some reason we wished to express the derivative as in (5.26), we could find a second-degree polynomial that goes through the three function values f_{-1}, f_1, and f_2. We could then differentiate the polynomial and evaluate the derivative at x_2. Conceptually the above procedure is simple; however, practically it is tedious—especially since the data are not equally spaced, so the Lagrange interpolating polynomial must be used.

It is much easier to use the method of undetermined coefficients, as will now be demonstrated. As usual, instead of (5.26) we will consider the normalized equation[2]

$$f_2' \approx d_{-1} f_{-1} + d_1 f_1 + d_2 f_2. \tag{5.27}$$

Since this relation contains three function values, it will be exact for a constant, linear, or second-degree function. Choosing the functions $f_s = 1$, $f_s = s$, and $f_s = s^2$ yields

$$\begin{bmatrix} 1 & 1 & 1 \\ -1 & 1 & 2 \\ 1 & 1 & 4 \end{bmatrix} \begin{bmatrix} d_{-1} \\ d_1 \\ d_2 \end{bmatrix} = \begin{bmatrix} 0 \\ 1 \\ 4 \end{bmatrix}. \tag{5.28}$$

Before proceeding, a comment should be made about the constant 4 in the column matrix, which came from

$$\frac{d}{ds} \left[f_s = s^2 \right] \bigg|_{s=2} = 2s \big|_{s=2} = 4.$$

The fact that we want to evaluate the derivative at $s = 2$ (instead of $s = 0$ as in the previous example) presents no difficulty for the method of undetermined coefficients.

The solution to (5.28) is $d_{-1} = \frac{1}{6}$, $d_1 = -\frac{9}{6}$, $d_2 = \frac{8}{6}$, so that

$$\frac{df}{dx} \bigg|_{x=x_2} \approx \frac{1}{6h} \left[f_{-1} - 9f_1 + 8f_2 \right]. \tag{5.29}$$

---

[2]We can still define a normalized variable $s = (x - x_0)/h$, even though the value of the function $f(x_0)$ is not used in (5.26). The normalized variable is used here to simplify notation.

In practice, one would not use this approximation, because a more accurate one can be obtained if the function value f_0 is also used (see Problem 5.8). However, an example of the use of (5.29) will be illuminating, because this is the first derivative formula we have had for unevenly spaced data.

EXAMPLE 5.3

The derivative of $f(x) = e^x$ can be estimated at $x = 1$ by using the data $x_{-1} = -0.5$, $x_1 = 0.5$, and $x_2 = 1$. For these values of x it follows that $f_{-1} = 0.607$, $f_1 = 1.649$, $f_2 = 2.718$. Substituting these numbers into (5.29) and using $h = 0.5$ yields an estimate for the derivative of 2.50, as compared with the analytical answer 2.72.

The answer in this example was quite inaccurate because the three values $f(-0.5) = 0.607$, $f(0.5) = 1.649$, and $f(1) = 2.718$ did not characterize the function $f(x) = e^x$ very well at the point $x = 1$. That is, the three values determined a unique second-degree polynomial. The slope of this polynomial was 2.5 at $x = 1$, while the slope of e^x is 2.72 at $x = 1$.

In the next section we will discuss an easy way of verifying that the second-degree polynomial actually did have a slope of 2.5 at $x = 1$.

5.4 APPLICATION OF INTERPOLATING PROGRAMS

In practice, one does not very often take experimental data and then predict high-order derivatives—because the predictions would be too inaccurate. In fact, the average reader will estimate the first derivative so infrequently it is not worth developing a special program for this; instead, an existing one can be used.

If data have been taken at $n + 1$ points, then an nth-degree interpolating polynomial is uniquely determined. If the points are evenly spaced, then the Newton-Gregory program can be applied to interpolate the data at any desired point. If the data are not evenly spaced, Lagrange interpolation can be used. The interpolated values can then be used to estimate the derivative.

EXAMPLE 5.4

The following data represent values for the function $f(x) = e^x$: $f(1.3) = 3.6693$, $f(1.5) = 4.4817$, $f(1.7) = 5.4739$, $f(1.9) = 6.6859$, $f(2.1) = 8.1662$, $f(2.3) = 9.9742$, $f(2.5) = 12.182$.

Since the data are evenly spaced, the Newton-Gregory program can be used to produce a sixth-degree interpolating polynomial. This polynomial can then be evaluated at any desired points. For example, if we want to evaluate the derivative at $x = 2$ by using the central-difference formula with $h = 0.001$, then we can use the program to yield $f(1.999) = 7.38169$ and $f(2.001) = 7.39647$, so that by the central-difference theorem

$$f'(2) \approx (7.39647 - 7.38169)/0.002 = 7.39.$$

The Newton-Gregory program can be applied to give a demonstration that small changes in input data can cause large changes in the derivative. Assume that the data in Example 5.4 were the result of an experiment, and an experimental error caused $f(1.9) = 6.7528$ (1% high) and $f(2.1) = 8.0854$ (1% low). Interpolating with a sixth-degree polynomial then yields $f(1.999)$ $= 7.38686$ and $f(2.001) = 7.39991$, so that this time the central-difference formula yields $f'(2) \approx 6.53$. Comparing this result with 7.39 from Example 5.4, we can see that a 1% change in some of the input data caused a greater than 10% change in the estimate of the derivative.

An example will next be presented that has unevenly spaced data and thus requires the use of the Lagrange interpolating program.

EXAMPLE 5.5

In Example 5.3 we calculated the derivative at $x = 1$ for the second-degree polynomial that matches

$$f(-0.5) = 0.607, \qquad f(0.5) = 1.649, \qquad f(1) = 2.718.$$

The answer, 2.50, can be verified by using the Lagrange program to produce a second-degree interpolating polynomial. Interpolating with the program yields $f(0.999) = 2.7155$ and $f(1.001) = 2.7205$, so that the central-difference formula indicates $f'(1) \approx 2.5$.

PROBLEMS

5.1 Evaluate $f(x)=2+3x+x^4$ at $x=1$, 1.1, 1.2, and 1.3. Use these function values to estimate the first derivative at $x=1$ by applying (5.4a), (5.4b), and (5.4c). Compare with the analytical answer.

5.2 Evaluate $f(x)=3\sin 2x$ at $x=0$, 0.1, 0.2, and 0.3. Use these function values to estimate the first derivative at $x=0$ by applying (5.4c).

5.3 Show that the derivative approximation in (5.4c) is exact for $f(x)=x^3$, but not for $f(x)=x^4$. Choose $x_0=1$ and $h=1$.

5.4 This problem shows that for $f(x)=e^x$ the derivative approximation in (5.4b) has an error that is proportional to h^2.
(a) Choose $x_0=0$ and $h=0.1$. Find error(0.1).
(b) Reduce h to 0.05 and find error(0.05).
(c) Calculate error(0.1)/error(0.05).

5.5 Show that the derivative approximation in (5.7) is exact for $f(x)=x^3$, but not for $f(x)=x^4$. Choose $x_0=1$ and $h=1$.

5.6 This problem shows that for $f(x)=e^x$ the derivative approximation $f''(x_0)\approx\Delta^2 f_0/h^2$ has an error that is proportional to h.
(a) Choose $x=0$ and $h=0.1$. Find error(0.1).
(b) Reduce h to 0.05 and find error(0.05).
(c) Calculate error(0.1)/error(0.05).

5.7 Find the coefficients for the following approximation by using the method of undetermined coefficients:
$$f'(x_0)\approx a_{-1}f_{-1}+a_3 f_3+a_4 f_4.$$

5.8 The central-difference formula for the first derivative was given as $f'(x_0)=(f_1-f_{-1})/2h$. An even better approximation would be of the form $f'(x_0)=a_{-2}f_{-2}+a_{-1}f_{-1}+a_0 f_0+a_1 f_1+a_2 f_2$. Find the coefficients.
Hint: Use the Gauss elimination program to help solve a set of equations.

5.9 Another approximation for the first derivative is $f(x_0)=(f_{-2}-8f_{-1}+8f_1-f_2)/12h$. Apply this to $f(x)=e^x$ as follows:
(a) Choose $x_0=0$ and $h=0.1$. Find error(0.1).
(b) Reduce h to 0.05 and find error(0.05).
(c) Calculate error(0.1)/error(0.05).
Beware: this requires at least 8-digit accuracy.

5.10 Problem 5.7 found the coefficients in the approximation

$$f'(x_0) \approx a_{-1} f_{-1} + a_3 f_3 + a_4 f_4.$$

In this problem, use the method of undetermined coefficients to find the unknowns in the equivalent approximation

$$f'(x_1) \approx b_0 f_0 + b_4 f_4 + b_5 f_5.$$

5.11 (a) Use the central-difference formula to approximate $f'(1)$ for $f(x) = e^{x^2}$. Choose $h = 0.1$.

(b) Reduce h to 0.05 and approximate $f''(1)$.

5.12 The following data represent values of the function $f(x) = 3x^2 + 2x + 1$:

$$f(1) = 6, \quad f(2) = 17, \quad f(3) = 34.$$

(a) Use (5.4a) to estimate the derivative at $x = 2$.

(b) Use the central-difference formula to find the derivative at $x = 2$. Why is this result exact?

5.13 The method of undetermined coefficients is not restricted to integer values of s. Demonstrate this fact by determining the coefficients for $f'(x_0 + h/2) \approx a_0 f_0 + a_1 f_1 + a_2 f_2$.

5.14 Use the result of Problem 5.13 to estimate the derivative at $x = 1.5$ from the following data:

$$f(1) = 6, \quad f(2) = 17, \quad f(3) = 34.$$

5.15 As an alternate solution to Problem 5.14, use the Newton-Gregory program to find a second-degree interpolating polynomial that matches $f(1) = 6$, $f(2) = 17$, and $f(3) = 34$. Interpolate to estimate $f(1.501)$ and $f(1.499)$. Apply the central-difference formula to estimate the derivative at $x = 1.5$.

5.16 A car was accelerated at a constant rate, and the following distances were measured as a function of time: $s(1) = 35$, $s(2) = 70$, and $s(2.2) = 78.2$.

(a) Apply the Lagrange interpolation program to find the velocity at $t = 1.5$ and $t = 2.2$.

(b) If the distance $s(2.2)$ had been incorrectly measured as 77, what velocities would be calculated at $t = 1.5$ and $t = 2.2$?

Chapter Six

Integration

6.1 INTRODUCTION

In a calculus course one is taught how to find the integral of certain types of functions. The integral of some functions, for example polynomials, can be written down by inspection. More complicated expressions may require some special tricks, such as integration by parts. Finally, if one runs out of time, patience, or knowledge, there are tables of integrals that can be consulted.

Even with integral tables it is not always possible to integrate a function analytically. Also, oftentimes we will not have a function, but will have experimental data to integrate, and this cannot be done analytically. Numerical integration can be used when analytical integration is impossible or impractical.

In numerical integration a function or set of data is approximated as a set of simple functions, such as a series of straight lines or parabolas. The area under each of the simple functions is then calculated, and the sum of the areas used to approximate the integral. The accuracy of the approximation to the integral will depend on how accurately the set of simple functions approximates the given function.

The first numerical method that will be studied is the trapezoidal rule, which approximates a given function by a set of straight lines. The shorter each straight line is, the better will be the approximation and the more accurate will be the answer. Shorter line segments imply that a larger total number of lines will be required to approximate the given function, which will in turn require more computation time.

Another way to improve the accuracy of numerical integration is to use a set of more complicated functions to approximate the given function. In addition to straight lines, second-order and third-order functions are commonly used.

6.2 TRAPEZOIDAL RULE

The concept of an integral is usually introduced in a calculus course by applying the trapezoidal rule to find areas under curves. Once analytical methods are derived for evaluating integrals, the trapezoidal rule is discarded as a tool that is no longer necessary. However, computer programs can be written which apply the trapezoidal rule to numerical integration.

The notation that will be used in discussing the trapezoidal rule is illustrated in Fig. 6.1. In order to integrate a function $f(x)$ from an initial point $x = A$ to a final point $x = B$, the function is divided into a series of n *panels*. The width of each of the panels is the same and is denoted by h.

This notation is reminiscent of that used in the study of interpolation of evenly spaced data. However, we are *not* going to fit an nth-degree polynomial to the function values at $x_0, x_1, \ldots, x_n$. We will instead work with a much simpler polynomial. The reason for this choice of polynomial will become clear later.

The trapezoidal rule finds the integral of a function such as the $f(x)$ shown in Fig. 6.1 by approximating the area in each one of the panels and then adding together all the areas. To learn how the trapezoidal rule estimates the area of a panel, consider the first one which is shown in Fig. 6.2.

Between x_0 and x_1 the function is approximated as a straight line, and the area under $f(x)$ is approximated as the area under the straight line. Because the area of a panel is approximated by the area of a trapezoid, this is termed the trapezoidal rule. The area of a trapezoid is given by the width

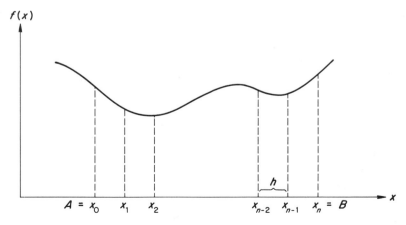

FIGURE 6.1. Illustration of notation used for various integration rules.

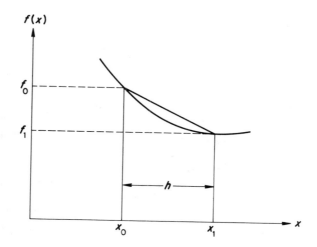

FIGURE 6.2. The trapezoidal rule approximates a panel by a trapezoid.

times the average height. The width in Fig. 6.2 is $x_1 - x_0 = h$ and the average height is $(f_0 + f_1)/2$, so that

$$\int_{x_0}^{x_1} f(x) \, dx \approx \frac{h}{2}(f_0 + f_1). \tag{6.1}$$

Similarly, the area of the second panel is approximated by $h(f_1 + f_2)/2$, the third by $h(f_2 + f_3)/2$, etc. Adding together these results gives the trapezoidal rule

$$\int_A^B f(x) \, dx \approx \frac{h}{2}(f_0 + 2f_1 + 2f_2 + \cdots + 2f_{n-2} + 2f_{n-1} + f_n). \tag{6.2}$$

Note that all function values except the first (f_0) and the last (f_n) are multiplied by two.

EXAMPLE 6.1

Estimate $\int_{-0.5}^{0.5} e^x \, dx$ by applying the trapezoidal rule to a total of ten panels.

SOLUTION

The increment size is $h = 1/10 = 0.1$, so that $x_0 = -0.5$, $x_1 = -0.4$, $x_2 = -0.3$, etc. Evaluating e^x at these locations yields $f_0 = 0.6065$, $f_1 = 0.6703$, $f_2 = 0.7408$, $f_3 = 0.8187$, $f_4 = 0.9048$, $f_5 = 1$, $f_6 = 1.1052$, $f_7 = 1.2214$, $f_8 = 1.3499$, $f_9 = 1.4918$, $f_{10} = 1.6487$.

Applying (6.2) to these data,

$$\int_{-0.5}^{0.5} e^x \, dx \approx \frac{0.1}{2} (0.6065 + 2 \times 0.6703 + \cdots + 2 \times 1.4918 + 1.6487) = 1.0431.$$

The analytical answer is $e^{0.5} - e^{-0.5} = 1.0422$.

A program for integration by the trapezoidal rule is given in Fig. 6.3. The trapezoidal rule is first applied for ten panels, and the approximate answer is printed out. Then the number of panels is doubled (that is, step size halved) and the trapezoidal rule is applied again. The number of panels is doubled until the answer is deemed to be accurate enough at which time the computations should be stopped interactively. Note that each time the number of panels is doubled, it is possible to reduce the number of calculations by using the function values that are already available from previous calculations; thus the DO loop at line 54 uses increments of two.

Each time the program of Fig. 6.3 is applied to a different function, the expression in line 900 must be rewritten. Note that the function in Fig. 6.3 is e^x.

EXAMPLE 6.2

The trapezoidal-rule program is applied in Fig. 6.4 to evaluate $\int_{-0.5}^{0.5} e^x \, dx$. For $n = 10$ the integral was approximated as 1.04306, while for $n = 20$ it was 1.04241, and for $n = 40$ it was 1.04224. Comparing the last two answers we can conclude that to four significant figures the answer is 1.042.

The program in Fig. 6.3 applies the trapezoidal rule to continuous data. That is, it is assumed that a subroutine contains the function $f(x)$, which can therefore be evaluated for any value of x. For these circumstances better and better approximations can be made to the integral by making the step size h smaller and smaller.

Instead of continuous data, we will often have discrete data. For example, we may have measured the velocity of a car at seven different times and want to estimate the distance that the car travelled. Problem 6.8 outlines how the program of Fig. 6.3 can be modified for discrete data.

Insight into the accuracy of the trapezoidal rule can be obtained by recalling from Example 1.3 that the trapezoidal rule is exact for every first-degree function, but not every second-degree function. It follows that the error for the trapezoidal rule is of the order of h^3. It must be stressed that this is the *local* error, that is, the error for one panel. The error for n panels (the global error) is of the order of nh^3. Since the number of panels

```
01C      TRAPEZOIDAL RULE
02       PROGRAM TR(INPUT,OUTPUT)
03 03    FORMAT(I4,1P,E14.5)
08       REAL INTGRL
10C
11C      INITIAL POINT=A   FINAL POINT=B
12       PRINT,*    A       B*
13       READ,A,B
14       PRINT,/,*   N          INTEGRAL*
16       F0=F(A) $FN=F(B)
18C
19C      INITIAL CONSTANTS N,H
21       N=10 $N1=9 $H=(B-A)/10.
23C
30C      APPLICATION OF TRAPEZOIDAL RULE (EQ. 6.2)
33       SUM=0.
35       DO 36 I=1,N1
36 36    SUM=SUM+F(A+I*H)
46       Z=F0+2.*SUM+FN
47       INTGRL=.5*H*Z
48       PRINT 3,N,INTGRL
49C
50C      DOUBLE THE # OF STEPS UNTIL INTERRUPTED
51 51    N=2*N    $N1=N-1    $H=.5*H
54       DO 55 I=1,N1,2
55 55    SUM=SUM+F(A+I*H)
56       Z=F0+2*SUM+FN
57       INTGRL=.5*H*Z
58       PRINT 3,N,INTGRL
59       GO TO 51
60       END
898C
899      FUNCTION F(X)
900      F=EXP(X)
950      RETURN
999      END
```

FIGURE 6.3. A program for the trapezoidal rule.

n is inversely proportional to h, it follows that

The global error for the trapezoidal rule is of the order of h^2.

This is equivalent to saying that, for h small enough, the global error for the trapezoidal rule is proportional to h^2. This fact will be used in Section 6.5 (Romberg prediction) to improve the accuracy of the trapezoidal rule. In fact, applying Romberg prediction to the trapezoidal rule yields

```
        A         B
    ? -.5        .5

    N          INTEGRAL
    10     1.04306E+00
    20     1.04241E+00
    40     1.04224E+00
```

FIGURE 6.4. An application of the trapezoidal-rule program.

Simpson's $\frac{1}{3}$ rule. Simpson's rule is a very popular integration formula which is discussed in the next section.

EXAMPLE 6.3

Example 6.2 found the following estimates of $\int_{-0.5}^{0.5} e^x dx$:

$$\text{Integral } (h=0.1) = 1.04306,$$
$$\text{Integral } (h=0.05) = 1.04241.$$

The analytical answer is 1.04219, so the errors for these two different values of h are error(0.1)=0.0087 and error(0.05)=0.0022. Thus when h was reduced by a factor of 2, the error was reduced by a factor of 4, which confirms that the error is proportional to h^2.

This section about the trapezoidal rule will conclude by rederiving the formula by the method of interpolating polynomials. This method will then be applied in the next section to derive Simpson's rules.

The trapezoidal rule for one panel was used to evaluate $\int_{x_0}^{x_1} f(x) dx$. Since we are assuming evenly spaced data, we can use the normalized variable $s = (x - x_0)/h$. For this normalization, integration over one panel can be expressed as

$$\int_{x_0}^{x_1} f(x) dx = h \int_0^1 f_s \, ds. \tag{6.3}$$

If we are integrating over one panel, we have just two data values (f_0, f_1) and can thus just use a first-degree polynomial to match the data. From (4.20), the first-degree Newton-Gregory polynomial is

$$f_s \approx f_0 + s(f_1 - f_0). \tag{6.4}$$

Substituting this into (6.3) yields

$$h \int_0^1 \left[f_0 + s(f_1 - f_0) \right] ds = \frac{h}{2} (f_0 + f_1), \tag{6.5}$$

which is the trapezoidal rule as it was expressed in (6.1).

6.3 SIMPSON'S RULES

The trapezoidal rule has a global error that is proportional to h^2; thus, for h small enough, every time the step size is reduced by a factor of 2 the error is reduced by a factor of 4. This implies that by using a sufficient number of panels the error can be made arbitrarily small.

In this section we will study Simpson's rules and discover that for the same number of panels they will produce a smaller error than the trapezoidal rule. Put another way, for the same accuracy, Simpson's rules require a smaller number of panels than does the trapezoidal rule. For this reason Simpson's rules are more widely used.

Simpson's first rule is derived by integrating over two panels at a time as indicated in Fig. 6.5. In terms of the normalized variable this can be expressed as

$$\int_{x_0}^{x_2} f(x)\,dx = h \int_0^2 f_s\,ds. \tag{6.6}$$

The two panels are described by the following data pairs: (x_0, f_0), (x_1, f_1), and (x_2, f_2). From (4.20), the following second-degree Newton-Gregory polynomial goes through the three values:

$$f_s \approx f_0 + s\Delta f_0 + \frac{s(s-1)}{2}\Delta^2 f_0 = f_0 + s(f_1 - f_0) + \frac{s(s-1)}{2}(f_2 - 2f_1 + f_0). \tag{6.7}$$

Substituting this into (6.6) yields

$$\int_{x_0}^{x_2} f(x)\,dx \approx \frac{h}{3}(f_0 + 4f_1 + f_2). \tag{6.8}$$

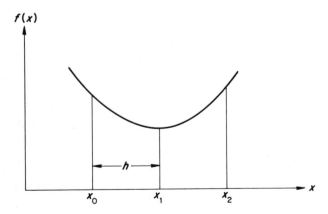

FIGURE 6.5. Simpson's $\frac{1}{3}$ rule integrates two panels at a time.

Similarly, the area of the second pair of panels is approximated by $h(f_2 + 4f_3 + f_4)/3$, the third pair of panels by $h(f_4 + 4f_5 + f_6)/3$, etc. Adding together these results gives Simpson's first rule, which is known as Simpson's $\frac{1}{3}$ rule:

$$\int_A^B f(x)\,dx \approx \frac{h}{3}(f_0 + 4f_1 + 2f_2 + 4f_3 + \cdots + 2f_{n-2} + 4f_{n-1} + f_n). \quad (6.9)$$

Note that all odd functions are multiplied by 4 and all even functions (except f_0 and f_n) are multiplied by 2.

It should be emphasized that Simpson's $\frac{1}{3}$ rule assumes that n is an even number. This is because it was derived by integrating over pairs of panels.

EXAMPLE 6.4

Estimate $\int_{-0.5}^{0.5} e^x\,dx$ by applying Simpson's rule to a total of ten panels.

SOLUTION

This has an even number of panels, so we can apply (6.9). The function values $f_0, f_1, \ldots, f_{10}$ were calculated in Example 6.1 for the trapezoidal rule. Using these data in (6.9), we have

$$\int_{-0.5}^{0.5} e^x\,dx \approx \frac{0.1}{3}(0.6065 + 4 \times 0.6703 + 2 \times 0.7408$$
$$+ 4 \times 0.8187 + 2 \times 0.9048 + 4 x 1 + 2 \times 1.1052 + 4 \times 1.2214$$
$$+ 2 \times 1.3499 + 4 \times 1.4918 + 1.6487) = 1.0422.$$

This answer agrees with the analytical answer to five significant figures.

A program written for Simpson's $\frac{1}{3}$ rule is given in Fig. 6.6. The function in the subroutine (see statement 900) is e^x. This program was applied to evaluate $\int_{-0.5}^{0.5} e^x\,dx$, and for $n = 10$ yielded 1.04219, which is the same as the first six figures of the analytical answer. This result for $n = 10$ is much more accurate than the corresponding trapezoidal result of Example 6.2.

Further insight into the accuracy of Simpson's $\frac{1}{3}$ rule can be obtained by recalling that it was derived by matching a second-degree polynomial to the function values of two panels, and thus it is exact for any second-degree function. Problem 6.13 demonstrates that Simpson's $\frac{1}{3}$ rule is also exact for any third-degree function, while Problem 6.14 demonstrates that it is not exact for every fourth-degree function. It follows that the local error (for two panels) is of the order of h^5, so that:

The global error for Simpson's $\frac{1}{3}$ rule is of the order of h^4.

```
01C      SIMPSON'S 1/3 RULE
02       PROGRAM SR(INPUT,OUTPUT)
03 03    FORMAT(I4,1P,E14.5)
08       REAL INTGRL
10C
11C      INITIAL POINT=A   FINAL POINT=B
12       PRINT,*    A        B*
13       READ,A,B
14       PRINT,/,*   N         INTEGRAL*
16       F0=F(A) $FN=F(B)
18C
19C      INITIAL CONSTANTS N,H
21       N=10  $N1=9   $N2=8   $H=(B-A)/10.
23C
30C      APPLICATION OF SIMPSON'S RULE   (EQ. 6.9)
33       SUM1=0.
35       DO 36 I=1,N1,2
36 36    SUM1=SUM1+F(A+I*H)
40       SUM2=0.
42       DO 43 I=2,N2,2
43 43    SUM2=SUM2+F(A+I*H)
46       Z=F0+4.*SUM1+2.*SUM2+FN
47       INTGRL=H*Z/3.
48       PRINT 3,N,INTGRL
49C
50C      DOUBLE THE # OF STEPS UNTIL INTERRUPTED
51 51    N=2*N  $N1=N-1   $H=.5*H
52       SUM2=SUM1+SUM2
53       SUM1=0.
54       DO 55 I=1,N1,2
55 55    SUM1=SUM1+F(A+I*H)
56       Z=F0+4.*SUM1+2.*SUM2+FN
57       INTGRL=H*Z/3.
58       PRINT 3,N,INTGRL
59       GO TO 51
60       END
898C
899      FUNCTION F(X)
900      F=EXP(X)
950      RETURN
999      END
```

FIGURE 6.6. A program for Simpson's $\frac{1}{3}$ rule.

This is equivalent to saying that, for h small enough, the global error is proportional to h^4.

Since matching a second-degree polynomial to the function values of two panels was much more accurate than matching a first-degree polynomial to the function values of one panel, the next logical step is to try matching a third-degree polynomial to the function values of three panels. This can be done as follows:

$$\int_{x_0}^{x_3} f(x)\,dx = h\int_0^3 f_s\,ds, \tag{6.10}$$

where from (4.20)

$$f_s \approx f_0 + s\,\Delta f_0 + \frac{s(s-1)}{2}\Delta^2 f_0 + \frac{s(s-1)(s-2)}{3!}\Delta^3 f_0. \tag{6.11}$$

Substituting (6.11) into (6.10) yields Simpson's $\frac{3}{8}$ rule:

$$\int_{x_0}^{x_3} f(x)\,dx \approx \frac{3h}{8}(f_0 + 3f_1 + 3f_2 + f_3). \tag{6.12}$$

From the derivation we know that Simpson's $\frac{3}{8}$ rule is exact for every third-degree function. Problem 6.15 shows that it is not exact for every fourth-degree function. From these two facts we can conclude that the local error is of the order of h^5, which is the same conclusion that was reached for Simpson's $\frac{1}{3}$ rule. Because Simpson's $\frac{3}{8}$ rule is no more accurate than the $\frac{1}{3}$ rule, people are usually content to apply the first rule.

The reason for the surprising accuracy of Simpson's $\frac{1}{3}$ rule can be seen from an examination of (6.11). That expression is exact for any third-degree function (since the fourth- and higher-order difference functions are zero for this case). If (6.11) is integrated over two panels, then the last term can be ignored because $\int_0^2 s(s-1)(s-2)\,ds = 0$.[1] Since the last term contributes nothing to the integral, Simpson's $\frac{1}{3}$ rule must be exact for any third-degree function.

The program in Fig. 6.6 applied Simpson's $\frac{1}{3}$ rule to continuous data. Because there was a subroutine that calculated $f(x)$, it was possible to make sure the number of panels was even, as is required by Simpson's $\frac{1}{3}$ rule. However, for discrete data one may encounter an odd number of panels. This situation may be treated by applying Simpson's $\frac{3}{8}$ rule to the first three panels; the remaining number of panels will be even, so the $\frac{1}{3}$ rule can be applied to these. Instead of using the $\frac{3}{8}$ rule for the first three panels, one can produce an even number of panels from an odd number

---

[1] An easy way to verify that the integral is zero is to make the substitution $s = S + 1$, so that the integral becomes $\int_{-1}^{1} S(S^2 - 1)\,dS$. This integral has an equal amount of positive and negative area, so that it must be equal to zero.

applying the trapezoidal rule to just the first panel. However, this will usually not be as accurate as using Simpson's $\frac{3}{8}$ rule.

6.4 EXAMPLES

The program in Fig. 6.6 for Simpson's $\frac{1}{3}$ rule can be used on a variety of different functions. This section will discuss a few applications that may be familiar to the reader.

In the study of probability theory, the normal (or Gaussian) probability density function is frequently encountered. This is also sometimes referred to as the "bell-shaped curve". Integrating a probability density function indicates the probability of a specific event. For example, the probability that a person's income is within two standard deviations of the average might be given by

$$\frac{2}{\sqrt{2\pi}} \int_0^2 e^{-x^2/2} dx. \tag{6.13}$$

This integral (without the factor $2/\sqrt{2\pi}$) was evaluated as indicated in Fig. 6.7 to yield 1.19629. Multiplying by $2/\sqrt{2\pi}$ yields a probability of 95.45%.

Another function encountered in probability theory is the gamma function, which is defined as

$$\Gamma(t) = \int_0^\infty x^{t-1} e^{-x} dx. \tag{6.14}$$

This definition applies whether or not t is an integer. If t is an integer n, then it can be shown that $\Gamma(n) = (n-1)!$. Thus, for example,

$$\Gamma(4) = \int_0^\infty x^3 e^{-x} dx = 3! = 6. \tag{6.15}$$

This equality is investigated in Fig. 6.8. The upper limit of integration is infinity in (6.15), but this is of course not practical for computer calculations. However, the factor of e^{-x} in the integral implies that the contributions to the integral will become smaller and smaller as x increases.

```
          A        B
     ?    0        2

          N        INTEGRAL
          10       1.19629E+00
          20       1.19629E+00
```

FIGURE 6.7. Integration of the Gaussian probability density function.

```
                 A        B
            ?    0        10

                 N           INTEGRAL
                 10       5.93265E+00
                 20       5.93646E+00
                 40       5.93786E+00
                 80       5.93798E+00
                160       5.93798E+00
                320       5.93798E+00
                640       5.93798E+00
```

(a)

```
                 A        B
            ?    0        100

                 N           INTEGRAL
                 10       6.05442E-01
                 20       5.77323E+00
                 40       6.55891E+00
                 80       6.00828E+00
                160       5.99697E+00
                320       5.99972E+00
                640       5.99998E+00
```

(b)

FIGURE 6.8. Evaluation of the gamma function $\Gamma(4)$ by integration. The infinite limit of integration is first approximated as (a) $B = 10$ and then as (b) $B = 100$.

In Fig. 6.8(a) the upper limit of integration was chosen as $B = 10$. With this as an approximation to infinity the integral was found to be 5.93798. In Fig. 6.8(b) the upper limit of integration was instead picked as $B = 100$, which yielded 5.99998 for the integral. This is extremely close to the analytical answer of 6.

Elliptic integrals are encountered in many branches of engineering and science. For example, electrical engineers use them to help design elliptic filters. The elliptic integral of the first kind is defined as

$$u(\phi, k) = \int_0^\phi (1 - k^2 \sin^2 x)^{-1/2} dx. \tag{6.16}$$

As the notation indicates, this is a function of two variables: ϕ and k. The elliptic integral is evaluated in Fig. 6.9 for the case $\phi = 190°$ (3.3161 radians) and $k = 0.5$. This figure indicates that $u(190°, 0.5) = 3.54623$.

```
        A      B
  ?     0      3.3161

        N      INTEGRAL
        10     3.54623E+00
        20     3.54623E+00
```

FIGURE 6.9. Evaluation of the elliptic integral $u(190°, 0.5)$.

6.5 ROMBERG PREDICTION

In Section 6.2 we found that, for h small enough, trapezoidal integration has a global error that is proportional to h^2. In Section 6.3 we found that for either of Simpson's rules the error is proportional to h^4. In this section we will treat the general case—we will assume that an integration process has an error that is proportional to h^r, where r is an integer.

The notation we will use is that Int is the exact value of the integral, while Int(h) is the value that is determined by the integration process; for example, by the trapezoidal rule. Since the error is assumed to be proportional to h^r, we can write

$$\text{Int} - \text{Int}(h) \approx \alpha h^r, \qquad (6.17)$$

where α is a constant of proportionality. The approximation symbol is used instead of an equality symbol to emphasize that the error is only proportional to h^r for h *small enough* (that is, as $h \to 0$).

In our integration programs, we let h be continually reduced by a factor of 2 until the error was small enough. To see the effect of halving h on the error, we can replace h by $h/2$ in (6.17).

$$\text{Int} - \text{Int}(h/2) \approx \alpha(h/2)^r. \qquad (6.18)$$

The relations in (6.17) and (6.18) have two unknowns: the exact value of the integral (Int) and the value of the proportionality constant (α). We can solve for Int by multiplying (6.18) by 2^r and then subtracting from (6.17). This yields

$$\text{Int} \approx \frac{2^r \text{Int}(h/2) - \text{Int}(h)}{2^r - 1}. \qquad (6.19)$$

This equation is the basis of Romberg prediction. To understand how it can be applied, recall that Int(h) is the estimate for the integral based on using a step size equal to h. Int($h/2$) is another estimate for the integral, but this is based on using a smaller step size $h/2$. Equation (6.19) indicates that the more accurate estimate [Int($h/2$)] is weighted by 2^r and then the less accurate estimate is subtracted from it.

As indicated in (6.19), Romberg prediction takes two estimates for an integral and calculates an even better estimate. The approximation symbol in (6.19) indicates that the true value of the integral is not calculated exactly—because the error was only approximately proportional to h^r. However, as h is made smaller, the approximation becomes better and better.

Romberg prediction has its biggest success when applied to the trapezoidal rule. Since this has an error proportional to h^2, (6.19) becomes

$$\text{Int} \approx \frac{4\,\text{Int}(h/2) - \text{Int}(h)}{3}. \tag{6.20}$$

EXAMPLE 6.5

Example 6.2 used the trapezoidal rule to estimate $\int_{-0.5}^{0.5} e^x \, dx$. For $n = 10$ the estimate was 1.04306, while for $n = 20$ it was 1.04241. Thus in our present notation,

$$\text{Int}(h) = 1.04306, \qquad \text{Int}(h/2) = 1.04241.$$

Substituting these values into (6.20) yields $\text{Int} \approx 1.04219$, which agrees with the analytical answer to six significant figures.

The above example demonstrated that two successive answers from a computer output could be taken and used to estimate a much more accurate answer. The same approach can be used if we have experimental data (instead of a continuous function as in the example. This is demonstrated in the next example.

EXAMPLE 6.6

The following function values were found by evaluating $f(x) = 4x^2 - 7x + 2$:

$$f(0) = 2, \quad f(1) = -1, \quad f(2) = 4, \quad f(3) = 17, \quad f(4) = 38.$$

This data can be used by the trapezoidal rule to estimate the integral from 0 to 4. The result is $\text{Int}(h = 1) = 40$. If we want to, we may instead consider only some of the data as indicated below:

$$f(0) = 2, \quad f(2) = 4, \quad f(4) = 38.$$

Applying the trapezoidal rule to this yields $\text{Int}(h = 2) = 48$.

Romberg prediction may be applied to these two estimates of the integral to yield a better answer:

$$\text{Int} \approx (4 \times 40 - 48)/3 = 37\tfrac{1}{3}.$$

This answer is also the analytical answer. Simpson's $\frac{1}{3}$ rule also would have given the analytical answer because it is exact for any third-degree function. We will now demonstrate the surprising fact that Romberg prediction applied to the trapezoidal rule always yields the same result as Simpson's $\frac{1}{3}$ rule.

The trapezoidal rule estimates the integral as

$$\text{Int}(h) \approx \frac{h}{2}(f_0 + 2f_1 + 2f_3 + 2f_4 + \cdots). \tag{6.21}$$

If we instead choose to use just half the data, we have

$$\text{Int}(2h) \approx h(f_0 + 2f_2 + 2f_4 + \cdots). \tag{6.22}$$

Applying Romberg prediction to these two results, we have

$$\text{Int} \approx \frac{4\,\text{Int}(h) - \text{Int}(2h)}{3}$$

$$= \frac{h}{3}(f_0 + 4f_1 + 2f_2 + 4f_3 + 2f_4 + \cdots), \tag{6.23}$$

which is Simpson's $\frac{1}{3}$ rule.

It has just been shown that Romberg prediction applied to the trapezoidal rule yields the same results as Simpson's $\frac{1}{3}$ rule. However, even though the results must be the same for the same step size, a program based on Romberg prediction can have features not available in a program based on Simpson's $\frac{1}{3}$ rule. A Romberg program can include an estimate of whether h is small enough (because answers for both h and $2h$ are obtained in the process). One would have to use Simpson's rule twice (with different h's) to get the same information. The Romberg method therefore is useful as the basis of programs which reduce h automatically until it is small enough (e.g., subroutine *QATR* of the IBM scientific subroutines package).

Because of the success we had in applying Romberg prediction to the trapezoidal rule, it is logical to attempt to apply it to Simpson's rules. However, the attempt is usually not worth the effort. To apply Romberg prediction to Simpson's rules, we would have to make the assumption that h is small enough so that the error is proportional to h^4. However, by that time the error is usually negligible anyway, so Romberg prediction is not necessary. An exception to this statement might occur if very high accuracy is desired; then integration rules that converge faster than fourth order may be needed.

6.6 METHOD OF UNDETERMINED COEFFICIENTS

The method of undetermined coefficients was applied in the previous chapter to help derive approximations for derivatives, but it is not restricted to derivatives. The method is based on the fact that the following approximation can be exact for any nth-degree polynomial:

$$f_s \approx c_0(s) f_0 + c_1(s) f_1 + c_2(s) f_2 + \cdots + c_n(s) f_n. \tag{6.24}$$

Since the coefficients $c_i(s)$ can be chosen so that the expression is exact for any nth-degree polynomial, it can be integrated and the result will also be exact.

The approximation for an integral will be expressed as

$$\int_{S_A}^{S_B} f_s \, ds \approx d_0 f_0 + d_1 f_1 + d_2 f_2 + \cdots + d_n f_n, \tag{6.25}$$

where the coefficients d_i are related to the coefficients $c_i(s)$ via

$$d_i = \int_{S_A}^{S_B} c_i(s) \, ds. \tag{6.26}$$

Actually, it is not necessary to apply (6.26) to determine the coefficients d_i; they can be determined by analogy with the method used for derivatives.

As an illustration of the application of the method of undetermined coefficients to the derivation of integral approximations, consider the following:

$$\int_0^2 f_s d_s \approx d_0 f_0 + d_1 f_1 + d_2 f_2. \tag{6.27}$$

The three unknown coefficients d_0, d_1, d_2 can be determined so that this equation is exact for any second-degree polynomial. In particular, it must be exact for the polynomials $f_s = 1$, $f_s = s$, and $f_s = s^2$.

The fact that (6.27) is exact for these three different functions can be used to obtain three equations in terms of the three unknowns d_0, d_1, d_2. For example, substituting the function $f_s = s^2$ into (6.27),

$$\int_0^2 s^2 \, ds = \frac{8}{3} = f_0 d_0 + f_1 d_1 + f_2 d_2 = 0 + d_1 + 4 d_2. \tag{6.28}$$

The results of applying the three different functions can be conveniently written in matrix notation as

$$\begin{bmatrix} 1 & 1 & 1 \\ 0 & 1 & 2 \\ 0 & 1 & 4 \end{bmatrix} \begin{bmatrix} d_0 \\ d_1 \\ d_2 \end{bmatrix} = \begin{bmatrix} 2 \\ 2 \\ \frac{8}{3} \end{bmatrix}. \tag{6.29}$$

This relation can be solved to yield $d_0 = \frac{1}{3}$, $d_1 = \frac{4}{3}$, $d_2 = \frac{1}{3}$, so that (6.27) becomes

$$\int_0^2 f_s \, ds \approx \frac{1}{3}(f_0 + 4 f_1 + f_2). \tag{6.30}$$

Since $s = (x - x_0)/h_1$, this expression is equivalent to

$$\int_{x_0}^{x_2} f(x)\, dx \approx \frac{h}{3}(f_0 + 4f_1 + f_2). \tag{6.31}$$

Either of the results in (6.30) or (6.31) can be recognized as Simpson's $\frac{1}{3}$ rule. Simpson's $\frac{1}{3}$ rule was obtained because the three unknown coefficients d_0, d_1, d_2 were selected so that the integral approximation would be exact for any second-degree polynomial. Other approximations can be obtained as illustrated in the following sections.

6.7 PREDICTOR AND CORRECTOR EQUATIONS

This section applies the method of undetermined coefficients to derive what are called predictor and corrector equations. There will be nothing profound about the derivations, but the results will be so useful to us in the next chapter that their importance will be emphasized by devoting this separate section to them.

In this section we will first assume that at the locations x_0, x_1, x_2, x_3 we have function values f_0, f_1, f_2, f_3 and we want to estimate the integral $\int_{x_3}^{x_4} f(x)\, dx$. This situation is illustrated (for the normalized variable s) in Fig. 6.10, which indicates we want to *predict* the value of the integral without knowing the value f_4.

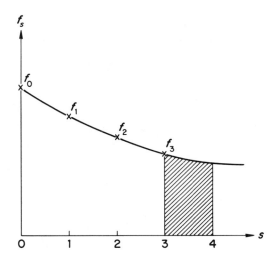

FIGURE 6.10. Extrapolation can be used to obtain a predictor integration equation.

It is possible to predict the integral without knowing f_4 because through four data values one can pass a third-degree polynomial and use this to estimate the value of $f(x)$ between x_3 and x_4. However, instead of actually finding the third-degree polynomial, we will apply the method of undetermined coefficients, which is simpler.

By analogy with the derivation of Simpson's $\frac{1}{3}$ rule, in this problem the integral can be approximated in terms of four function values as

$$\int_3^4 f_s\, ds \approx d_0 f_0 + d_1 f_1 + d_2 f_2 + d_3 f_3. \tag{6.32}$$

Using the four functions $f_s = 1$, $f_s = s$, $f_s = s^2$, $f_s = s^3$ then yields

$$\begin{bmatrix} 1 & 1 & 1 & 1 \\ 0 & 1 & 2 & 3 \\ 0 & 1 & 4 & 9 \\ 0 & 1 & 8 & 27 \end{bmatrix} \begin{bmatrix} d_0 \\ d_1 \\ d_2 \\ d_3 \end{bmatrix} = \begin{bmatrix} 1 \\ 3.5 \\ \frac{37}{3} \\ 43.75 \end{bmatrix}. \tag{6.33}$$

The above matrix equation can be solved by using the Gauss elimination method of Chapter 2. The result is $d_0 = -\frac{9}{24}$, $d_1 = \frac{37}{24}$, $d_2 = -\frac{59}{24}$, $d_3 = \frac{55}{24}$, so that the predictor equation becomes

$$\int_{x_3}^{x_4} f(x)\, dx \approx \frac{h}{24}(-9f_0 + 37f_1 - 59f_2 + 55f_3). \tag{6.34}$$

EXAMPLE 6.7

Using $x_0 = 0$, $x_1 = 0.1$, $x_2 = 0.2$, and $x_3 = 0.3$ for $f(x) = e^x - 1$ yields that $f_0 = 0$, $f_1 = 0.10517$, $f_2 = 0.22140$, and $f_3 = 0.34986$. Substituting these values into the predictor integration formula with $h = 0.1$ produces

$$\int_{0.3}^{0.4} (e^x - 1)\, dx \approx 0.04196,$$

compared with the analytical answer 0.04197.

We have developed an equation that can be used to predict the value of $\int_{x_3}^{x_4} f(x)\, dx$ without having the value of the function at x_4. If the value of the function f_4 is known, then the four function values f_1, f_2, f_3, f_4 can be used to estimate the integral, as illustrated in Fig. 6.11. In the Adams method described in Chapter 7, an integral of the type shown in Fig. 6.11 will be used to "correct" a "predicted" value; thus the relation derived for this figure will be called a corrector integration formula.

The method of undetermined coefficients can be used to find the coefficients in

$$\int_3^4 f_s\, ds \approx d_1 f_1 + d_2 f_2 + d_3 f_3 + d_4 f_4. \tag{6.35}$$

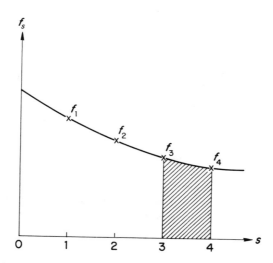

FIGURE 6.11. Interpolation can be used to obtain a corrector integration equation.

Applying the method for $f_s = 1$, $f_s = s$, $f_s = s^2$, and $f_s = s^3$ yields

$$\begin{bmatrix} 1 & 1 & 1 & 1 \\ 1 & 2 & 3 & 4 \\ 1 & 4 & 9 & 16 \\ 1 & 8 & 27 & 64 \end{bmatrix} \begin{bmatrix} d_1 \\ d_2 \\ d_3 \\ d_4 \end{bmatrix} = \begin{bmatrix} 1 \\ 3.5 \\ \frac{37}{3} \\ 43.75 \end{bmatrix}. \tag{6.36}$$

The solution to this matrix equation is $d_1 = \frac{1}{24}$, $d_2 = -\frac{5}{24}$, $d_3 = \frac{19}{24}$, $d_4 = \frac{9}{24}$, so that the corrector equation becomes

$$\int_{x_3}^{x_4} f(x)\,dx \approx \frac{h}{24}(f_1 - 5f_2 + 19f_3 + 9f_4). \tag{6.37}$$

The corrector equation is more accurate than the predictor equation because the integration range x_3 to x_4 is within the region where the corrector values are specified (see Fig. 6.11), but outside the region where the predictor values are specified (see Fig. 6.10). That is, the corrector uses interpolation, while the predictor uses extrapolation. The better accuracy of the corrector equation is also evident by comparing (6.34) and (6.37). The predictor equation has the difference $55f_3 - 59f_2$, which is very sensitive to changes in f_2 or f_3 (because of the large coefficients which are approximately the same), while the corrector equation is much less sensitive.

More insight into the predictor and corrector equations may be obtained by considering the coefficients of the various derivatives as weights. For example, reexamine the corrector equation

$$\int_{x_3}^{x_4} f(x)\,dx \approx \frac{h}{24}(9f_4 + 19f_3 - 5f_2 + f_1).$$

Since the integral is from x_3 to x_4, it is logical that the derivatives f_3 and f_4 should have the largest weights.

6.8 GAUSSIAN QUADRATURE[2]

The integration formulas that have been presented in this chapter were for equally spaced data. If the data are not constrained to be equally spaced, then the extra degrees of freedom can be used to give a more accurate solution. This section will explain how two data pairs can be located so that a third-degree polynomial can be integrated exactly. A program, similar to the one developed for Simpson's $\frac{1}{3}$ rule, will then be given and applied.

As mentioned in the next section, higher-order Gaussian-quadrature programs are possible and in fact widely used. They have the advantage that, for the same accuracy, they require fewer function evaluations than an equally spaced evaluation would.

Gaussian quadrature can be developed by generalizing the method of undetermined coefficients. The generalization will be introduced by considering the following approximation:

$$\int_0^2 f_s\,ds \approx d_a f_a + d_b f_b. \tag{6.38}$$

The left side of this relation indicates that we want to find an approximation for integration over two panels. The right side indicates that we want to express the approximation in terms of two function values: f_a and f_b. As usual, there are some coefficients to be determined: d_a and d_b. However, the notation in (6.38) implies there are two more quantities to be determined: a and b. That is, we have indicated we want to express the approximation in terms of two function values, but we have not specified their locations.

It should be emphasized that we are assuming once a and b have been determined the function values f_a and f_b will be available. Thus Gaussian quadrature will only work for continuous functions, not for experimental data.

There are four unknowns in (6.38): the locations a, b, and the coefficients d_a, d_b. Since there are four unknowns, the approximation for the integral can be *exact* for any polynomial which is of third degree or

[2]Quadrature is another term for integration.

less. In particular it is exact for the polynomials $f_s = 1$, $f_s = s$, $f_s = s^2$, and $f_s = s^3$. Substituting these polynomials into (6.38) yields

$$d_a + d_b = 2$$
$$ad_a + bd_b = 2$$
$$a^2 d_a + b^2 d_b = \tfrac{8}{3} \qquad (6.39)$$
$$a^3 d_a + b^3 d_b = 4.$$

This is not a linear set of equations, so the techniques derived in Chapter 2 cannot be applied to yield a solution. Some methods for solving nonlinear equations such as these will be mentioned in the next section; here it will be stated without derivation that a solution to (6.39) is

$$d_a = 1 = d_b, \qquad a = 1 - 1/\sqrt{3}, \qquad b = 1 + 1/\sqrt{3}. \qquad (6.40)$$

Combining (6.38) and (6.40), and also using the fact that $s = (x - x_0)/h$, we have

$$\int_{x_0}^{x_2} f(x)\,dx \approx h[\, f_a + f_b\,], \qquad (6.41)$$

where

$$f_a = f\big(x_0 + h - h/\sqrt{3}\,\big), \qquad (6.42)$$
$$f_b = f\big(x_0 + h + h/\sqrt{3}\,\big).$$

EXAMPLE 6.8

Use the Gaussian quadrature formula to estimate $\int_1^5 f(x)\,dx$, where $f(x) = x^3 + 2$.

SOLUTION

Since $x_0 = 1$ and $x_2 = 5$, it follows that $h = 2$, and

$$f_a = f\big(1 + 2 - 2/\sqrt{3}\,\big) = 8.2835$$
$$f_b = f\big(1 + 2 + 2/\sqrt{3}\,\big) = 73.717.$$

Substituting into (6.41) yields 164 as the value of the integral.

Since (6.41) is exact for any third-degree polynomial, the answer to Example 6.8 must be exact. Recall that Simpson's $\tfrac{1}{3}$ rule was also exact for any third-degree polynomial, but it required four function values instead of two as in Gaussian quadrature.

An integration program can be based on (6.41) and (6.42) by analogy with the development of the Simpson integration program. That program applied Simpson's $\frac{1}{3}$ rule to an even number of panels by going from x_0 to x_n in steps of two panels at a time. Using this approach for Gaussian quadrature, we can write from (6.41) and (6.42)

$$\int_{A=x_0}^{B=x_n} f(x)\,dx \approx h \sum_{i=0,2,\ldots}^{n-2} \left[f\left(x_i + h - \frac{h}{\sqrt{3}}\right) + f\left(x_i + h + \frac{h}{\sqrt{3}}\right) \right]. \quad (6.43)$$

A better form for a computer program can be obtained by substituting $x_i = A + ih$:

$$\int_A^B f(x)\,dx \approx h \sum_{i=0,2,\ldots}^{n-2} \left[f(ih + \delta_1) + f(ih + \delta_2) \right], \quad (6.44)$$

```
01C     GAUSSIAN QUADRATURE
02      PROGRAM GQ(INPUT,OUTPUT)
03 03   FORMAT(I4,1P,E14.5)
08      REAL INTGRL
10C
11C     INITIAL POINT=A    FINAL POINT=B
12      PRINT,*    A        B*
13      READ,A,B
14      PRINT,/,*   N         INTEGRAL*
18C
19C     INITIAL CONSTANTS N,H
21      N=10 $N2=8 $H=(B-A)/10.
23C
24C     APPLICATION OF GAUSS. QUAD.  (EQ. 6.43)
27 27   DEL1=A+H-H/1.73205 $DEL2=A+H+H/1.73205
28      Z=F(DEL1)+F(DEL2)
29      DO 30 I=2,N2,2
30 30   Z=Z+F(A+I*H+DEL1)+F(A+I*H+DEL2)
32      INTGRL=H*Z
34C
36      PRINT 3,N,INTGRL
40C
41C     NEW CONSTANTS N,H
42      N=2*N $N2=N-2 $H=.5*H
50      GO TO 27
60      END
898C
899     FUNCTION F(X)
900     F=X**3/EXP(X)
950     RETURN
999     END
```

FIGURE 6.12. A program for Gaussian quadrature.

$$
\begin{array}{ccc}
 & A & B \\
? & \emptyset & 1\emptyset
\end{array}
$$

N	INTEGRAL
10	5.94038E+00
20	5.93897E+00
40	5.93806E+00
80	5.93799E+00
160	5.93798E+00
320	5.93798E+00

FIGURE 6.13. An application of the Gaussian-quadrature program.

where

$$\delta_1 = A + h - h/\sqrt{3} ,$$

$$\delta_2 = A + h + h/\sqrt{3} . \tag{6.45}$$

A program that implements these equations is shown in Fig. 6.12. This program is very similar to the one for Simpson's $\frac{1}{3}$ rule that was shown in Fig. 6.6 and thus should need no further explanation. Fig. 6.13 shows the application of the Gaussian quadrature program to $\int_0^{10} x^3 e^{-x} dx$.

6.9 SUGGESTED READING IN RELATED TOPICS

In this chapter we started our investigation of numerical methods for integration by first considering the trapezoidal rule, which can be obtained by matching a first-degree polynomial to two data values. Similarly, using a second-degree polynomial to match three points leads to Simpson's $\frac{1}{3}$ rule, and using a third-degree polynomial for four points leads to Simpson's $\frac{3}{8}$ rule. This process has been continued by other authors. For example, using a fourth-degree polynomial for five points leads to Boole's rule. It is not practical to keep extending this approach and use high-degree polynomials to match many points. The reason is the same as the one mentioned in Section 4.12: increasing the degree of an interpolating polynomial need not result in a smaller error, and may actually increase it. Thus, in practice, one uses a low-degree polynomial (e.g., third-degree) to match a few points and then finds the total integral by adding up a series of such contributions. That is, one uses composite integration such as Simpson's $\frac{1}{3}$ rule.

The error analysis that was used in this chapter consisted mainly in determining the order of the truncation error for a particular process. For example, for the trapezoidal rule we found that the (global) error was of the order of h^2. This allowed the use of Romberg prediction to improve trapezoidal results. There are more definitive error statements available for the various integration rules.[3] Again using the trapezoidal rule for an illustration, the truncation error can be approximated as $-h^2(x_n - x_0)^2 f^{(2)}(\xi)/12$, where $f^{(2)}(\xi)$ is the second derivative at some point ξ which is between x_0 and x_n. However, since the location of the point ξ is unknown, this formula conveys little more information than the statement that the error is of the order of h^2. Because the error is proportional to h^2, we know that by reducing h we can make the error arbitrarily small (until roundoff error is larger than truncation error).

For special types of integrals, more efficient algorithms have been developed than the general-purpose procedures. One important algorithm, Filon's method, treats oscillatory functions of the form $\int_a^b f(x)\sin x\,dx$. In fact, the Gaussian quadrature method as presented in this chapter was very elementary; the theory has been extended to treat many different types of special functions.

The Gaussian procedure developed in this chapter chose the location of two function values f_a, f_b and their "weights" d_a, d_b. The resulting approximation was exact for any third-degree function. If n function values and n weights were used, then the resulting approximation would be exact for any $(2n-1)$-degree polynomial. This is a factor of 2 better than if the function locations were constrained to be equally spaced and accounts for the widespread popularity of the Gaussian quadrature method.

Finding the value of the function locations and their weights requires the solution of some nonlinear equations. One way these equations could be solved would be to use optimization techniques as outlined in Chapter 8. However, a more efficient solution is based on the use of Legendre polynomials. It should be emphasized that once the locations and weights have been obtained, they can be tabulated and the average user need never worry about solving the nonlinear equations. Stroud and Secrest (1966) provide tables containing values of the locations and weights. It should be noted that these tables (and most of those in other books) are for the normalized integral $\int_{-1}^1 f(x)\,dx$.

If the integral is of a special form, often other polynomials are more useful than the Legendre polynomials. If the integral is of the form $\int_0^\infty e^{-x} f(x)\,dx$, then Laguerre polynomials are used. Hermite polynomials are used for $\int_{-\infty}^\infty e^{-x^2} f(x)\,dx$, and Chebyshev polynomials are used for

$$\int_{-\infty}^\infty \frac{f(x)}{\sqrt{1-x^2}}\,dx.$$

---

[3]One way of deriving these error estimates [e.g. see McCormick and Salvadori (1965)] is to use a Taylor series expansion and include the remainder term which is due to truncation.

Besides these special polynomials, special transformations are often useful if the limits of integration are infinite or if there are singularities (locations at which division by zero is encountered).

The Gaussian quadrature method did not require equally spaced data. Adaptive quadrature routines (Forsythe 1977) also do not require equally spaced points. Such routines use small distances between the points where the integrand varies rapidly and larger distances elsewhere. This can substantially reduce the number of points which are necessary to achieve an accurate approximation of the integral.

PROBLEMS

6.1 Apply the trapezoidal rule to evaluate $\int_2^7 (2x+3)\,dx$ using just one panel. Compare with the analytical answer.

6.2 Integrate x^2-2 from 0 to 4 by using the trapezoidal rule with four panels.

6.3 Apply the trapezoidal rule to evaluate $\int_1^2 e^{-x}\,dx$, using four panels. Compare with the analytical answer.

6.4 Use the trapezoidal program of Fig. 6.3 to evaluate $\int_0^2 e^{-x^2}\,dx$. Stop the calculations when the answer is accurate to three significant figures.

6.5 Use the trapezoidal program to evaluate $\int_0^1 e^{-2x}\,dx$ for ten panels and for twenty panels. Find the error for these answers by comparing with the analytical answer. Verify that the error is proportional to h^2.

6.6 Integrate the following data from $x=1$ to $x=2$: $f(1)=1$, $f(1.2)=2$, $f(1.6)=3$, $f(1.8)=3$, $f(2)=2.5$. In this problem the data are not evenly spaced, but the trapezoidal rule can still be applied to each panel and then the individual results can be added to yield the overall answer.

6.7 The data in Problem 6.6 would be evenly spaced if we had $f(1.4)$.

(a) Interpolate with a fourth-degree polynomial to estimate $f(1.4)$.

(b) Apply the trapezoidal rule for evenly spaced data to estimate $\int_1^2 f(x)\,dx$.

6.8 Modify the trapezoidal program of Fig. 6.3 so that it can be used for discrete data. This can be done as follows:

(a) Input data rather than calculate them via a subroutine.

(b) Input a value for N instead of setting it equal to 10.

6.9 Apply the program that was developed in Problem 6.8 to integrate the following data from $x = 1$ to $x = 3$: $f(1) = 1$, $f(1.25) = 1.5$, $f(1.5) = 1.6$, $f(2) = 1.6$, $f(2.25) = 1.4$, $f(2.5) = 1$, $f(2.75) = 0$, $f(3) = -2$.

6.10 Problem 6.2 integrated $x^2 - 2$ from 0 to 4 by using the trapezoidal rule with four panels. The answer was not exact. In this problem evaluate the same integral by using Simpson's $\frac{1}{3}$ rule with two panels. Note that this result will be exact because Simpson's rule is exact for any second- (or third-) degree function.

6.11 Repeat Problem 6.3 with Simpson's $\frac{1}{3}$ rule.

6.12 Repeat Problem 6.4 with Simpson's $\frac{1}{3}$ rule.

6.13 For two panels, Simpson's $\frac{1}{3}$ rule is $\int_0^2 f_s\, ds \approx \frac{1}{3}(f_0 + 4f_1 + f_2)$. This is exact for any second-degree function. Any third-degree function can be written as $f_s = (\text{second-degree}) + cs^3$, where c is an arbitrary constant. This implies that if Simpson's rule is exact for the function s^3, it must be exact for every third-degree function. Show that Simpson's $\frac{1}{3}$ rule is exact for $f_s = s^3$.

6.14 Show that Simpson's $\frac{1}{3}$ rule applied to $\int_0^2 f_s\, ds$ does not give the exact answer for $f_s = s^4$.

6.15 Show that Simpson's $\frac{3}{8}$ rule applied to $\int_0^3 f_s\, ds$ does not give the exact answer for $f_s = s^4$.

6.16 The following data represent the sine function: $f(0) = 0$, $f(0.1) = 0.0998$, $f(0.2) = 0.1987$, $f(0.3) = 0.2955$, $f(0.4) = 0.3894$, $f(0.5) = 0.4794$, $f(0.6) = 0.5646$.

(a) Use Simpson's $\frac{1}{3}$ rule to estimate the integral from 0 to 0.6.

(b) Use Simpson's $\frac{3}{8}$ rule to estimate the integral from 0 to 0.6.

6.17 For an odd number of panels, Simpson's $\frac{3}{8}$ rule can be used for the first three and Simpson's $\frac{1}{3}$ rule for the rest. Use this technique to integrate the following data: $f(1.8) = 6.05$, $f(2.0) = 7.389$, $f(2.2) = 9.025$, $f(2.4) = 11.023$, $f(2.6) = 13.464$, $f(2.8) = 16.445$.

6.18 The complete elliptic integral of the first kind is defined as

$$K(k) = \int_0^{\pi/2} (1 - k^2 \sin^2 x)^{-1/2}\, dx.$$

Use the program in Fig. 6.6 to find $k(0.5)$.

6.19 The elliptic integral $u(190°, 0.5)$ was found in Section 4 to be equal to 3.5462. An alternate method of calculating this is to use

$$u(190°, 0.5) = 2K(0.5) + u(10°, 0.5),$$

where $K(0.5)$ is the complete elliptic integral as defined in Problem

6.18. Use the Simpson integration program to evaluate $u(10°, 0.5)$, and combine this with $2K(0.5)$ to yield a value for $u(190°, 0.5)$.

6.20 The elliptic integral of the first kind can also be written as

$$u(\phi, k) = \int_0^{\sin \phi} \left[(1 - z^2)(1 - k^2 z^2) \right]^{-1/2} dz.$$

Use the program in Fig. 6.6 to evaluate $u(10°, 0.5)$.

6.21 Problem 6.3 applied the trapezoidal rule to evaluate $\int_1^2 e^{-x} dx$ by using four panels. The result was 0.23375. In this problem, also apply the trapezoidal rule for two panels and then use Romberg prediction to obtain a better answer.

6.22 What is the Romberg prediction formula for Simpson's $\frac{1}{3}$ rule?

6.23 Romberg prediction is not restricted to integration processes; it can also be applied to differentiation. As an illustration of this use, evaluate $f(x) = 2 + 3x + x^4$ at $x = 1$, 1.1, and 1.2. Use $f(1)$ and $f(1.1)$ to estimate the derivative at $x = 1$. Also use $f(1)$ and $f(1.2)$ to estimate the derivative at $x = 1$. Then use Romberg prediction to provide a better estimate.

6.24 Apply the method of undetermined coefficients to derive the trapezoidal rule.

6.25 Apply the method of undetermined coefficients to derive Simpson's $\frac{3}{8}$ rule.

6.26 Use the predictor equation to estimate $\int_{1.5}^2 (2 + 4x^3) dx$ by choosing $x_0 = 0$ and $h = 0.5$. Compare the results with the analytical answer.

6.27 Equation (6.34) expresses a function in terms of four function values, so it should be exact for any third-degree polynomial. Problem 6.26 was one illustration of this fact. Show that the predictor equation is *not* exact for $f_s = s^4$.

6.28 Use the predictor equation to estimate $\int_{1.5}^{2.5} x^4 dx$ by choosing $x_0 = 0$ and $h = 0.5$. Compare the result with the analytical answer.

6.29 Assume that the three equally spaced data points x_1, x_2, x_3 have function values f_1, f_2, f_3. Use the method of undetermined coefficients to show that

$$\int_{x_0}^{x_4} f(x) dx \approx \frac{4h}{3} \left[2f_1 - f_2 + 2f_3 \right].$$

6.30 Use the result of the previous problem to estimate $\int_0^2 e^x dx$. (*Hint:* For this problem, $x_1 = 0.5$, $x_2 = 1$, $x_3 = 1.5$.) Compare your answer with the exact answer.

6.31 The approximation

$$\int_{x_0}^{x_4} f(x)\,dx \approx \frac{4h}{3}\left[2f_1 - f_2 + 2f_3\right]$$

is exact for any second-degree polynomial. Show that it is also exact for $f(x) = x^3$. [*Hint*: It is equivalent (and easier) to show instead that it is exact for the normalized problem $f_s = s^3$.] Note that the result of this problem implies that the relation is exact for any third-degree polynomial.

6.32 In Problem 6.27 the predictor equation was used to integrate $f_s = s^4$ from $s = 3$ to $s = 4$. The answer is 147.83, compared to the analytical answer of 156.2. Use the corrector equation and see whether it is better or worse than the predictor's result.

6.33 Apply Gaussian quadrature to evaluate $\int_1^2 e^{-x}\,dx$, using four panels. Compare with the analytical answer.

Chapter Seven

Solution of Differential Equations

7.1 INTRODUCTION

Very often the laws describing natural phenomena are most easily expressed in terms of differential equations. For example, the motion of a pendulum might be described by

$$\frac{d^2\theta}{dt^2} + \frac{g}{l}\sin\theta = 0, \tag{7.1}$$

where θ is the angular displacement, g the gravitational constant, and l the length of the pendulum. Or the variation of voltage in an electrical circuit might be described by

$$C\frac{d^2v}{dt^2} + \frac{1}{R}\frac{dv}{dt} + \frac{v}{L} = \cos 2t, \tag{7.2}$$

where v, R, L, and C represent voltage, resistance, inductance, and capacitance, respectively.

The above differential equations are easy to solve, and one need not resort to numerical methods.[1] Later in this chapter, we will encounter other differential equations that are not so easily solved. Comparing our numerical solutions with analytical solutions will allow us to simultaneously develop confidence in the numerical methods and also become familar with some well-known differential equations. Of course, the purpose of the numerical methods is not comparison with known results, but the solution of problems for which no analytical results have been found.

As in the preceding chapters, sample programs are included in this one about differential equations. These programs are adequate for many problems, but again it should be mentioned that experts have written far better programs for solving differential equations than the novice can. If the reader anticipates developing a sophisticated program he will be well advised to consult the literature or someone in a computation center.

---

[1] The pendulum differential equation is only easy to solve if the small-angle approximation $\sin\theta \cong \theta$ is made.

7.2 CLASSIFICATION OF DIFFERENTIAL EQUATIONS

There are two types of differential equations, *ordinary* and *partial*. We will restrict our attention to the type that has only one independent variable, the ordinary differential equation—for example,

$$\left(\frac{d^2y}{dx^2}\right)^3 + xy\frac{dy}{dx} + y^2 = 6x. \tag{7.3}$$

The order of the highest derivative determines the *order* of the differential equation, while the exponent of the highest derivative determines the *degree*. The above differential equation is of second order and third degree.

A *linear differential equation* is one which has only first-degree derivatives and a first-degree dependent variable. For example,

$$x^3\frac{d^3y}{dx^2} + 6\frac{d^2y}{dx^2} + (\sin x)y = \tan x \tag{7.4}$$

is a linear differential equation. For a linear differential equation it can be shown that if $y_1(x)$ is a solution and $y_2(x)$ is a solution, then the sum $y_1(x) + y_2(x)$ is also as solution.

The methods we study in this chapter will initially be discussed in terms of first-order differential equations. However, this will not be restrictive, because we will learn later how to change a higher-order differential equation into a set of first-order differential equations which can then be solved.

7.3 EULER METHOD

A general form for a first-order differential equation is

$$\frac{dy}{dx} = f(x,y). \tag{7.5}$$

This implies that, in general, the first derivative (slope) is a function of the dependent variable y as well as the independent variable x. Equation (7.5) is simple enough in appearance, but unfortunately there is no general method for obtaining an analytical solution.

For some special cases of (7.5), analytical solutions can be obtained. One such case is if the variables are separable, as in

$$\frac{dy}{dx} = \frac{2y^{3/2}}{x^2}. \tag{7.6}$$

It can be shown that the solution to this equation is

$$y = \left(\frac{x}{1 + Cx}\right)^2. \tag{7.7}$$

The above solution contains an arbitrary constant C, which can be evaluated if an initial condition is given. For example, if $y_0 = 1$ at $x_0 = 1$, then the constant must be $C = 0$. From the analytical answer $y = x^2$ one can plot a continuous curve to represent the solution. This is not possible for a numerical solution. As will be demonstrated next for the Euler method, a numerical solution yields answers only at discrete points. Because the Euler method is simple and easy to understand, it will serve as a good introduction to the numerical solution of differential equations. We will eventually study much more efficient algorithms.

Given the initial point x_0, y_0, the slope there can be calculated from $dy/dx = f(x_0, y_0)$. As illustrated in Fig. 7.1, one can proceed from x_0, y_0 in the direction of the slope until the abscissa is $x_0 + h = x_1$, where the solution will be $y_1 = y_0 + hf(x_0, y_0)$. At this new point x_1, y_1 the new slope $f(x_1, y_1)$ can be calculated, and one can proceed in that direction until the abscissa is $x_0 + 2h = x_2$. This procedure can be continued indefinitely by using the equation

$$y_{i+1} = y_i + hf(x_i, y_i). \tag{7.8}$$

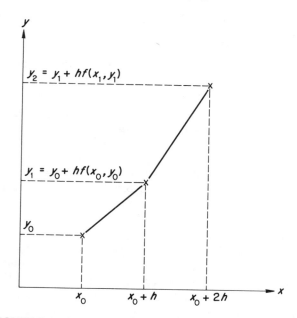

FIGURE 7.1. A graphical interpretation of the Euler method.

EXAMPLE 7.1

Apply the Euler method to the first-order differential equation

$$\frac{dy}{dx} = \frac{2y^{3/2}}{x^2} = f(x,y)$$

to estimate $y(2)$. Use $y(1) = 1$ as the initial value, and choose $h = 0.25$ as the step size.

SOLUTION

From (7.8), $y_1 = y_0 + hf(x_0, y_0)$. For this problem, at the initial point $x_0 = 1$ the value of y was given as $y_0 = 1$. Evaluating the function for these values yields $f(1, 1) = 2$. Substituting these values into the Euler equation yields

$$y_1 = 1 + 0.25 \times 2 = 1.50$$

This completes one cycle of the Euler solution.

The next cycle sets $i = 1$ in (7.8) to yield $y_2 = y_1 + hf(x_1, y_1)$. Using $x_1 = 1.25$, $y_1 = 1.50$, $f(1.25, 1.50) = 2.3515$ produces $y_2 = 2.088$.

Advancing the solution to $x_3 = 1.75$ yields $y_3 = 2.758$, and finally one more cycle yields that at $x_4 = 2$, $y_4 = 3.506$.

The numerical answer found in Example 7.1 was 3.506, while the analytical answer is 4. The numerical accuracy would have been better if the step size h had been smaller.

All the numerical methods that are discussed in this chapter will have a step size h which influences the accuracy and speed of the solution to the differential equation. The step size should be made small enough so that the answer has the desired accuracy, but large enough so that an unnecessary number of calculations is not performed.

Care must be taken that the step size is not too large because the errors are cumulative, as illustrated in the previous example. That is, after one cycle of the Euler method the result was $y_1 = 1.50$, while the analytical value is $y(1.25) = 1.5625$. This error affected the next value y_2, since we used $y_2 = y_1 + f(x_1, y_1)$. Similarly, the error in y_2 affects the value found for y_3, etc. In general, if h is too large, by the time the last point is reached the answer may be meaningless.

Numerical methods will normally be applied when one does not have an analytical solution. In that case the accuracy of the solution can be checked by solving the problem twice, once for a step size of h and again for a step size of $h/2$. If the answers do not agree to the desired number of significant figures, then the step size can usually be halved until they do. This will be demonstrated in the following sections.

7.4 STABILITY ANALYSIS

The step size can usually be halved until the solution is sufficiently accurate; however, this is not always possible. Some algorithms are unstable—even if the step size is infinitesimally small there may be errors that grow exponentially as the solution is advanced.

This section will demonstrate the instability of one particular numerical method. It will also indicate how stability can be investigated for other numerical methods. However, so that the reader does not imagine that all numerical methods of solving differential equations are unstable, it should be emphasized that this is not the case. The following sections will introduce the Runge-Kutta method and the Adams method, both of which can be stable numerical methods. They are also fairly efficient procedures and thus are quite popular algorithms.

The unstable algorithm that will be investigated in this section is based on an attempt to improve the Euler method, which we recall is described by

$$y_{i+1} = y_i + hf(x_i, y_i). \tag{7.9}$$

This method was derived by using $(y_{i+1} - y_i)/h$ as an approximation to the first derivative. The central-difference approximation is more accurate, and can hopefully be used to improve the Euler method. Applying the central difference equation (5.21) yields

$$y_{i+1} = y_{i-1} + 2hf(x_i, y_i). \tag{7.10}$$

As noted in Chapter 5, the standard approximation for the first derivative results in an error that is proportional to h, while the central-difference approximation results in an error that is proportional to h^2. Thus we would expect that (7.10) would yield more accurate results than (7.9). To investigate this assumption for a particular example, consider the following differential equation:

$$y'(x) = -y(x), \qquad y(0) = 2. \tag{7.11}$$

Its analytical solution is $y(x) = 2e^{-x}$, which implies $y(1) = 0.73576$ and $y(10) = 9.0800 \times 10^{-5}$. These values should be compared with the results shown in Table 7.1. This table indicates the effect of reducing the step size h for Euler's method and for the central-difference method. In the table, y_E is the Euler answer and y_{CD} is the central-difference answer.[2]

---

[2] The central-difference method of (7.10) requires two values (y_{i-1}, y_i) to be available before y_{i+1} can be calculated. Usually just one "initial" value is given [$y_0 = y(x_0)$]. A second value can be obtained by applying Euler's method [$y_1 = y_0 + hf(x_0, y_0)$].

Table 7.1
An Illustration of numerical Instability

H	$Y_E(1)$	$Y_{CD}(1)$	$Y_E(10)$	$Y_{CD}(10)$
0.1	0.69736	0.74862	5.3123×10^{-5}	107.51
0.01	0.73206	0.73589	8.6342×10^{-5}	1.1011
0.001	0.73539	0.73576	9.0347×10^{-5}	-1.0934×10^{-2}
0.0001	0.73572	0.73576	9.0754×10^{-5}	-1.9353×10^{-5}
0.00001	0.73576	0.73576	9.0795×10^{-5}	8.9689×10^{-5}

We will first compare the solutions from the two numerical methods with the analytical answer $y(1) = 0.73576$. For any particular step size the central-difference method was more accurate than Euler's method. For example, with $h = 0.001$ the central-difference answer agrees with the analytical answer to five significant figures. On the other hand, $y_E(1) = 0.73539$ agrees only to three significant figures. However, reducing the step size to 0.00001 caused the Euler answer to be accurate to five significant figures.[3] This is as would be anticipated, since a smaller step size causes less truncation error.

We will next compare the solutions from the two numerical methods with the analytical answer $y(10) = 9.0800 \times 10^{-5}$. This time the Euler answers are more accurate than the corresponding central-difference answers; in fact, for large step sizes the central-difference answers are meaningless. The source of the trouble is in the accumulation of truncation error. In the central-difference method the errors grow exponentially as the independent variable x is increased,[4] and the method is thus said to be unstable. Reducing the step size h can alleviate this behavior, as it reduces the truncation error. However, as the step size is reduced, more calculations must be performed before the end point is reached; thus there will be more chance for roundoff error. In fact, if the step size is reduced too much, the roundoff error may become worse than the truncation error.[5]

As is indicated by Table 7.1, whether or not a numerical method is stable for a particular problem can be determined by seeing whether or not the answer changes significantly as the step size is reduced. An alternative stability investigation can be performed by solving the difference equation that corresponds to that problem. This will be illustrated next for Euler's method and for the central-difference method.

---

[3]For this same step size the central-difference answer was accurate to nine significant figures.

[4]This will be demonstrated in (7.21).

[5]The optimum step size would depend on the computer, the algorithm, and the problem.

Euler's method is described by

$$y_{i+1} = y_i + hf(x_i, y_i). \tag{7.12}$$

For the differential equation $y'(x) = -y(x)$, Euler's equation becomes the difference equation

$$y_{i+1} = y_i - hy_i. \tag{7.13}$$

It thus follows that

$$y_1 = (1-h)y_0$$
$$y_2 = (1-h)y_1 = (1-h)^2 y_0 \tag{7.14}$$
$$\vdots$$
$$y_i = (1-h)^i y_0.$$

For example, if $h = 0.1$, $y_0 = 2$, and $x = 1$ ($i = 10$), then $y_{10} = 2(0.9)^{10} = 0.69736$, which agrees with the result in Table 7.1.

The central-difference method is described by

$$y_{i+1} = y_{i-1} + 2hf(x_i, y_i). \tag{7.15}$$

For the differential equation $y'(x) = -y(x)$ the central-difference equation becomes the difference equation

$$y_{i+1} = y_{i-1} - 2hy_i. \tag{7.16}$$

As noted previously, this requires values for y_0 and y_1 before the equation can be applied. We will again assume that y_1 is obtained from the Euler solution, i.e., $y_1 = (1-h)y_0$. It thus follows that

$$y_2 = y_0 - 2hy_1 = (1 - 2h + 2h^2)y_0$$
$$y_3 = y_1 - 2hy_2 = (1 - 3h + 4h^2 - 4h^3)y_0 \tag{7.17}$$

Unfortunately, these equations are difficult to generalize. We can circumvent this problem by solving the *linear* difference equation (7.16) by assuming[6,7] the solution is of the form $y_i = \lambda^i$ and seeing what this implies about λ. Substituting $y_i = \lambda^i$ into (7.16) yields

$$\lambda^2 = 1 - 2h\lambda. \tag{7.18}$$

The solutions to this quadratic equation are

$$\lambda_{1,2} = -h \pm \sqrt{1+h^2}. \tag{7.19}$$

---

[6] This is analogous to the assumption $y = e^{\lambda x}$ that would be made for a homogeneous linear differential equation.

[7] See Section 6.2 of Conte and deBoor (1972).

Because (7.16) is a *linear* difference equation, the general solution is found by taking a linear combination of $y_i = \lambda_1^i$ and $y_i = \lambda_2^i$. That is,

$$y_i = C_1(\sqrt{1+h^2} - h)^i + C_2(-1)^i(\sqrt{1+h^2} + h)^i. \qquad (7.20)$$

The constants C_1, C_2 can be found in terms of y_0 and $y_1 = (1-h)y_0$. This yields

$$y_i = \frac{1}{2}\left(1 + \frac{1}{\sqrt{1+h^2}}\right)(\sqrt{1+h^2} - h)^i y_0$$

$$+ \frac{(-1)^i}{2}\left(1 - \frac{1}{\sqrt{1+h^2}}\right)(\sqrt{1+h^2} + h)^i y_0. \qquad (7.21)$$

For example, if $h = 0.1$, $y_0 = 2$, $x = 1$ ($i = 10$), then

$$y_{10} = \left(1 + \frac{1}{\sqrt{1.01}}\right)(\sqrt{1.01} - 0.1)^{10}$$

$$+ \left(1 - \frac{1}{\sqrt{1.01}}\right)(\sqrt{1.01} + 0.1)^{10} \qquad (7.22)$$

$$= 0.73515 + 0.01347 = 0.74862,$$

which agrees with the result in Table 7.1.

We are now in a position to see why the central-difference solution is unstable. The second term in (7.21) contains $(\sqrt{1+h^2} + h)^i$; thus it raises to the power i a term which is greater than unity. Therefore as i approaches infinity (i.e., as x gets large), the second term also approaches infinity. This is very unfortunate, since the correct solution is $y = 2e^{-x}$, which approaches zero as x becomes large.

To obtain more insight into this instability we can rewrite (7.21) making the assumption that h is much less than unity:

$$y_i \approx (1-h)^i y_0 + \frac{(-1)^i h^2}{4}(1+h)^i y_0. \qquad (7.23)$$

This should be compared with the Euler solution, which was $y_i = (1-h)^i y_0$. Thus the first term in (7.21) represents the desired solution, and the second term represents an extraneous solution which becomes larger and larger and finally dominates the desired solution.

We have just investigated the stability of Euler's method and the central-difference method for the differential equation $y'(x) = -y(x)$. The same approach could have been used for another differential equation or another algorithm (e.g., for the Runge-Kutta method which is described in the next section). In general, an algorithm that approximates the solution of a differential equation does so by replacing the differential equation with a difference equation. In the difference equation the solution is advanced by using previous values. These previous values will contain errors (because of poor starting data, roundoff error, or truncation error), and thus the future calculations will also contain errors. If these errors grow exponentially then the algorithm is unstable.

A detailed stability analysis will not be performed for each of the algorithms that is introduced in the remaining part of this chapter. However, to allay any fears this section may have generated about their stability, it should be noted that one of the reasons the algorithms in the following sections are popular is their good stability characteristics.

7.5 MODIFIED EULER METHOD

The Euler method for solving differential equations is not very popular, because (for the same step size h) it is less accurate than most other methods. Insight into its accuracy can be obtained by realizing that it yields exact solutions for first-degree functions, but not for second-degree ones. From Section 1.5, this implies that the error at each step is of the order of h^2, so that the global error is of the order of h; thus Euler's method is said to be a first-order method.

In this section we will study the modified Euler method, which uses an additional function evaluation at each step and is thus a second-order method instead of a first-order one. In addition to improved accuracy, another reason for studying the modified Euler method is that it uses a predictor-corrector approach which will be very important in other sections of this chapter. Also, the Runge-Kutta method of the next section can be considered to be a generalization of the modified Euler method. The Runge-Kutta method is a practical and accurate approach to solving differential equations. In fact, it can be shown to be exact for fourth-degree functions, so that its global error is proportional to the fourth power of h: the Runge-Kutta method is fourth-order.

As illustrated in Fig. 7.2, the Euler method *predicts* a new value of y by using the derivative at x,y. That is,

$$y_p = y(x) + h d_1, \tag{7.24}$$

where $d_1 = f(x,y)$ is the derivative[8] at x,y. The derivative at this predicted value of y is

$$y_p' = f(x + h, y_p) = d_2. \tag{7.25}$$

---

[8]Throughout this chapter, the symbol d will be used for derivatives.

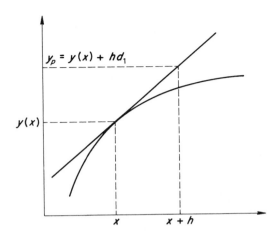

FIGURE 7.2. A value of $y(x+h)$ can be predicted by assuming a constant derivative $d_1 = f(x,y)$.

The predicted value y_p was found in (7.24) by assuming a constant slope d_1; but as is evident in Fig. 7.2, the slope will usually not be constant. A more accurate value for $y(x+h)$ can be obtained by using the average value of the derivatives d_1, d_2 to *correct* the predicted value[9]

$$y_c = y(x) + 0.5h(d_1 + d_2). \tag{7.26}$$

Equation (7.24) is termed a predictor equation; given a value $y(x)$, it is used to predict the value $y(x+h)$. For this predicted value, the slope can be found by applying (7.25). Finally, this predictor slope can be used to provide a better estimate of $y(x+h)$, which is given by the corrector equation (7.26).

EXAMPLE 7.2

For $dy/dx = 2x - y = f(x,y)$ and the initial condition $y(1) = 1$, estimate $y(2)$ by using the modified Euler method with $h = 0.25$.

SOLUTION

Applying (7.24), $y_p = 1 + 0.25f(1, 1) = 1.25$. Next (7.25) yields $d_2 = f(1.25, 1.25) = 1.25$. Substituting these values into (7.26) gives $y_C = 1.28125$. The modified Euler method can now be applied again, except this time

---

[9]This equation is merely a restatement of the trapezoidal rule (6.1). For this reason, the modified Euler method is also called the trapezoidal method.

with $x,y = 1.25, 1.28125$. This yields a predictor value of 1.5859 and a corrector value of 1.6104.

Applying the modified Euler method to $x,y = 1.5, 1.6104$ produces $x,y = 1.75, 1.9768$, and finally one more application gives $x,y = 2.00, 2.3725$.

The modified Euler method in the above example yielded an answer of 2.3725, compared to the analytical answer 2.3679. On the other hand, without modification the Euler method would yield 2.3164 (see Problem 7.1). Thus, the modification certainly improved the result, but the next method is even more accurate.

7.6 RUNGE-KUTTA METHOD

As a preliminary to the Runge-Kutta method we will consider a refinement of the modified Euler method. Instead of going from x to $x+h$ directly, we will first go to $x+0.5h$ by predicting and correcting, then we will continue to $x+h$ by again predicting and correcting. The predicted, corrected pair at $x+0.5h$ will be denoted as y_{p1}, y_{c1}, and the pair at $x+h$ will be denoted as y_{p2}, y_{c2}.

EXAMPLE 7.3

For $dy/dx = 2x - y = f(x,y)$ and the initial condition $y(1) = 1$, estimate $y(1.5)$ by using the above refinement of the modified Euler method with $h = 0.5$.

SOLUTION

To advance the solution to $x+0.5h$, we apply (7.24) to (7.26) as follows:

$$y' = d_1 = f(x,y) = f(1,1) = 1,$$
$$y_{p1} = y + 0.5h d_1 = 1 + 0.25 = 1.25,$$
$$y'_{p1} = d_2 = f(x+0.5h, y_{p1}) = f(1.25, 1.25) = 1.25,$$
$$y_{c1} = y + 0.25h(d_1 + d_2) = 1.28125.$$

Thus, half way to $x+h$ the solution is $1.25, 1.28125$. The modified Euler method can next be applied to this point and be used to advance the solution to $x+h$ as follows:

$$y'_{c1} = d_3 = f(x+0.5h, y_{c1}) = f(1.25, 1.28125) = 1.21875,$$
$$y_{p2} = y_{c1} + 0.5h d_3 = 1.58594,$$
$$y'_{p2} = d_4 = f(x+h, y_{p2}) = f(1.5, 1.58594) = 1.41406,$$
$$y_{c2} = y_{c1} + 0.25h(d_3 + d_4) = 1.60992.$$

The procedure used in the above example is summarized by the following set of equations:

$$y' = d_1 = f(x,y), \qquad y_{p1} = y + 0.5hd_1,$$
$$y'_{p1} = d_2 = f(x + 0.5h, y_{p1}), \qquad y_{c1} = y + 0.25h(d_1 + d_2),$$
$$y'_{c1} = d_3 = f(x + 0.5h, y_{c1}), \qquad y_{p2} = y_{c1} + 0.5hd_3, \qquad (7.27)$$
$$y'_{p2} = d_4 = f(x + h, y_{p2}), \qquad y_{c2} = y_{c1} + 0.25h(d_3 + d_4).$$

Substituting the expression for y_{c1} into the expression for y_{c2} allows us to approximate $y(x+h)$ as

$$y(x+h) \approx y + 0.25h(d_1 + d_2 + d_3 + d_4). \qquad (7.28)$$

This equation is very similar to the modified Euler equation (7.26), except instead of averaging two derivatives this one averages four derivatives.

Recall that d_1 and d_4 are estimates of the derivative at x and $x+h$ respectively, while d_2 and d_3 are both estimates of the derivative at the midpoint $x + 0.5h$. Equation (7.28) weights all these derivatives equally, while the Runge-Kutta method can be viewed as weighting them differently. Actually, there are many different Runge-Kutta methods. The most popular one weights the derivatives at the midpoint twice as heavily as those at the end points, that is,

$$y(x+h) \approx y(x) + h(d_1 + 2d_2 + 2d_3 + d_4)/6. \qquad (7.29)$$

Also, the Runge-Kutta method does not use the same values for d_3 and d_4 as those given in (7.27). Instead, in the expression for d_3, y_{c1} is approximated as[10] $y + 0.5hd_2$. Similarly, in the expression for d_4, y_{p2} is approximated as $y + hd_3$. Thus, in the Runge-Kutta method the d's are written as[11]

$$d_1 = f(x,y),$$
$$d_2 = f(x + 0.5h, y + 0.5hd_1),$$
$$d_3 = f(x + 0.5h, y + 0.5hd_2), \qquad (7.30)$$
$$d_4 = f(x + h, y + hd_3).$$

EXAMPLE 7.4

For $dy/dx = 2x - y = f(x,y)$ and the initial condition $y(1) = 1$, estimate $y(2)$ by using the Runge-Kutta method with $h = 0.5$.

---

[10]This is obtained by using $d_1 \approx d_2$.

[11]Instead of the constants d_i, most texts use constants $k_i = hd_i$. The notation d_i was choosen here to emphasize that the constants are derivatives.

SOLUTION

Applying (7.30) yields $d_1 = 1$, $d_2 = 1.25$, $d_3 = 1.1875$, $d_4 = 1.40625$. Substituting these values into (7.29) produces $y(1.5) = 1.60677$. This completes one cycle of the Runge-Kutta method.

The value for $y(1.5)$ can now be taken as the initial value and (7.30) applied again to yield $d_1 = 1.39323$, $d_2 = 1.54492$, $d_3 = 1.50700$, $d_4 = 1.63973$. Substituting these values into (7.29) produces $y(2) = 2.3682$.

The Runge-Kutta method was applied in this example to yield an answer of 2.3682, compared to the analytical answer 2.3679. Since the step size was chosen as 0.5, the Runge-Kutta method needed two cycles to reach $x = 2$. For each of these cycles the function $f(x,y)$ had to be evaluated four times (once for each of the d_i); thus, there were a total of eight function evaluations.

```
01C     RUNGE-KUTTA METHOD
02      PROGRAM RK(INPUT,OUTPUT)
03 03   FORMAT(F8.2,1P,E14.5)
10C
11      PRINT,*H*, $READ,H
12      PRINT,/,*INITIAL VALUES*,/,*      X0          Y0*
13      READ,X,Y
15      PRINT,/,*      X              Y*
22C
23C     FIND D1,D2,D3,D4   (EQ. 7.30)
31 31   D1=F(X,Y)
32      D2=F(X+.5*H,Y+.5*H*D1)
33      D3=F(X+.5*H,Y+.5*H*D2)
34      D4=F(X+H,Y+H*D3)
35C
36C     FIND Y(X+H)   (EQ. 7.29)
37      Y=Y+H*(D1+2.*D2+2.*D3+D4)/6.
39C
40C     ADVANCE SOLUTION
41      X=X+H
42      PRINT 3,X,Y
78      GO TO 31
99      END
898C
899     FUNCTION F(A,B)
900     F=-(2.*B*ALOG(B))/A
950     RETURN
999     END
```

FIGURE 7.3. A program for the Runge-Kutta method.

The modified Euler method was applied to the same problem in Example 7.2 and produced an answer of 2.3725, compared to the analytical answer 2.3679. Since the step size was chosen as 0.25, the modified Euler method needed four cycles to reach $x = 2$. For each of these cycles the function $f(x,y)$ was evaluated twice; thus, this also had a total of eight function evaluations.

Since the number of function evaluations is a good indication of the computer time, the above example demonstrates that the Runge-Kutta method is much more efficient than the modified Euler method. Because of its efficiency, the Runge-Kutta method is widely used in computer programs that numerically solve differential equations.

A program for the Runge-Kutta method is given in Fig. 7.3.

EXAMPLE 7.5

For $dy/dx = -(2y \ln y)/x$ and the initial condition $y(1) = e^2$, find $y(2)$ accurate to four significant figures.

SOLUTION

Results obtained by using the Runge-Kutta program are shown in Fig. 7.4. A step size of $h = 0.2$ was tried first and yielded $y(2) \approx 1.6504$. Reducing the step size by a factor of 2 to $h = 0.1$ then produced $y(2) \approx 1.6489$, while reducing it by another factor of 2 to $h = 0.05$ yielded $y(2) \approx 1.6487$. Comparing the last two answers, we can conclude that to four significant figures $y(2) = 1.649$.

7.7 ADAMS METHOD AND AUTOMATIC ERROR CONTROL

Given an initial value $y(x)$, the Runge-Kutta method requires four function evaluations to extend the solution to $y(x + h)$. The Adams method is just as accurate as the Runge-Kutta method and only needs two function evaluations per cycle. However, the Adams method needs more data than are contained in the initial conditions, that is, it is not "self-starting". As we will shortly see, the Runge-Kutta method can be used to advance the solution a sufficient number of times so that the more efficient Adams method can then take over.

In Section 6.7 the method of undetermined coefficients was applied to yield the following predictor integration formula:

$$\int_{x_3}^{x_4} f(x) \, dx \approx \frac{h}{24} (-9f_0 + 37f_1 - 59f_2 + 55f_3). \tag{7.31}$$

```
                                    H  ?  .1

                                    INITIAL VALUES
                                         X0              Y0
                                    ?    1          7.38906
H  ?  .2
                                         X               Y
INITIAL VALUES                          1.10        5.22294E+00
     X0              Y0                  1.20        4.01117E+00
?    1          7.38906                  1.30        3.26616E+00
                                        1.40        2.77478E+00
     X               Y                   1.50        2.43278E+00
    1.20        4.01897E+00              1.60        2.18449E+00
    1.40        2.77961E+00              1.70        1.99802E+00
    1.60        2.18753E+00              1.80        1.85408E+00
    1.80        1.85615E+00              1.90        1.74039E+00
    2.00        1.65036E+00              2.00        1.64886E+00
           (a)                                     (b)
                     H  ?  .05

                 INITIAL VALUES
                      X0              Y0
                 ?    1          7.38906

                      X               Y
                     1.05        6.13534E+00
                     1.10        5.22212E+00
                     1.15        4.53715E+00
                     1.20        4.01044E+00
                     1.25        3.59668E+00
                     1.30        3.26560E+00
                     1.35        2.99638E+00
                     1.40        2.77435E+00
                     1.45        2.58896E+00
                     1.50        2.43245E+00
                     1.55        2.29900E+00
                     1.60        2.18422E+00
                     1.65        2.08470E+00
                     1.70        1.99780E+00
                     1.75        1.92143E+00
                     1.80        1.85390E+00
                     1.85        1.79387E+00
                     1.90        1.74024E+00
                     1.95        1.69211E+00
                     2.00        1.64873E+00
                            (c)
```

FIGURE 7.4. An application of the Runge-Kutta program.

We can use this relation to predict a solution to the first-order differential equation

$$\frac{dy}{dx} = f(x,y). \tag{7.32}$$

Integrating from x_3 to x_4 yields

$$y_4 = y_3 + \int_{x_3}^{x_4} f(x,y)\,dx. \tag{7.33}$$

Comparing this with (7.31), we see that y_4 can be *predicted* by

$$y_{4p} = y_3 + \frac{h}{24}(-9f_0 + 37f_1 - 59f_2 + 55f_3). \tag{7.34}$$

To use this predictor equation we must have $y(x)$ at four points. That is, we must have the initial value $y_0 = y(x_0)$ and the next three values y_1, y_2, and y_3 so that we can calculate the derivatives f_0, f_1, f_2, and f_3. Given an initial value y_0, the next three values can be calculated by using the Runge-Kutta method; then the value y_4 can be predicted by using (7.34).

From the predicted value y_{4p} a predicted derivative f_{4p} can be evaluated. This predicted derivative can then be used in the corrector equation which was derived in Section 6.7 to yield

$$y_{4c} = y_3 + \frac{h}{24}(f_1 - 5f_2 + 19f_3 + 9f_{4p}). \tag{7.35}$$

This corrected value y_{4c} is assumed to be an accurate estimate of the value of $y(x+4h)$. Thus, we can now calculate the derivative f_4. From the value y_4 and the derivatives f_1, f_2, f_3, f_4 the value y_5 can first be predicted and then corrected. In this manner the Adams method can be used to advance the solution indefinitely.

EXAMPLE 7.6

For $dy/dx = 2x - y = f(x,y)$ and the initial condition $y(1)=1$, estimate $y(3)$ by using the Adams method with $h = 0.25$.

SOLUTION

Table 7.2 contains data obtained for this solution. The Runge-Kutta method was used to obtain $y(1.25)$, $y(1.50)$, and $y(1.75)$. The predictor equation of (7.34) then gave $y_p = 2.36810$. The derivative was evaluated at this point, and the corrector equation of (7.35) yielded $y(2.00) = 2.36786$. This completes one cycle of the Adams method; the next cycle yielded $y(2.25) = 2.78646$, etc.

Table 7.2

x	y	$f(x,y)$	y_p	$f(x,y_p)$
1.00	1.00000	1.00000		
1.25	1.27881	1.22119		
1.50	1.60654	1.39346		
1.75	1.97238	1.52762	2.36810	1.63190
2.00	2.36786	1.63214	2.78666	1.71334
2.25	2.78646	1.71354	3.22322	1.77678
2.50	3.22308	1.77692	3.67384	1.82616
2.75	3.67372	1.82628	4.13537	1.86463
3.00	4.13528			

One is not normally interested in six significant figures, but there is a reason Table 7.2 was made that detailed: it allows the predicted value y_p to be compared with the corrected value y. For example, the first predicted value was 2.36810, and the corrected value was 2.36786, which differs by 0.00024. On the other hand, the last predicted value was 4.13537, and the corrected value was 4.13528, which differs by 0.00009.

The predicted value can be made arbitrarily close to the corrected value by choosing h small enough. If the predicted value and corrected value are extremely close, then the solution will be very accurate, but there is a price for this—a small step size implies many cycles of the Adams method must be performed before the desired value of x is reached.

A very important property of a predictor-corrector technique such as the Adams method is that it allows for *automatic error control*. If the predicted value is not close enough to the corrected value, then the step size can be reduced, or if they are closer than necessary, then the step size can be increased.

A program that incorporates automatic error control into the Adams method is shown in Fig. 7.5. As indicated in line 21, the Runge-Kutta method is first applied three times to provide starting values for the Adams method. The important calculations of the Adams method are indicated in lines 51–58. It should be noted that each cycle of the Adams method requires two evaluations of the function $f(x,y)$; this is half as many as required by the Runge-Kutta method, so that there are substantial time savings.

The allowable size of the error is controlled by the parameters δ_{min} and δ_{max} (i.e., DMIN, DMAX). These are related to the quantity $\delta = |y_p - y_c|$; that is, δ indicates the difference between the predicted value and the corrected value.[12] If $\delta_{min} \leqslant \delta \leqslant \delta_{max}$, then the step size h is correct and the Adams

---

[12] As shown on p. 352 of Conte and deBoor (1972), the error in $y \approx \frac{19}{270}(y_p - y_c)$; thus some prefer to include a scale factor of approximately $\frac{19}{270}$ when calculating δ.

```
01C    ADAMS METHOD
02     PROGRAM A(INPUT,OUTPUT)
03 03  FORMAT(F8.2,1P,E14.5)
06     DIMENSION G(5)
10C
11     PRINT,*H,DMIN,DMAX*, $READ,H,DMIN,DMAX
12     PRINT,/,*INITIAL VALUES*,/,*    X0         Y0*
13     READ,X,Y
15     PRINT,/,*    X          Y*
19C
20C    ADVANCE 3 STEPS BY RUNGE-KUTTA METHOD
21 21  DO 39 I=1,3
22C
23C        FIND D1,D2,D3,D4   (EQ. 7.30)
31         D1=G(I)=F(X,Y)
32         D2=F(X+.5*H,Y+.5*H*D1)
33         D3=F(X+.5*H,Y+.5*H*D2)
34         D4=F(X+H,Y+H*D3)
35C
36C        FIND Y(X+H)   (EQ. 7.29)
37         Y=Y+H*(D1+2.*D2+2.*D3+D4)/6.
38         X=X+H
39 39      PRINT 3,X,Y
41C
42C    FIND F3 WHICH IS DEFINED AS G(4)
43 43  G(4)=F(X,Y)
49C
50C    FIND Y PREDICTED   (EQ. 7.34)
51     YP=Y+H*(-9*G(1)+37*G(2)-59*G(3)+55*G(4))/24
52C
53C    FIND Y4P WHICH IS DEFINED AS G(5)
54     G(5)=F(X+H,YP)
56C
57C    FIND Y CORRECTED   (EQ. 7.35)
58     Y=Y+H*(G(2)-5*G(3)+19*G(4)+9*G(5))/24
60C
61C    ADVANCE SOLUTION
62     X=X+H
63     PRINT 3,X,Y
64     G(1)=G(2) $G(2)=G(3) $G(3)=G(4)
69C
70C    ERROR CONTROL
71     DEL=ABS(YP-Y)
72     IF(DEL.GE.DMIN.AND.DEL.LE.DMAX) GO TO 43
74     IF(DEL.LT.DMIN) H=2.*H
76     IF(DEL.GT.DMAX) X=.5*H
78     GO TO 21
99     END
898C
899    FUNCTION F(A,B)
900    F=2.*B**1.5/A/A
950    RETURN
999    END
```

FIGURE 7.5. A program for the Adams method.

method continues cycle after cycle. However, if the error δ is not within the above limits, the step size is automatically changed and the Runge-Kutta method is applied again to help restart the Adams method.[13]

As an example of how the program can be applied, consider again the differential equation $dy/dx = 2y^{3/2}/x^2$, which was discussed in Section 7.3. For the initial condition $y(1) = 1$ the analytical solution is $y = x^2$, which can be used to check a numerical solution. For example, Fig. 7.6[14] indicates that choosing $h = 1$ yielded $y(10) \approx 81.68$, while the analytical answer is $y(10) = 100$. But suppose we do not know the analytical answer. Insight into the accuracy of the numerical answer can then be obtained by doing another computer run with $h = 0.1$. This yielded $y(10) \approx 99.9913$, while choosing $h = 0.5$ yielded $y(10) \approx 99.9996$.

```
H,DMIN,DMAX ?  1      0      1000

INITIAL VALUES
      X0              Y0
?     1               1

      X               Y
    2.00       3.84632E+00
    3.00       8.45697E+00
    4.00       1.47210E+01
    5.00       2.25371E+01
    6.00       3.18071E+01
    7.00       4.24394E+01
    8.00       5.43489E+01
    9.00       6.74553E+01
   10.00       8.16834E+01
```

FIGURE 7.6. An application of the Adams program.

If one uses automatic error control, the number of cycles can be reduced. This can be illustrated by choosing $\delta_{min} = 0.00001$, $\delta_{max} = 0.001$, and $h = 0.1$. A rough estimate[15] for the maximum error can be obtained by assuming it takes ninety cycles to reach $x = 10$ and each cycle has an error $\delta_{max} = 0.001$; thus, the maximum error should be the order of 0.1. If the

---

[13]In this program, when the difference between predictor and corrector is too large, the result is accepted anyway, and then the step is halved. With little added complexity, this could be modified so the answer is instead recalculated for the smaller step.

[14]Note that DMIN = 0 and DMAX = 1000 so that, in essence, there was no automatic error control.

[15]This is very rough, because the errors cannot simply be added to get a final error estimate. Truncation errors can grow, even for a stable method, for nonlinear problems.

```
H,DMIN,DMAX ? .1    .00001    .001

INITIAL VALUES
     X0           Y0
?     1            1

     X            Y
   1.10      1.20999E+00
   1.20      1.43999E+00
   1.30      1.68998E+00
   1.40      1.95998E+00
   1.60      2.55990E+00
   1.80      3.23981E+00
   2.00      3.99971E+00
   2.20      4.83962E+00
   2.60      6.75888E+00
   3.00      8.99797E+00
   3.40      1.15568E+01
   3.80      1.44356E+01
   4.20      1.76340E+01
   4.60      2.11521E+01
   5.00      2.49899E+01
   5.80      3.36229E+01
   6.60      4.35338E+01
   7.40      5.47225E+01
   8.20      6.71889E+01
   9.00      8.09325E+01
   9.80      9.59529E+01
  10.60      1.12250E+02
```

(a)

```
H,DMIN,DMAX ? -.6    0    1000

INITIAL VALUES
     X0           Y0
?    10.6        112.25

     X            Y
   10.00     9.99077E+01
```

(b)

FIGURE 7.7. An illustration of automatic error control.

difference δ between any predicted value y_p and its corrected value y is greater than δ_{max}, then h will be halved.

On the other hand, if $\delta < \delta_{min}$, then the step size can be doubled and the point $x = 10$ will be reached much faster. For this example (as shown in Fig. 7.7) the step size was automatically increased from 0.1 to 0.2, etc., until it was finally $h = 0.8$. Because of this continually increasing step size, the point $x = 10$ was reached much quicker. Actually, the answer was not computed at $x = 10$, but instead at $x = 10.6$, where it was found that $y(10.6) \approx 112.25$. Using this as an initial value and choosing $h = -0.6$ then gave $y(10) \approx 99.91$, which is within the desired accuracy of $y(10) = 100$.

7.8 SOLUTION OF HIGHER-ORDER DIFFERENTIAL EQUATIONS

The previous sections have presented methods that can be used to solve first-order differential equations. In this section we will learn how these methods can be extended to solve higher-order differential equations. We will first learn how to solve a set of simultaneous first-order differential equations. This does not imply one often wants to solve a set of first-order differential equations as such, but an nth-order differential equation can be represented as n first-order ones, so that learning how to solve such sets of equations will be very useful to us.

We have studied different numerical methods for solving the differential equation $dy/dx = f(x,y)$ subject to the initial condition $y(x_0) = y_0$. Any of these methods can be extended to solve a set of first-order equations. However, the following discussion will be restricted to the Runge-Kutta method because it is easy to program and relatively efficient.

For one first-order differential equation the Runge-Kutta method advances the solution by using

$$y(x+h) \approx y(h) + h(d_1 + 2d_2 + 2d_3 + d_4)/6, \qquad (7.36)$$

where

$$
\begin{aligned}
d_1 &= f(x,y), \\
d_2 &= f(x+0.5h, y+0.5hd_1), \\
d_3 &= f(x+0.5h, y+0.5hd_2), \\
d_4 &= f(x+h, y+hd_3).
\end{aligned}
\qquad (7.37)
$$

Next consider the following first-order differential equations:

$$\frac{dy}{dx} = g(x,y,y_1), \qquad \frac{dy_1}{dx} = f(x,y,y_1), \qquad (7.38)$$

subject to the initial conditions $y(x_0)$, $y_1(x_0)$. The equations can be solved by considering two sets of d parameters: d_{11}, d_{21}, d_{31}, d_{41} corresponding to the function $g(x,y,y_1)$, and d_{12}, d_{22}, d_{32}, d_{42} corresponding to $f(x,y,y_1)$. For just one differential equation, d_2 was a function of d_1; d_3 was a function of d_2; and d_4 was a function of d_3. For two equations, d_{21}, d_{22} are functions of d_{11}, d_{12}; d_{31}, d_{32} are functions of d_{21}, d_{22}; and d_{41}, d_{42} are functions of d_{31}, d_{32}, as is illustrated by the following set of equations:

$$\begin{aligned}
d_{11} &= g(x,y,y_1), \\
d_{12} &= f(x,y,y_1), \\
d_{21} &= g(x+0.5h, y+0.5h\,d_{11}, y_1+0.5h\,d_{12}), \\
d_{22} &= f(x+0.5h, y+0.5h\,d_{11}, y_1+0.5h\,d_{12}), \\
d_{31} &= g(x+0.5h, y+0.5h\,d_{21}, y_1+0.5h\,d_{22}), \\
d_{32} &= f(x+0.5h, y+0.5h\,d_{21}, y_1+0.5h\,d_{22}), \\
d_{41} &= g(x+h, y+h\,d_{31}, y_1+h\,d_{32}), \\
d_{42} &= f(x+h, y+h\,d_{31}, y_1+h\,d_{32}).
\end{aligned} \tag{7.39}$$

The Runge-Kutta method advances the solution for y and y_1 by using the following equations, which are analogous to (7.36):

$$\begin{aligned}
y(x+h) &\approx y(x) + h(d_{11}+2d_{21}+2d_{31}+d_{41})/6, \\
y_1(x+h) &\approx y_1(x) + h(d_{12}+2d_{22}+2d_{32}+d_{42})/6.
\end{aligned} \tag{7.40}$$

Even if we are not interested in solving two first-order differential equations, the previous work is very useful because a second-order can be expressed as two first-orders.

A second-order differential equation can be written as

$$\frac{d^2y}{dx^2} = f\left(x,y,\frac{dy}{dx}\right). \tag{7.41}$$

This general second-order differential equation can be expressed as two first-order equations by introducing the notation $dy/dx = y_1$, from which it follows that $d^2y/dx^2 = dy_1/dx$. Substituting into (7.41) yields

$$\frac{dy}{dx} = y_1 = g(x,y,y_1), \qquad \frac{dy_1}{dx} = f(x,y,y_1). \tag{7.42}$$

EXAMPLE 7.7

The second-order differential equation (7.3) was $(d^2y/dx^2)^3 + xy\,dy/dx + y^2 = 6x$. Putting this into the form of (7.41),

$$\frac{d^2y}{dx^2} = \left(6x - y^2 - xy\frac{dy}{dx}\right)^{1/3}. \tag{7.43}$$

Introducing the notation $dy/dx = y_1$, we can rewrite this as $dy_1/dx = (6x - y^2 - xyy_1)^{1/3}$. Comparison with (7.42) yields

$$g(x,y,y_1) = y_1, \qquad f(x,y,y_1) = (6x - y^2 - xyy_1)^{1/3}.$$

The Runge-Kutta method for two first-order differential equations has the set of derivatives (7.39) that must be evaluated. For the special case $g(x,y,y_1) = y_1$ these derivative equations can be simplified considerably:

$$d_{11} = y_1,$$

$$d_{12} = f(x,y,y_1),$$

$$d_{21} = y_1 + 0.5h d_{12},$$

$$d_{22} = f(x + 0.5h, y + 0.5h d_{11}, d_{21}), \qquad (7.44)$$

$$d_{31} = y_1 + 0.5h d_{22},$$

$$d_{32} = f(x + 0.5h, y + 0.5h d_{21}, d_{31}),$$

$$d_{41} = y_1 + h d_{32},$$

$$d_{42} = f(x + h, y + h d_{31}, d_{41}).$$

Before an example is done, this technique will be extended to an nth-order differential equation so a general purpose program can be developed. An nth-order differential equation can be written as

$$\frac{d^n y}{dx^n} = f\left(x, y, \frac{dy}{dx}, \ldots, \frac{d^{n-1}y}{dx^n}\right). \qquad (7.45)$$

This is equivalent to

$$\frac{dy}{dx} = y_1,$$

$$\frac{dy_1}{dx} = y_2, \qquad (7.46)$$

$$\frac{dy_{n-2}}{dx} = y_{n-1},$$

$$\frac{dy_{n-1}}{dx} = f(x, y, y_1, \ldots, y_{n-1}).$$

By analogy with (7.44), the d coefficients for this set of first-order differential equations are

$$d_{1i} = y_i, \qquad\qquad\qquad\qquad i = 1, 2, \ldots, n-1,$$

$$d_{1n} = f(x, y, y_1, \ldots),$$

$$d_{2i} = y_i + 0.5h\,d_{1, i+1}, \qquad\qquad i = 1, 2, \ldots, n-1,$$

$$d_{2n} = f(x + 0.5h, y + 0.5h\,d_{11}, d_{21}, d_{22}, \ldots), \qquad\qquad (7.47)$$

$$d_{3i} = y_i + 0.5h\,d_{2, i+1}, \qquad\qquad i = 1, 2, \ldots, n-1,$$

$$d_{3n} = f(x + 0.5h, y + 0.5h\,d_{21}, d_{31}, d_{32}, \ldots),$$

$$d_{4i} = y_i + h\,d_{3, i+1}, \qquad\qquad\quad i = 1, 2, \ldots, n-1,$$

$$d_{4n} = f(x + h, y + h\,d_{31}, d_{41}, d_{42}, \ldots).$$

The Runge-Kutta method can advance the solution for $y, y_1, y_2, \ldots, y_{n-1}$ by using the following equations:

$$y(x+h) \approx y(x) + h(d_{11} + 2d_{21} + 2d_{31} + d_{41})/6,$$

$$y_i(x+h) \approx y_i(x) + h(d_{1, i+1} + 2d_{2, i+1} + 2d_{3, i+1} + d_{4, i+1})/6. \qquad (7.48)$$

A program for the solution of an nth-order differential equation is given in Fig. 7.8. This program is a generalization of the Runge-Kutta program of Fig. 7.3; thus many of the steps are similar. If the program in Fig. 7.8 is compared with equations (7.47), (7.48), it should be noted that the subscripts in this figure have been shifted by one so that Y(1) corresponds to y, Y(2) corresponds to the first derivative, etc. Two examples will be described next to illustrate the application of the program.

EXAMPLE 7.8

The third-degree equation (7.3) can be rewritten as

$$\frac{d^2y}{dx^2} = \left(6x - xy\frac{dy}{dx} - y^2\right)^{1/3} = f(x, y, y_1),$$

where $y_1 = dy/dx$. Figure 7.9(a) contains a computer output for the initial conditions $y(1) = 1$ and $y'(1) = -1$. The solution indicates that $y(2) = 0.9827$. The accuracy of the solution was verified by also using $h = 0.05$ instead of $h = 0.1$.

EXAMPLE 7.9

The third-order differential equation

$$\frac{d^3y}{dx^3} - 3\frac{dy}{dx} + 2y = 2(\sin x - 2\cos x)$$

```
01C     NTH-ORDER DIFFERENTIAL EQUATION
02      PROGRAM NTH(INPUT,OUTPUT)
03 03   FORMAT(F8.2,1P,E14.5)
06      DIMENSION D1(10),D2(10),D3(10),D4(10),Y(10)
15C
16      PRINT,*N,H*, $READ,N,H
17      N1=N+1
19      PRINT,/,*INITIAL VALUES*
20      PRINT,*     X0*, $READ,X
22      PRINT,*Y0,Y1,...*
24      READ,(Y(I),I=1,N)
26      PRINT,/,*     X          Y*
29C
30C     CALCULATE D1(I)
32 32   DO 34 I=1,N
34 34   D1(I)=Y(I)
36      D1(N1)=F(X,Y)
39C
40C     CALCULATE D2(I)
42      DO 44 I=1,N
44 44   D2(I)=Y(I)+.5*H*D1(I+1)
46      D2(N1)=F(X+.5*H,D2)
49C
50C     CALCULATE D3(I)
52      DO 54 I=1,N
54 54   D3(I)=Y(I)+.5*H*D2(I+1)
56      D3(N1)=F(X+.5*H,D3)
59C
60C     CALCULATE D4(I)
62      DO 64 I=1,N
64 64   D4(I)=Y(I)+H*D3(I+1)
66      D4(N1)=F(X+H,D4)
69C
70C     CALCULATE Y(X+H)   (EQ. 7.29)
71      DO 72 I=2,N1
72 72   Y(I-1)=Y(I-1)+H*(D1(I)+2.*D2(I)+2.*D3(I)+D4(I))/6.
75C
76C     ADVANCE SOLUTION
77      X=X+H
78      PRINT 3,X,Y(1)
79      GO TO 32
99      END
897C
898     FUNCTION F(X,Y)
899     DIMENSION Y(10)
900     F=3*Y(2)-2*Y(1)+2*(SIN(X)-2*COS(X))
950     RETURN
999     END
```

FIGURE 7.8. A program for the solution of an *n*th-order differential equation.

```
N,H ? 2,.1

INITIAL VALUES
     X0 ? 1
Y0,Y1,...
? 1   -1

     X              Y
    1.10     9.09185E-01
    1.20     8.37111E-01
    1.30     7.84277E-01
    1.40     7.51120E-01
    1.50     7.38025E-01
    1.60     7.45324E-01
    1.70     7.73289E-01
    1.80     8.22123E-01
    1.90     8.91936E-01
    2.00     9.82723E-01
```

(a)

```
N,H ? 3,.01

INITIAL VALUES
     X0 ? 0
Y0,Y1,...
? 4   -2   17

     X              Y
    .01      3.98085E+00
    .02      3.96338E+00
    .03      3.94757E+00
    .04      3.93341E+00
    .05      3.92089E+00
    .06      3.90998E+00
    .07      3.90068E+00
    .08      3.89296E+00
    .09      3.88681E+00
    .10      3.88223E+00
```

(b)

FIGURE 7.9. Application of the program in Fig. 7.8 to (a) $y'' = (6x - xyy' - y^2)^{1/3}$, (b) $y''' - 3y' + 2y = 2(\sin x - 2\cos x)$.

has as a general solution

$$y = (C_1 + C_2 x)e^x + C_3 e^{-2x} + \sin x.$$

For the initial conditions $y(0) = 4$, $y'(0) = -2$, and $y''(0) = 17$, the constants are $C_1 = 1$, $C_2 = 2$, and $C_3 = 4$. Using these values for the constants, the analytical answer at $x = 0.1$ is $y(0.1) = 3.8822$. Figure 7.9(b) contains a computer output for this problem, which demonstrates that for $h = 0.01$ the numerical method yields the same result as the analytical method.

7.9 BOUNDARY-VALUE PROBLEMS

All the problems presented thus far in this chapter have been initial-value problems: the conditions on the function and its derivatives were given at the same point. For example, the third-degree equation

$$\left(\frac{d^2 y}{dx^2}\right)^3 = 6x - xy\frac{dy}{dx} - y^2 \qquad (7.49)$$

had the initial conditions $y(1) = 1$ and $y'(1) = -1$. Both conditions were given at the point $x = 1$.

Differential equations are important because they often describe practical physical problems. Sometimes the conditions pertaining to these problems are not initial conditions, but are boundary values. For example, the deflection of a beam can be described by a differential equation. If the beam is supported at both ends, then boundary values are that the deflection at both ends must be zero.

The program in Fig. 7.8 is for initial-value problems, but with a little insight it can also be used for boundary-value problems. That is, one can iteratively guess initial values until the proper boundary values are obtained; then this equivalent initial-value problem can be solved by normal methods.

As an example, consider the differential equation (7.49) with the boundary values $y(1) = 1$, $y(2) = 0.75$. One can guess values for $y'(1)$ until the solution $y(2) = 0.75$ is obtained. To be specific, for $h = 0.1$ the program yielded

$$y(2) = 0.5090 \quad \text{if} \quad y'(1) = -1.5,$$
$$y(2) = 0.9827 \quad \text{if} \quad y'(1) = -1.0,$$
$$y(2) = 1.4420 \quad \text{if} \quad y'(1) = -0.5.$$

Instead of making further guesses, we can treat this as an inverse interpolation problem. That is, we can match a second-degree polynomial to the above three data pairs and then find the value of $y'(1)$ corresponding to $y(2) = 0.75$. The Lagrange interpolation program of Section 4.7 was used to yield $y'(1) = -1.2476$.

With $h = 0.1$ and initial values of $y(1) = 1$, $y'(1) = -1.2476$, the differential equation program of Fig. 7.9 yielded $y(2) = 0.7498$, which is very close to the desired boundary value of 0.75. Of course, the initial value could be perturbed slightly from $y'(1) = -1.2476$ to yield an even better match to the boundary value; but in practice $y(2) = 0.7498$ would certainly be accurate enough.

Most boundary-value problems are of second order, but if higher-order equations are encountered the same type of approach can be used: guess initial conditions until the proper boundary values are obtained. If more than one boundary value has to be matched, then optimization techniques (described later in the book) can be used to determine the equivalent initial conditions. Optimization techniques can simultaneously vary more than one parameter (such as the initial conditions in the above problem) to match a desired response.

However, for the few times one is likely to encounter a higher-order differential equation that is subject to boundary values, it is probably not worth the effort to develop a general-purpose optimization program. Instead, one can optimize the initial parameters one at a time, as illustrated by the next example.

EXAMPLE 7.10

The following fourth-order differential equation is solved in Problem 7.19 for a set of initial conditions:

$$\left(\frac{d^4y}{dx^4}\right)^2 - x\left(\frac{d^3y}{dx^3}\right)^2 + \frac{d^2y}{dx^2} + \left(\frac{dy}{dx}\right)^2 - xy^2 = x + 1 - \sin x.$$

This example will demonstrate how a set of boundary values can be transformed into an equivalent set of initial conditions.

The boundary values for this example are[16] $y(0) = 1$, $y'(0) = 1$, $y(0.5) = 0.4$, and $y'(0.5) = 0.62$. A set of equivalent initial conditions can be obtained by an iterative procedure. We will first concentrate on making $y(0.5) = 0.4$.

As illustrated in Table 7.3, there are many different sets of initial conditions that can make $y(0.5) = 0.4$. For example, the initial conditions $y''(0) = -0.8212$, $y'''(0) = 0$ result in a boundary value of $y(0.5) = 0.3999$, which is essentially 0.4 as desired. The initial conditions $y''(0) = -0.8212$,

---

[16]Originally, the last boundary value was $y'(0.5) = 0.60$; however, one of the intermediate guesses in the solution yielded this value, so it was changed to $y'(0.5) = 0.62$ to keep the problem from being trivial.

Table 7.3

INITIAL CONDITIONS[a]		BOUNDARY VALUES	
$y''(0)$	$y'''(0)$	$y(0.5)$	$y'(0.5)$
0.0	0	0.5001	1.0012
−0.5	0	0.4395	0.7663
−1.0	0	0.3778	0.5230
−0.8212	0	0.3999	0.6103
−0.7	0.25	0.4201	0.7004
−0.8	0.25	0.4077	0.6517
−0.9	0.25	0.3954	0.6029
−0.8625	0.25	0.4000	0.6212
−0.7	−0.25	0.4097	0.6384
−0.8	−0.25	0.3974	0.5897
−0.9	−0.25	0.3850	0.5409
−0.7789	−0.25	0.4000	0.6000
−0.7	0.2232	0.4195	0.6970
−0.8	0.2232	0.4072	0.6483
−0.9	0.2232	0.3948	0.5996
−0.8582	0.2232	0.4000	0.6200

[a]The initial conditions $y(0)$ and $y'(0)$ are fixed at 0 and 1 respectively.

$y'''(0) = 0$ were obtained by

(a) setting $y'''(0) = 0$,

(b) choosing three values for $y''(0)$ and finding the corresponding values for $y(0.5)$,

(c) using Lagrange interpolation to pass a second-degree polynomial through the three data pairs

$$0.5001, 0; \qquad 0.4395, -0.5; \qquad 0.3778, -1.0,$$

(d) interpolating for the value $y(0.5) = 0.4$, which yielded $y''(0) = -0.8212$.

Table 7.3 also indicates that the initial values $y''(0) = -0.8625$, $y'''(0) = 0.25$ results in $y(0.5) = 0.4$, as do the initial values $y''(0) = -0.7789$, $y'''(0) = -0.25$.

None of the above sets of initial values result in the desired boundary value $y'(0.5) = 0.62$. However, Lagrange interpolation can be used on the three data pairs $y'(0.5)$, $y'''(0)$, which are 0.6103, 0; 0.6212, 0.25; 0.6000, −0.25, to yield $y'''(0) = 0.2232$. With this value for $y'''(0)$ it was then possible to find $y''(0)$ such that $y(0.5) = 0.4$.

As indicated in Table 7.3, the initial values $y(0) = 0$, $y'(0) = 1$, $y''(0) = -0.8582$, $y'''(0) = 0.2232$ are equivalent to the boundary values

$$y(0) = 0, \quad y'(0) = 1, \quad y(0.5) = 0.4, \quad y'(0.5) = 0.62.$$

7.10   SUGGESTED READING IN RELATED TOPICS

This chapter stressed the numerical solution of ordinary differential equations. Numerical solutions have the advantage of being applicable to any ordinary differential equation, but they have the disadvantage of being given only at discrete points. Also, if the initial conditions are changed, then the solution must be found again. On the other hand, analytical solutions cannot be found for all differential equations; but it should be mentioned that there are many classes of problems that can be solved by systematic procedures. These analytical solutions can be evaluated for any value of the independent variable. Furthermore, if the initial conditions or boundary conditions are changed, then only some constants need be reevaluated. A good introductory text about differential equations is the one by Rainville (1969).

We have studied three different methods for solving differential equations: the (modified) Euler method, Runge-Kutta method, and Adams method. The Euler method is not a very efficient approach; it was presented to serve as a simple introduction to the numerical solution of differential equations. Another simple introduction could have been a Taylor-series method which uses the first few terms in the Taylor series and evaluates the first and higher derivatives from $dy/dx = f(x,y)$.

The Runge-Kutta method is much more efficient than the Euler method. It was developed in this chapter by analogy with the predictor-corrector technique used in the modified Euler method. An alternate approach matches coefficients to a Taylor series expansion. However, the Taylor-series approach is more involved than the one presented here—though it does have the advantage of being more general.

The Runge-Kutta method is self-starting: it only needs the initial values, and then the solution can be advanced indefinitely. The Adams method is not self-starting, but once it has been supplied four function values it can advance the solution with half the effort of the Runge-Kutta method. Because of this, numerical analysis programs for solving differential equations often use the Runge-Kutta method to start the solution and then continue it with the Adams method. Other methods, such as one proposed by Milne, have been used instead of the Adams method, but none are as popular.

Actually, there are many different formulas due to the work of Adams—only the most popular one was described in this chapter. The ones that use explicit relations are often termed Adams-Bashforth methods, and the ones that use implicit relations are termed Adams-Moulton methods. The explicit methods express the current value of the variable y as a function of the previous derivatives; thus the predictor equation

(7.34) is an explicit relation for y. In this chapter we did not solve differential equations by just applying this predictor equation, although that is possible. Instead, we used it in the implicit corrector equation (7.35).

The implicit methods express the current value of the independent variable y as a function of previous derivatives and the present derivative. Since this present derivative is not accurately available, the current value of y cannot be solved for explicitly; but an estimated (predicted) value of y can be used to approximate the derivative. In fact, some methods go through this cycle a few times—each time estimating the derivative more and more accurately. However, it is usually more practical to use the additional computations to reduce the step size, which is an alternative way of improving the predicted value.

The implicit (Adams-Moulton) algorithms are used more frequently than the explicit (Adams-Bashforth) methods for two reasons. First, the addition of a corrector equation provides increased accuracy by reducing truncation error. Second, these algorithms are more stable, and thus errors do not propagate as freely as they might in an Adams-Bashforth algorithm.

Boundary-value problems, as contrasted with initial-value problems, were only briefly mentioned here. The approach described in Section 7.9 has been termed the "shooting method" because of the analogy with an artillery problem. To determine the proper direction of a cannon one can shoot, observe the result, correct the direction, shoot again, etc. In Section 7.9 we aimed at the boundary values and adjusted the initial conditions until the results were satisfactory. Another approach that is sometimes used is to approximate the differential equations by difference equations. This can be done by applying the equations that were developed in Chapter 5. In fact, partial differential equations can also be solved by using the difference-equation approach.

In closing this chapter, it is worthwhile mentioning that sometimes the step size h must be chosen very small in order to ensure accurate answers. This is the situation in the case of "stiff differential equations" as described by Hamming (1973). A stiff differential equation is examined in Problem 7.20. Stiff differential equations may result, for example, if one describes a chemical process that has time constants that are orders of magnitude different: then the step size may have to be made small enough so that variations due to the short time constant are not overlooked. However, even if the variations due to the small time constant are past, care must still be taken that a large step size does not cause instability. Methods have been described (Fowler and Warten, 1967)[17] for reducing the number of

---

[17] See also, Gear, C. W. (1971), *Numerical Initial Value Problems in Ordinary Differential Equations* (Englewood Cliffs, N.J.: Prentice-Hall).

computations needed in the numerical solution of stiff differential equations.

PROBLEMS

7.1 For $y'=2x-y=f(x,y)$ and the initial condition $y(1)=1$, estimate $y(2)$ by using Euler's method as given in Eq. (7.8), with $h=0.25$. Compare with the analytical answer of 2.3679.

7.2 For $y'=x^2-2y$ and the initial condition $y(0)=0$, estimate $y(0.4)$ by using Euler's method with $h=0.1$. Compare with the analytical answer of 0.0177.

7.3 Apply the modified Euler method to Problem 7.2 and compare the result with that answer.

7.4 Write a program for the modified Euler method and apply it to the differential equation in Problem 7.2.

7.5 For $y'=x^2-2y$ and the initial condition $y(0)=0$, apply one cycle of the Runge-Kutta method with $h=0.1$ to find $y(0.1)$.

7.6 Use the Runge-Kutta program to find $y(2)$ for $dy/dx=-(1+e^x)$ subject to the initial conditon $y(0)=0$. First have $h=0.2$, and then $h=0.1$. Compare the answers and determine how many digits are probably accurate.

7.7 The Runge-Kutta program in Fig. 7.3 calculates the d-parameters based on (7.30). Modify the program so it instead calculates the derivatives based on (7.27). Apply this modified program to Problem 7.6.

7.8 The Runge-Kutta method produces an error which is of the order of h^4; thus, for Problem 7.6 we can write $y(2)=y(h)+\alpha h^4$. Use Romberg prediction on the results of Problem 7.6 to yield a better estimate of $y(2)$.

7.9 The nth-order Chebyshev polynomial T_n is the solution to the following differential equation:

$$\left(\frac{dT_n}{dx}\right)^2 = n^2 \frac{1-T_n^2}{1-x^2}.$$

Using the initial condition $T_3(0)=0$, apply the Runge-Kutta method to evaluate $T_3(0.3)$. Choose $h=0.1$ and use the negative slope for dT_n/dx.

7.10 For $y' = x^2 - 2y$ and the initial condition $y(0) = 0$, applying the Runge-Kutta method with $h = 0.1$ yields $y(0.1) = 0.0003175$, $y(0.2) = 0.0024204$, $y(0.3) = 0.0077979$. Apply the Adams method to find $y(0.4)$. Compare with the Euler-method result of Problem 7.2, which was 0.01284, and the analytical result, which is 0.0176678.

7.11 Use the Adams-method program to estimate the solution of

$$\frac{dy}{dx} = -y\left(\frac{2x}{e^x} + \ln y\right)$$

at $x = 0.1$. Use the initial condition $y(0) = 1$, and choose $\delta_{min} = 0.0001$, $\delta_{max} = 0.01$, $h = 0.001$.

Hint: The closest printout to $x = 0.1$ will be $x = 0.092$; thus, for an initial condition of $y(0.092)$ use the program again with $h = 0.008$. Compare with the analytical answer $y = \exp(-x^2 e^{-x})$.

7.12 In Section 7.8 the Runge-Kutta method was applied to solve the set of equations

$$\frac{dy}{dx} = g(x,y,y_1), \qquad \frac{dy_1}{dx} = f(x,y,y_1).$$

This problem will instead illustrate the application of the Euler method, which can advance the solution by $y(x+h) \approx y(x) + hg(x,y,y_1)$ and $y_1(x+h) \approx y_1(x) + hf(x,y,y_1)$. Use this approach to estimate $y(0.2)$ and $y_1(0.2)$ for $g(x,y,y_1) = x + y_1$, $f(x,y,y_1) = x - 2y - 3y_1$, subject to the initial conditions $y(0) = 0$ and $y_1(0) = 0$. Choose $h = 0.5$.

7.13 Express the following third-order differential equation as a set of first-order differential equations:

$$\frac{d^3y}{dx^3} + 4y\frac{d^2y}{dx^2} + \sin y = e^x.$$

What is $f(x,y,y_1,y_2)$?

7.14 The set of first-order differential equations in Problem 7.12 can be transformed into a second-order differential equation in terms of x and y. Find this equation and give the initial conditions. If familiar with differential equations, find the analytical solution.

7.15 Use the program in Fig. 7.8 to find $y(1.5)$ for

$$\frac{d^2y}{dx^2} + 2\frac{dy}{dx} + 2y = 0$$

subject to the initial conditions $y(0) = 0$, $y'(0) = 1$. First let $h = 0.3$, and then let $h = 0.1$.

7.16 The differential equation in the above problem is said to be homogeneous, because the right side is zero. Re-solve the problem for the right side instead equal to 3. For initial conditions use $y(0)=1.5$, $y'(0)=1$.

7.17 Find $y(1.2)$ for the following nonhomogeneous differential equation:

$$\frac{d^2y}{dx^2} + 3\frac{dy}{dx} + 2y = 3.$$

Use $h=0.1$, $y(0)=-1$, $y'(0)=0$.

7.18 Legendre's differential equation is

$$(1-x^2)\frac{d^2y}{dx^2} - 2x\frac{dy}{dx} + n(n+1)y = 0.$$

Find $y(0.1)$ for $n=5$ and the initial conditions $y(0)=0$, $y'(0)=1.875$. First let $h=0.01$, and then let $h=0.001$. For $h=0.001$ modify the program so that the output is printed only for $x=0.1$. Compare with the analytical answer which is

$$y(x) = \frac{63}{8}x^5 - \frac{35}{4}x^3 + \frac{15}{8}x.$$

7.19 Find $y(0.5)$ for the following fourth-order second-degree differential equation:

$$\left(\frac{d^4y}{dx^4}\right)^2 - x\left(\frac{d^3y}{dx^3}\right)^2 + \frac{d^2y}{dx^2} + \left(\frac{dy}{dx}\right)^2 - xy^2 = x+1-\sin x.$$

Use the initial conditions $y(0)=0$, $y'(0)=1$, $y''(0)=0$, $y'''(0)=-1$, and choose $h=0.1$.

7.20 An example of a stiff differential equation is

$$\frac{d^2y}{dx^2} + 100\frac{dy}{dx} + y = 2.$$

(a) For the initial conditions $y(0)=0$ and $y'(0)=100$, show that $y = 2 - e^{-0.01x} - e^{-99.99x}$.

(b) Examine the solution where the small time constant predominates by evaluating the solution in (a) for $x=0.001$, 0.01, 0.02, and 0.05.

(c) Examine the solution where the large time constant predominates by evaluating the solution in (a) for $x=5$, 50, and 300.

(d) Use the program of Fig. 7.8 to find $y(0.05)$, and compare with the answer found in (b). Use $h=0.001$.

(e) In the region where the large time constant predominates, one would like to use a large step size. Try the program of Fig. 7.8 for this differential equation with $y(1)=1$, $y'(1)=0$, and $h=0.1$. Explain what happened.

Chapter Eight

Introduction to Optimization Theory

8.1 PRELIMINARY REMARKS

In our everyday experiences we often consciously or subconsciously try to optimize results. Some of the problems we encounter are rather trivial, such as finding the shortest path between two points: a straight line. However, if the problem is to reach the airport in a minimum amount of time so as not to miss a flight, then the optimum solution is not so easily found. Perhaps the geometrically shortest route goes through the city and is therefore rather slow. If one decides to drive on the freeway to the airport, other choices will have to be made: for example the speed (we do not want to get a ticket or get in an accident), the exit to use, etc.

Optimization problems become increasingly difficult to solve as the number of variables is increased. In practical applications there may be many parameters that can be varied independently to improve results. However, while optimization problems may be involved and thus require the use of a computer, the benefits of using optimization theory can be great.

Optimization theory has been used to great advantage in electrical engineering. For example, an electrical network may contain many resistors, inductors, and capacitors. These elements, which may be considered as the independent variables, can be adjusted by optimization techniques so that a desired electrical response is obtained. An example in Section 8.6 illustrates one application of this approach.

Optimization theory has influenced the design of many different types of manufacturing processes. A chemical product, for instance, may contain variable proportions of ingredients, may be subjected to various temperatures for different amounts of time, etc. It may be possible to write functional relations for these different parameters, but it will probably be impossible to obtain an analytical answer for the optimum result. However, often the problem can be formulated in a manner that allows iterative methods to adjust the parameters and obtain an optimum solution. These optimization techniques can thus be viewed as a collection of numerical methods that have been linked together in a specific way.

177

In the next section, it is shown that optimization can correspond to minimizing a function, which will be termed the error function E. If the error E is a function of only one variable x, then we will assume it can be expanded in terms of a Taylor series as

$$E(x + \delta x) = E(x) + \frac{dE}{dx}\delta x + \frac{d^2E}{dx^2}\frac{(\delta x)^2}{2} + \cdots . \tag{8.1}$$

In an introductory calculus course, an equation such as this could be used to prove that at a minimum the first derivative dE/dx must be zero and the second derivative d^2E/dx^2 must be positive.

In optimization problems, the error E may be influenced by many variables $x_1, x_2, \ldots, x_n$ and thus will often be written as $E(\mathbf{x})$, where $\mathbf{x}$ is a vector having components $x_1, x_2, \ldots, x_n$. As mentioned in Section 9.6, the equation that corresponds to (8.1) for this general case is

$$E(\mathbf{x} + \delta\mathbf{x}) = E(\mathbf{x}) + \nabla E^T \delta\mathbf{x} + \frac{\delta\mathbf{x}^T \mathbf{H} \delta\mathbf{x}}{2} + \cdots . \tag{8.2}$$

The symbol ∇E represents the gradient, which is defined in Section 9.3. The gradient is the n-dimensional analogue of the first derivative. In fact, it is shown in Section 9.3 that the gradient must be zero at a minimum.

The symbol $\mathbf{H}$ represents a matrix termed the Hessian, which is defined in Section 9.6. The Hessian is the n-dimensional analogue of the second derivative. In fact, by analogy it can be shown that at a minimum we must have $\delta\mathbf{x}^T \mathbf{H} \delta\mathbf{x}$ positive for any nonzero vector $\delta\mathbf{x}$. A matrix such as this is said to be positive definite.

Four different optimization techniques are discussed in detail in this book: simplex, steepest descent, Fletcher-Powell, and least pth. After comparing optimization techniques in general in Section 8.3, the simplex algorithm is described in detail in Section 8.4. Simplex was chosen for this introductory chapter because it is unsophisticated yet can still be a powerful optimization program. At the end of the chapter, the simplex algorithm is applied to various test functions such as the Rosenbrock function.

Another simple optimization technique is the steepest-descent method, which searches for the minimum by proceeding in the direction of the negative gradient. The Fletcher-Powell optimization technique modifies this direction slightly by using information that is contained in the Hessian matrix. The least-pth optimization procedure (a generalization of least squares) also calculates the gradient to help determine the search direction, but it calculates this very efficiently by assuming that the error function is of a special form.

The reader may be wondering why the text discusses four different optimization techniques, when any one theoretically can be used to minimize a function. A major reason is that often one technique is not able to find a minimum, so another must be tried. Which program is best will often depend on the particular error function that must be minimized. In fact, as shown in Section 9.5, even scaling the parameters (e.g., replacing x_1 by $10x_1$) can drastically affect the rate of convergence.

When an optimization program finds a minimum, the user may not be happy with the minimum that is found. One reason (see Section 9.5) may be that the point found was only a *local* minimum; that is, if different initial parameter values had been chosen, then an even smaller value could have been obtained. Another reason may be that the parameter values at the minimum were unrealistic (e.g., if the parameters represent dimensions of an object, then the "optimum" product may be too large to manufacture). Chapter 11 indicates how parameter values can be constrained to have practical values.

Before proceeding with this introduction to optimization theory, a warning should be given about the optimization programs that are included in the rest of this text. As was true for the previous programs, these optimization programs have been written with clarity as the first goal and not efficiency. (In an optimization program, it can be worthwhile to save a few milliseconds of computation time because the computations may be done many times before the optimization loop is completed.) While it should be acknowledged that these programs are not sophisticated, it also should be emphasized that they can be used to solve practical optimization problems —but interaction might be required in certain cases. This interaction could consist of choosing a better set of initial parameters; or if a particular algorithm (e.g., steepest descent) does not perform satisfactorily for a specific problem, then another algorithm (e.g., least pth) could be tried.

8.2 FORMULATION OF OPTIMIZATION PROBLEMS

Before optimization techniques can be applied to a specific problem, it must be stated in terms of mathematical relations. We will assume the problem can be formulated so that we wish to *minimize* an *error function*[1] E. The error function E may depend on many variables $x_1, x_2, \ldots, x_n$ and thus will often be written as $E(\mathbf{x})$, where $\mathbf{x}$ is a vector having components $x_1, x_2, \ldots, x_n$.

The fact that the optimization techniques we study are formulated so as to minimize functions is not so restrictive as it might seem. If instead we want to maximize a function $F(\mathbf{x})$, we can let $E(\mathbf{x}) = -F(\mathbf{x})$ and minimize $E(\mathbf{x})$.

---

[1]This is often called the *objective function*.

Often, we will not want to minimize an error, but instead minimize the magnitude of the error. That is, a large negative error may be as objectionable as a large positive error. As an example of this, assume we want to find a solution of the nonlinear equation $\ln x = x$. If we define an error function as $e(x) = \ln x - x$, then a solution of the nonlinear equation can be found by adjusting x so that the error function $e(x)$ becomes zero. If we want to make a function $e(x)$ become zero, we can instead minimize the square of that function, i.e.,

$$E = [e(x)]^2. \tag{8.3}$$

This idea can be generalized in numerous ways; for example, the function we want to make zero may depend on many parameters $x_1, x_2, \ldots, x_n$. Then we write

$$E(\mathbf{x}) = [e(\mathbf{x})]^2. \tag{8.4}$$

Or we may have many functions $e_1(\mathbf{x}), e_2(\mathbf{x}), \ldots, e_m(\mathbf{x})$ we wish to simultaneously set equal to zero; then we can define the error function as

$$E(\mathbf{x}) = \sum_{i=1}^{m} [e_i(\mathbf{x})]^2. \tag{8.5}$$

EXAMPLE 8.1

A set of nonlinear equations can be solved by using an error function of the type in (8.5). As a simple case, consider

$$x_1^2 + 3\cos x_2 = 2,$$
$$\cos x_1 + 2x_1 x_2 = 4.$$

For this case, if we define the individual errors as

$$e_1(x_1, x_2) = x_1^2 + 3\cos x_2 - 2,$$
$$e_2(x_1, x_2) = \cos x_1 + 2x_1 x_2 - 4,$$

then minimizing the following error function will produce a solution

$$E(\mathbf{x}) = e_1(x_1, x_2)^2 + e_2(x_1, x_2)^2.$$

The exponent in (8.5) was picked as 2 so that the contribution of each individual error was always positive. In general, any even positive number p could have been used:

$$E(\mathbf{x}) = \sum_{i=1}^{m} [e_i(\mathbf{x})]^p. \tag{8.6}$$

This is called the *least-p th error criterion*, while the special case of $p = 2$ is called the *least-squares error criterion*.

In a practical problem, some of the individual errors may be more important than others. In this case we can assign nonnegative weighting factors ω_i so that

$$E(\mathbf{x}) = \sum_{i=1}^{m} \omega_i \left[e_i(\mathbf{x}) \right]^p. \qquad (8.7)$$

The more important an error is, the larger is the weight we assign it. Of course we could make the substitution $\omega_i [e_i(\mathbf{x})]^p \rightarrow [e_i(\mathbf{x})]^p$ and transform the weighted problem to a nonweighted one.

In some problems a requirement[2] $f(t)$ may be given and we may wish to adjust the parameters $x_1, x_2, \ldots, x_n$ so that the response $h(t)$ of a system is as close as possible to $f(t)$. For this case we could define an error as

$$e(t) = f(t) - h(t). \qquad (8.8)$$

However, a computer can only treat discrete functions, so we will instead define

$$e_i = f_i - h_i, \qquad (8.9)$$

where the subscript i indicates that the functions are evaluated at $t = t_i$. For this case, (8.6) can be rewritten as

$$E(\mathbf{x}) = \sum_{i=1}^{m} \left[f_i - h_i(\mathbf{x}) \right]^p. \qquad (8.10)$$

8.3 OVERVIEW OF VARIOUS OPTIMIZATION TECHNIQUES[3]

Just as there are various numerical methods for finding the roots of an equation, there are different optimization techniques that can be used to minimize the error function $E(\mathbf{x})$. Which is the best will depend on the specific application. However, it is possible to divide optimization techniques into certain categories and then to compare the categories. This section will give a brief overview of various optimization techniques, and the next section will give a more detailed presentation of a specific one. The following two chapters will give detailed descriptions of additional optimization techniques.

---

[2]The variable t can be considered to be time in this discussion, but of course it could have a different meaning.

[3]This is essentially the same as Section 13.4 of Daniels (1974).

1. Simple Search Methods (Nonderivative)

The sophisticated optimization techniques evaluate the first and/or higher derivatives; however, there are some procedures that do not require derivatives. Perhaps one of the simplest ways to minimize the error function is to vary one available parameter at a time—for example, first minimize the error for the parameter x_1, then for x_2, and so on; after doing this for all parameters, one would start over again at x_1. Since each step in this minimization procedure is a single parameter search, the quadratic interpolation method may be used to find the minimum.

The simplex method can be used for multiparameter searches, that is, searches in which one does not examine the behavior of the error function for one parameter at a time. In n-dimensional space, a set of $n+1$ points forms a simplex. In the simplex method we start with an arbitrary simplex and then let it tumble and shrink toward the region where the error is a minimum. The direction in which we allow the simplex to move is determined by evaluating the error function at each of the $n+1$ points of the simplex.

2. Slope-Following Methods

Slope-following methods evaluate the first derivatives of the error function $(\partial E/\partial x_i)$ and use this information to indicate how the parameters should be changed in order to minimize the error. The first derivatives determine the gradient of the error function. The gradient points in the direction of the greatest change in error; thus, to minimize the error one proceeds in the direction opposite to the gradient. This is the basis of the steepest-descent method, which uses the gradient to predict parameter changes for error minimization. Steepest descent can be considered to be an attempt to change parameter values so as to proceed down an error slope most rapidly. Assuming that the error function $E(\mathbf{x})$ has the special form given in (8.6) leads to the least-pth optimization technique, which is a generalization of the least-squares method.

3. Second-Order Methods

The slope-following methods tend to reduce the error rapidly in the initial stages of an optimization procedure; however, their convergence is rather slow as the minimum is approached. To improve the rate of convergence, one can use not only the first derivatives of the error function $(\partial E/\partial x_i)$, but also the second derivatives $(\partial^2 E/\partial x_i \partial x_j)$. Just as the first derivatives determined the gradient of the error function, the second derivatives determine the Hessian.

The various second-order methods differ mainly in the way they try to approximate the second derivatives. The second derivatives are not usually found by using a perturbation scheme based on varying elements; they are instead approximated by using knowledge of the error function and its gradient at previous iterations. The Fletcher-Powell minimization procedure is one of the best known second-order methods.

8.4 THE SIMPLEX OPTIMIZATION TECHNIQUE[4]

As previously mentioned, we are trying to minimize an error function $E(\mathbf{x})$ which is a function of n variables $x_1, x_2, \ldots, x_n$. Because $\mathbf{x}$ is an n-dimensional vector, we are led to the concept of an n-dimensional space. Even though our imagination may balk at something larger than a three-dimensional space, our mathematical symbols will not.

The simplex method of nonlinear programming begins by choosing $n+1$ parameter vectors to span an n-dimensional space. The geometric figure which is formed by these points is called a simplex—hence the name of the method. In particular, a two-dimensional simplex is a triangle and a three-dimensional simplex is a tetrahedron. In the simplex method we will start with an initial simplex and then cause it to approach the region where the error is a minimum.

In any optimization technique an initial guess must be made for the variables $x_1, x_2, \ldots, x_n$. The optimization technique is then supposed to adjust the parameters to minimize $E(\mathbf{x})$. In the simplex method we will identify this initial guess as point $\mathbf{P}_0$ in the n-dimensional space. That is,

$$\mathbf{P}_0 = (x_1, x_2, x_3, \ldots, x_n). \tag{8.11}$$

We will use this initial point to generate other points $\mathbf{P}_1, \mathbf{P}_2, \ldots, \mathbf{P}_n$. These points will define the initial simplex.

Point $\mathbf{P}_1$ will be arbitrarily related to $\mathbf{P}_0$ via

$$\mathbf{P}_1 = (1.1x_1, x_2, x_3, \ldots, x_n), \tag{8.12}$$

and in general

$$\mathbf{P}_i = (x_1, x_2, \ldots, 1.1x_i, \ldots, x_n), \tag{8.13}$$

where $i = 1, 2, \ldots, n$.

[4]This is not related to Dantzig's simplex algorithm of linear programming. The nonlinear simplex method described here was originally proposed by Nelder, J. A., and Mead, R. (Jan. 1965), "A Simplex Method for Function Minimization", *Comput. J.*, pp. 308–313. The values for α, β, and γ in this section were suggested by P. E. Fleischer and D. M. Bohling (private correspondence).

The iterative part of the simplex algorithm begins by ordering the points $\mathbf{P}_0, \mathbf{P}_1, \ldots, \mathbf{P}_n$ according to the values of $E(\mathbf{P}_0), E(\mathbf{P}_1), \ldots, E(\mathbf{P}_n)$. The points that yield the lowest, highest, and next highest values of the error function are identified as $\mathbf{P}_L$, $\mathbf{P}_H$, and $\mathbf{P}_{NH}$. The simplex algorithm repetitively replaces $\mathbf{P}_H$, the highest point. It will be illuminating to adopt a geometric language in a description of the algorithm. We will picture the simplex as moving towards a minimum by a series of operations termed reflections, contractions, and expansions. These are illustrated in Fig. 8.1 for the case of a two-dimensional simplex.

1. Reflection

The first attempt at replacing $\mathbf{P}_H$ is by reflection about the *centroid*, defined as

$$\mathbf{C} = \frac{1}{n} \sum_{\substack{i=0 \\ i \neq H}}^{n} \mathbf{P}_i. \tag{8.14}$$

That is, the centroid is the average of all the points except $\mathbf{P}_H$, which is going to be replaced shortly.

EXAMPLE 8.2

The error function for this example is $E(\mathbf{x}) = 2x_1 - x_2$. If the initial point

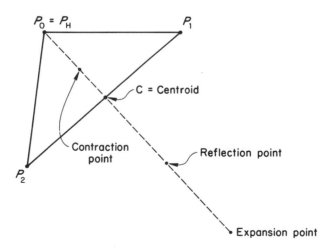

FIGURE 8.1. Illustration of reflection, contraction, and expansion for a two-dimensional simplex.

is chosen as $P_0 = (2, 1)$:

(a) Find P_1 and P_2.
(b) What point is P_H?
(c) Find the centroid.

SOLUTION

(a) Applying (8.13) yields $P_1 = (2.2, 1)$ and $P_2 = (2, 1.1)$.
(b) To determine which point has the highest error we must evaluate $E(x)$
   for each of the points:

$$E(P_0) = E(2, 1) = 3,$$
$$E(P_1) = E(2.2, 1) = 3.4,$$
$$E(P_2) = E(2, 1.1) = 2.9;$$

thus $P_H = P_1$.

(c) Applying (8.14) with $H = 1$ yields

$$C = \tfrac{1}{2}(P_0 + P_2) = \tfrac{1}{2}(2 + 2, 1 + 1.1) = \tfrac{1}{2}(4, 2.1) = (2, 1.05).$$

The reflected point is defined by

$$P_R = (1 + \alpha)C - \alpha P_H. \qquad (8.15)$$

If $\alpha = 1$, then the reflected point is the same distance from the centroid as is P_H, but on the opposite side (see Fig. 8.1 or Problem 8.10). However, this value will be modified slightly to $\alpha = 0.9985$ to prevent any of the computed parameters from becoming zero, which could cause computational difficulties.

EXAMPLE 8.3

This example will demonstrate reflection for the data given in Example 8.2. The parameter α will be chosen as unity to simplify computations.

For $\alpha = 1$, (8.15) becomes $P_R = 2C - P_H$. Substituting the results from the previous example,

$$P_R = 2(2, 1.05) - (2.2, 1) = (1.8, 1.1).$$

If the reflection is moderately successful, namely if

$$E(P_L) \leqslant E(P_R) < E(P_H), \qquad (8.16)$$

then P_R replaces P_H, thereby forming a new simplex. Another reflection is then attempted for this new simplex.

The reflected point may not be described by (8.16), for one of two possible reasons. One of the possibilities can be illustrated by calculating the error function for the reflected point of Example 8.3. Since for those data the error function was defined as $E(\mathbf{x}) = 2x_1 - x_2$, it follows that for $\mathbf{P}_R = (1.8, 1.1)$, $E(\mathbf{P}_R) = 2.5$. From Example 8.2, the error at the low point was $E(\mathbf{P}_L) = 2.9$; thus $E(\mathbf{P}_R) < E(\mathbf{P}_L)$. The other reason the reflected point may not be described by (8.16) is that in some cases $E(\mathbf{P}_R) > E(\mathbf{P}_H)$.

2. Expansion

If the reflection operation is highly successful and produces a new minimum, so that $E(\mathbf{P}_R) < E(\mathbf{P}_L)$, then it seems likely we are proceeding in a good direction, so we will go further in that direction by expanding according to the expression

$$\mathbf{P}_{\mathrm{Ex}} = \beta \mathbf{P}_R + (1 - \beta)\mathbf{C}. \tag{8.17}$$

If $\beta = 2$, then the expanded point will be twice as far from the centroid as is the reflected point (see Fig. 8.1 or Problem 8.10). However, this value will be modified slightly to 1.95 to prevent possible instabilities. Depending on whether $E(\mathbf{P}_R)$ or $E(\mathbf{P}_{\mathrm{Ex}})$ is smaller, either $\mathbf{P}_R$ or $\mathbf{P}_{\mathrm{Ex}}$ replaces $\mathbf{P}_H$. A new centroid is then calculated and the reflection process is again attempted.

3. Contraction

If the reflection operation is not successful, but results in $E(\mathbf{P}_R) \geqslant E(\mathbf{P}_H)$, then it seems likely we are searching on the wrong side of the centroid, so contraction is performed according to

$$\mathbf{P}_C = (1 - \gamma)\mathbf{C} + \gamma \mathbf{P}_H. \tag{8.18}$$

If $\gamma = \frac{1}{2}$, then the contracted point is midway between $\mathbf{P}_H$ and the centroid (see Fig. 8.1). This value of γ will be modified slightly to 0.4985 for practical reasons. If contraction is successful and $E(\mathbf{P}_C) < E(\mathbf{P}_H)$, then the result is the same as if reflection had been successful, and we proceed accordingly.

Contraction is usually successful; however, if it is not and $E(\mathbf{P}_C) \geqslant E(\mathbf{P}_H)$, then drastic measures are taken.

4. Scaling

In the unlikely event that neither reflecting nor contracting can find a better point than $\mathbf{P}_H$, then the simplex itself is modified by a scaling process described by

$$\mathbf{P}_i + k(\mathbf{P}_L - \mathbf{P}_i) \rightarrow \mathbf{P}_i, \qquad i = 0, 1, \ldots, n. \tag{8.19}$$

A two-dimensional representation of the scaling process for $k = 0.5$ is shown in Fig. 8.2. As demonstrated there, if $k = 0.5$, then the scaling process moves every point towards the best point $\mathbf{P}_L$; in fact, the distance is halved. In general, if k is positive (and also less than unity), then the scaling process of (8.19) causes the simplex to *shrink* about the point $\mathbf{P}_L$.

On the other hand, if k is negative, then every point moves away from $\mathbf{P}_L$ and the simplex increases in size. For example, if $k = -1$, then the distance between $\mathbf{P}_L$ and a point $\mathbf{P}_i$ doubles. Suggested values for the scale factor k are 0.5 to reduce the size of the simplex and -1 to increase it.

A program for the simplex algorithm is shown in Fig. 8.3. The notation in the program is very similar to that used in the preceeding discussion, but one comment should be made. As usual, because FORTRAN does not allow a subscript to be zero, the subscripts have been translated by unity in this program. For example, the initial point is identified as P(1) and not P(0).

Any point in the simplex has n components; since there are $n + 1$ points in the simplex, this implies there is a total of $n(n + 1)$ quantities that describe the simplex. The most convenient way to store this information is in a matrix. In the program, row$_1$ of the matrix represents $\mathbf{P}_1$, row$_2$ represents $\mathbf{P}_2$, and in general row$_i$ represents $\mathbf{P}_i$. The matrix is denoted by P in the program, so the general term $P(i,j)$ in the matrix represents the jth component of the ith simplex point $\mathbf{P}_i$.

In the program L, H, and NH represent lowest, highest, and next highest. For example, if $L = 4$, then $\mathbf{P}_4$ is the simplex point that has the lowest error value and this error value is E_4. It should be noted that extra memory locations are not needed for the lowest point $\mathbf{P}_L$ or its error E_L. Instead, the memory location L is used to indicate which simplex point produces the lowest error. The error at point $\mathbf{P}_i$ is stored as E(i); thus the lowest,

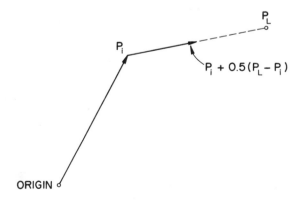

FIGURE 8.2. Illustration of scaling for a two-dimensional simplex.

```
01C        SIMPLEX
02         PROGRAM S(INPUT,OUTPUT)
03 03      FORMAT(7H  X(I)=,1P,4E14.5)
04 04      FORMAT(7H ERROR=,1P,E14.5,/)
06         DIMENSION C(10),E(10),P(10,10),R(10),X(10)
07         INTEGER H
08         REAL K
09C
10C        INITIAL VALUES
11         PRINT,*N*, $READ,N
12         N1=N+1
14         PRINT,/,*X(I)   I=1,2,...N*
15         READ,(X(I),I=1,N)
16         E(1)=ERROR(X)
17         PRINT 4,E(1)
19C
20C        INITIALIZE SIMPLEX   (EQ. 8.13)
21         DO 22 J=1,N
22 22      P(1,J)=X(J)
24         DO 28 I=2,N1
25         DO 26 J=1,N
26 26      P(I,J)=X(J)
27         P(I,I-1)=1.1*X(I-1)
28 28      IF(ABS(X(I-1)).LT.1E-12) P(I,I-1)=.0001
29C
30C        FIND PL,PH
31 31      L=H=1
32         DO 38 I=1,N1
34         DO 35 J=1,N
35 35      X(J)=P(I,J)
36         E(I)=ERROR(X)
37         IF(E(I).LT.E(L)) L=I
38 38      IF(E(I).GT.E(H)) H=I
39C
40C        FIND PNH
41 41      NH=L
42         DO 43 I=1,N1
43 43      IF(E(I).GE.E(NH).AND.I.NE.H) NH=I
49C
50C        CALCULATE CENTROID   (EQ. 8.14)
51         DO 56 J=1,N
52         C(J)=-P(H,J)
53         DO 54 I=1,N1
54 54      C(J)=C(J)+P(I,J)
56 56      C(J)=C(J)/N
59C
60C        REFLECT   (EQ. 8.15)
61 61      DO 62 J=1,N
62 62      R(J)=1.9985*C(J)-.9985*P(H,J)
64         ER=ERROR(R)
```

(a)

FIGURE 8.3. A program for simplex.

```
70C         REFLECT AGAIN  (IF MODERATELY SUCCESSFUL)
71          IF(ER.LT.E(L)) GO TO 91
73          IF(ER.GE.E(H)) GO TO 122
79  79      DO 80 J=1,N
80  80      P(H,J)=R(J)
81          E(H)=ER
83          IF(ER.GT.E(NH)) GO TO 61
85          H=NH
86          GO TO 41
89C
90C         EXPAND  (EQ. 8.17)
91  91      L=H $H=NH
92          DO 93 J=1,N
93  93      X(J)=1.95*R(J)-.95*C(J)
94          EX=ERROR(X)
96          IF(EX.LT.ER) GO TO 104
98          DO 99 J=1,N
99  99      P(L,J)=R(J)
100         E(L)=ER
101         GO TO 110
104 104     DO 105 J=1,N
105 105     P(L,J)=X(J)
106         E(L)=EX
109C
110 110     PRINT 3,(P(L,J),J=1,N)
114         PRINT 4,E(L)
117         GO TO 41
119C
120C        CONTRACT  (EQ. 8.18)
122 122     DO 123 J=1,N
123 123     R(J)=.5015*C(J)+.4985*P(H,J)
124         ER=ERROR(R)
126         IF(ER.LT.E(L)) GO TO 91
128         IF(ER.LT.E(H)) GO TO 79
132C
133C        SCALE  (EQ. 8.19)
134         PRINT,*K*, $READ,K
136         DO 138 I=1,N1
137         DO 138 J=1,N
138 138     P(I,J)=P(I,J)+K*(P(L,J)-P(I,J))
139         GO TO 31
140         END
897C
898         FUNCTION ERROR(X)
899         DIMENSION X(10)
900         ERROR=100.*(X(1)*X(1)-X(2))**2+(1-X(1))**2
950         RETURN
999         END
```

(b)

FIGURE 8.3. (Continued.)

highest, and next highest errors would be stored as E(L), E(H), and E(NH). The location of the centroid **C** is found by calculating

$$C = \frac{1}{n} \sum_{\substack{i=0 \\ i \neq H}}^{n+1} P_i = \frac{1}{N}\left[-P_H + \sum_{i=1}^{n+1} P_i \right]. \tag{8.20}$$

The second form of the equation is used because it avoids the necessity of checking each point to determine whether or not it is P_H.

In the program, the point produced by contraction is identified as P_R (i.e., R). Actually this is the value P_C that would be calculated by applying (8.18). It is identified in the program as P_R (and not as P_C) because if contraction is successful we proceed exactly the same as we would have proceeded if reflection had been successful. Thus coding the result of contraction as P_R eliminates an unnecessary substitution (i.e., it eliminates $P_C \rightarrow P_R$).

8.5 APPLICATIONS OF SIMPLEX

This section discusses some applications of the simplex program to serve as an introduction to the use of an optimization program. Compared with most optimization problems, these examples are quite simple, but they should thus be relatively easy to understand.

EXAMPLE 8.4

This uses the simplex algorithm to solve the following nonlinear equations, which were first presented in Example 8.1:

$$x_1^2 + 3\cos x_2 = 2,$$
$$\cos x_1 + 2x_1 x_2 = 4.$$

That example derived a suitable form for the error function, which can be coded in statements 900 and 910 as

900 ERROR = (X(1)*X(1)+3.*COS(X(2))−2.)**2
910 ERROR = ERROR+(COS(X(1))+2.*X(1)*X(2)−4.)**2

In this example, each contribution to the error function was given a separate statement which makes for ease in reading.

Figure 8.4 indicates the output of the simplex program for this example. The top of the printout indicates that for the initial set of parameters $x_1 = 1$, $x_2 = 1$ the error function was 2.52. After a few iterations, the simplex algorithm indicated that a better set of parameters would be $x_1 = 1.26222$, $x_2 = 1.44424$, for which the error function was 0.00333.

```
N ? 2

X(I)   I=1,2,...N
? 1          1
  ERROR=     2.51624E+00

   X(I)=     1.14735E+00     1.14735E+00
  ERROR=     1.21597E+00

   X(I)=     1.02242E+00     1.36449E+00
  ERROR=     5.89749E-01

   X(I)=     1.16965E+00     1.41160E+00
  ERROR=     1.18917E-01

   X(I)=     1.31655E+00     1.45862E+00
  ERROR=     1.32776E-02

   X(I)=     1.28842E+00     1.42986E+00
  ERROR=     7.99136E-03

   X(I)=     1.26222E+00     1.44424E+00
  ERROR=     3.33276E-03
```

FIGURE 8.4. The solution of two nonlinear equations by simplex.

In most optimization problems exact knowledge about the final value of an error function will not be very enlightening. The fact that the final error function in Example 8.4 was 0.00333 does not convey much information. However, comparing this value with the initial error value which was 2.52, we can note that the final error function is about a factor of 1000 smaller. This gives us some confidence that the final set of values for x_1, x_2 is much better than the initial set.

Much more insight into the accuracy of the optimization result may be obtained by returning to the set of equations we were trying to solve. Consider the first one: $x_1^2 + 3\cos x_2 = 2$. If $x_1 = 1.2622$, $x_2 = 1.4442$ is substituted into the left side, the number 1.972 results instead of 2. Similarly, substituting into the second equation yields 3.949 instead of 4.

Of course, improved accuracy could be obtained by using more iterations of the simplex algorithm. When one is finally satisfied that a set of parameter values is close enough to the optimum answer, the number of important digits in the parameter values should be determined. The mere fact that a computer has been programmed to print out six significant figures certainly does not imply that they are all important. For example, changing the solution from $x_1 = 1.2622$, $x_2 = 1.4442$ in the previous problem to $x_1 = 1.26$, $x_2 = 1.44$ changes the left side of the equations to 1.979 and 3.935, which are probably still sufficiently close to the desired values of 2 and 4.

In a practical optimization problem, the accuracy of a parameter value may indicate the tolerance of a component that is used. For example, if x represents the value of a resistor in an electrical network, then specifying four significant figures may imply that a component with a tolerance of 0.1% should be used. Since increased tolerance usually results in increased cost, an effort should be made to ascertain how many digits in the optimized parameter values are really important.

EXAMPLE 8.5

Figure 8.5 demonstrates the minimization of

$$E(x) = 2\sin x_1 \cos x_2 + (\cos x_1)^2 (\sin x_2)^4.$$

For the initial set of parameters $x_1 = 1$, $x_2 = 1$ the error function was 1.056. After many iterations the parameters were adjusted to $x_1 = 1.56$, $x_2 = 3.12$, which yielded an error function of -2.00.

It should be noted that the minimum that was found in Example 8.5 was a negative number. The simplex algorithm is a general procedure that *minimizes* a function of several variables. Often the function $E(\mathbf{x})$ is formulated as a sum of squares [see (8.5)], so that the minimum will be positive; but as this example demonstrates, that is not necessary.

The processes reflection, expansion, and contraction were used in the two previous examples. However, it was never necessary to scale the entire simplex. In fact this is generally true; the scale operation in simplex is not used often. The following example was especially concocted so that scaling would be necessary. Singularities (places where the function approaches infinity) were put near $\mathbf{P}_R$ (the reflected point) and $\mathbf{P}_C$ (the contracted point) so that these points would have large error values.

EXAMPLE 8.6

The error function for this example is $E(x_1, x_2) = (x_1 + 5x_2)^2 + 1/(x_1 + x_2 - 2.04)^2 + 1/(x_1 + x_2 - 2.19)^2$. Choosing the initial parameter vector as $\mathbf{P}_0 = (1, 1)$, the remaining points of the initial simplex are calculated as $\mathbf{P}_1 = (1.1, 1)$ and $\mathbf{P}_2 = (1, 1.1)$. For these points the error function is $E_0 = 688.7$, $E_1 = 438.4$, and $E_2 = 443.5$; thus $\mathbf{P}_H = \mathbf{P}_0$.

Applying (8.14) yields that the centroid is $\mathbf{C} = (1.05, 1.05)$. Reflecting with the parameter α chosen as unity for simplicity produces $\mathbf{P}_R = (1.1, 1.1)$, so that the error at the reflected point is $E_R = 1008.3$. This error is greater than the error at the high point $\mathbf{P}_0$, so contraction is attempted.

```
N ? 2

X(I)   I=1,2,...,N
? 1         1
  ERROR=   1.05566E+00

  X(I)=    8.52867E-01   1.29460E+00
  ERROR=   7.81547E-01

  X(I)=    9.77610E-01   1.38689E+00
  ERROR=   5.95195E-01

  X(I)=    7.50202E-01   1.80949E+00
  ERROR=   1.54609E-01

  X(I)=    8.85399E-01   2.18931E+00
  ERROR=  -7.21224E-01

  X(I)=    6.58230E-01   2.61100E+00
  ERROR=  -1.01418E+00

  X(I)=    7.93395E-01   2.98993E+00
  ERROR=  -1.40886E+00

  X(I)=    1.06468E+00   2.75167E+00
  ERROR=  -1.61306E+00

  X(I)=    1.15443E+00   3.16823E+00
  ERROR=  -1.82848E+00

  X(I)=    1.42524E+00   2.93001E+00
  ERROR=  -1.93468E+00

  X(I)=    1.51465E+00   3.34612E+00
  ERROR=  -1.95522E+00

  X(I)=    1.53787E+00   3.07897E+00
  ERROR=  -1.99500E+00

  X(I)=    1.57620E+00   3.17595E+00
  ERROR=  -1.99879E+00

  X(I)=    1.56456E+00   3.11956E+00
  ERROR=  -1.99948E+00
```

FIGURE 8.5. Demonstration that simplex can produce a minimum that is a negative number.

```
N ? 2

X(I)    I=1,2,...N
? 1         1
  ERROR=    6.88701E+02

K ? -1
  X(I)=     1.19471E+00      6.10585E-01
  ERROR=    4.29520E+01

  X(I)=     9.44848E-01      4.26182E-01
  ERROR=    1.31858E+01

  X(I)=     1.40035E+00     -4.19359E-01
  ERROR=    2.06083E+00

  X(I)=     1.20316E+00     -4.16675E-01
  ERROR=    1.91885E+00

  X(I)=     1.20648E+00     -2.31504E-01
  ERROR=    1.56140E+00

  X(I)=     8.24123E-01     -1.38592E-01
  ERROR=    1.00409E+00

  X(I)=     4.99346E-01     -1.96285E-01
  ERROR=    8.44714E-01

  X(I)=    -2.09031E-01      9.16705E-02
  ERROR=    4.64853E-01

  X(I)=    -5.32790E-01      3.38486E-02
  ERROR=    4.25601E-01

  X(I)=    -1.23986E+00      3.21415E-01
  ERROR=    3.52595E-01
```

FIGURE 8.6. Illustration of the simplex scale feature.

Contracting with $\gamma = \frac{1}{2}$ produces $\mathbf{P}_c = (1.025, 1.025)$, so that the error at the contracted point is $E_c = 1008.9$, which is still worse than the error at $\mathbf{P}_H$. Because all else has failed, scaling must be done.

Figure 8.6 shows the results of using the simplex program. In this computer run the scale factor k was chosen as equal to -1, so the initial simplex was increased in size about the low point P_1. Simplex was the able to make the error function arbitrarily close to zero.[5]

---

[5] If $x_1 = -5x_2$, then the error approaches zero as x_2 approaches infinity.

8.6 TEST FUNCTIONS

The simplex algorithm that was just described is but one of many optimization techniques that can be used to minimize an error function $E(\mathbf{x})$. Numerous techniques have been described in the literature; which is best depends on the application. However, for a specific problem one can make meaningful comparisons between different optimization techniques.

Over the years researchers have encountered (or concocted) various functions that are difficult to minimize. Many of these functions have been described in the literature and are now commonly used as test functions. In this section a few of the "classical" test functions will be discussed; then in the following chapters we will be able to compare different optimization techniques.

Perhaps the most famous test function is the Rosenbrock function

$$E(\mathbf{x}) = 100(x_1^2 - x_2)^2 + (1 - x_1)^2. \tag{8.21}$$

That this is a difficult function to optimize can be appreciated by studying Fig. 8.7.[6] This figure indicates contours of constant $E(\mathbf{x})$. Because the contours are close together it is difficult for an optimization program to search for the minimum.

The amount of computation time required by an optimization technique to reach a minimum can be greatly influenced by the values selected for the initial parameters. For the Rosenbrock function the values customarily chosen are $x_1 = -1.2$ and $x_2 = 1$.

Figure 8.8 shows the output of the simplex program for the Rosenbrock function. For $\mathbf{P}_0 = (-1.2, 1)$ the initial error was 24.2. After one iteration the parameters were adjusted to $x_1 = -1.08$, $x_2 = 1.10$, which reduced the error to 4.77. However, after this initial reduction in the error function, the simplex algorithm was very slow in approaching the minimum. The path taken due to the simplex optimization is indicated by the dashed line in Fig. 8.7. Following the thin curving contours is time consuming, but depending on how patient one is, the algorithm can get arbitrarily close to the minimum $x_1 = 1 = x_2$, at which point $E(\mathbf{x})$ is equal to zero.

A function very similar to the Rosenbrock function is "cube"

$$E(\mathbf{x}) = 100(x_1^3 - x_2)^2 + (1 - x_1)^2. \tag{8.22}$$

This function is plotted in Fig. 8.9, and the simplex optimization results are given in Fig. 8.10. The initial point $\mathbf{P}_0 = (-1.2, 1)$ was the same as for the Rosenbrock function. The initial error of 749 was worse than the corresponding Rosenbrock error, but the optimal point $\mathbf{P} = (1, 1)$ was approached much more quickly.

---

[6]The dashed line in this figure will be explained later.

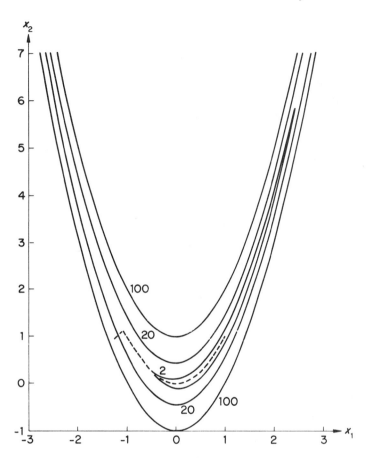

FIGURE 8.7. The Rosenbrock function.

Both of the test functions that were just discussed were functions of just two variables. As the number of parameters is increased, an optimization technique may encounter difficulties. A four-parameter function due to Powell is

$$E(x) = (x_1 + 10x_2)^2 + 5(x_3 - x_4)^2 + (x_2 - 2x_3)^4 + (10x_1 - x_4)^4. \quad (8.23)$$

Customary initial values for this function are $P_0 = (3, -1, 0, 1)$. Choosing a component to be zero causes line 28 in the program to be executed. If this statement had not been included in the program, then the algorithm would never have been able to vary the third component of P_0 from zero. The computer output in Fig. 8.11 indicates that the simplex algorithm was able to reduce the error functions slowly from an initial value of 707,336 to 90.9 in ten iterations.

```
N ? 2

X(I)   I=1,2,...N
? -1.2   1
  ERROR=    2.42000E+01

  X(I)=  -1.08018E+00   1.09992E+00
  ERROR=    4.77423E+00

  X(I)=  -1.08027E+00   1.19978E+00
  ERROR=    4.43505E+00

  X(I)=  -1.07276E+00   1.14058E+00
  ERROR=    4.30682E+00

  X(I)=  -1.05606E+00   1.10709E+00
  ERROR=    4.23406E+00

  X(I)=  -1.03521E+00   1.09768E+00
  ERROR=    4.20976E+00

  X(I)=  -1.00992E+00   1.01948E+00
  ERROR=    4.03978E+00

  X(I)=  -9.30016E-01   8.53469E-01
  ERROR=    3.73810E+00

  X(I)=  -8.02573E-01   6.04726E-01
  ERROR=    3.40449E+00

  X(I)=  -6.41337E-01   3.50679E-01
  ERROR=    3.06163E+00

  X(I)=  -5.48732E-01   2.51302E-01
  ERROR=    2.64661E+00
```

FIGURE 8.8. Minimization of the Rosenbrock function by simplex.

In the next two chapters these three test functions (Rosenbrock, "cube", and Powell) will be used to compare the efficiency of different optimization techniques. This will give insight into how the programs would be expected to perform on problems *similar* to these test functions. However, if one wants to know how different optimization techniques compare for a particular type of problem, then a problem of that type should be selected.

For an example of a "particular type of problem", the technique of coefficient matching will be explained. The electrical circuit in Fig. 8.12 is

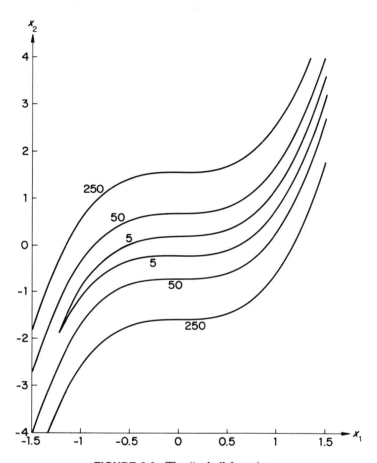

FIGURE 8.9. The "cube" function.

termed an active filter—it is made up of resistors, capacitors, and an operational amplifier. In a design problem the resistors and capacitors should have their element values chosen to yield a specified response. We will assume for this example that the response should have the form

$$T(s) = \frac{s}{s^2 + s + 40}, \tag{8.24}$$

where s is a normalized variable related to the frequency of an electrical signal.

Some of the element values for the circuit can be arbitrarily selected, and the response still made to have the form shown in (8.24). For this

```
N ? 2

X(I)   I=1,2,...,N
? -1.2   1
 ERROR=   7.49038E+02

 X(I)=  -9.66351E-01   1.14735E+00
 ERROR=   4.24020E+02

 X(I)=  -8.55709E-01   1.02242E+00
 ERROR=   2.75366E+02

 X(I)=  -3.48384E-01   1.25017E+00
 ERROR=   1.68863E+02

 X(I)=   1.07280E-01   1.11477E+00
 ERROR=   1.24794E+02

 X(I)=   1.31085E+00   1.49410E+00
 ERROR=   5.76125E+01

 X(I)=   1.23542E+00   1.33145E+00
 ERROR=   3.07595E+01

 X(I)=   9.83418E-01   1.33872E+00
 ERROR=   1.50273E+01

 X(I)=   1.09020E+00   1.29437E+00
 ERROR=   8.32327E-03

 X(I)=   1.07322E+00   1.23345E+00
 ERROR=   6.07770E-03

 X(I)=   1.05875E+00   1.18485E+00
 ERROR=   3.83487E-03
```

FIGURE 8.10. Minimization of "cube" by simplex.

example, the following choices will be made:

$$R_a = 1000, \qquad R_b = 5000, \qquad C_1 = C_2 = 10^{-8}. \qquad (8.25)$$

It can then be shown that the response of the circuit is given by

$$T(s) = \frac{a_1 s}{s^2 + b_1 s + b_0}, \qquad (8.26)$$

```
N ? 4

X(I)   I=1,2,...N
? 3    -1    0    1
  ERROR=   7.07336E+05

   X(I)=   2.41588E+00   -1.07368E+00    7.36769E-05    1.07368E+00
   ERROR=  2.84082E+05

   X(I)=   2.03217E+00   -1.01175E+00    1.93810E-05    1.28777E+00
   ERROR=  1.31328E+05

   X(I)=   1.31910E+00   -1.02041E+00    2.28368E-04    1.23140E+00
   ERROR=  2.05456E+04

   X(I)=   3.33829E-01   -1.15493E+00    8.58329E-05    1.38571E+00
   ERROR=  1.51702E+02

   X(I)=   1.57127E-01   -1.07911E+00    1.62529E-04    1.51571E+00
   ERROR=  1.25923E+02

   X(I)=   3.12163E-01   -1.03953E+00    1.99599E-04    1.51494E+00
   ERROR=  1.20975E+02

   X(I)=   7.84367E-02   -1.00796E+00    1.84177E-04    1.64235E+00
   ERROR=  1.15083E+02

   X(I)=   1.70012E-01   -9.83617E-01    2.59339E-04    1.57024E+00
   ERROR=  1.06697E+02

   X(I)=   2.24448E-01   -9.24915E-01    2.01309E-04    1.71597E+00
   ERROR=  9.69756E+01

   X(I)=   3.54463E-01   -8.41895E-01    2.58020E-04    1.82053E+00
   ERROR=  9.09423E+01
```

FIGURE 8.11. Minimization of "Powell" by simplex.

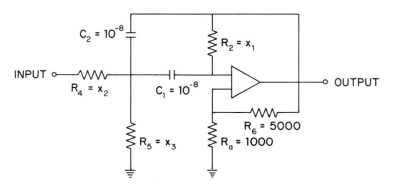

FIGURE 8.12. An active filter circuit that is used to illustrate coefficient matching.

where

$$a_1 = 1.2 \times 10^5 / x_2,$$

$$b_0 = \frac{(x_2 + x_3) \times 10^{10}}{x_1 x_2 x_3}, \qquad (8.27)$$

$$b_1 = \frac{2 \times 10^5}{x_1} - \frac{2 \times 10^4 (x_2 + x_3)}{x_2 x_3}.$$

The coefficient-matching technique consists of adjusting the parameters x_1, x_2, x_3 so that the coefficients a_1, b_0, b_1 have the specified values. For this problem (8.24) implies that the specified values are $a_1 = 1$, $b_0 = 40$, and $b_1 = 1$. Optimization techniques can be applied to this problem if the following error function is defined:

$$E(x) = (a_1 - 1)^2 + (b_0 - 40)^2 + (b_1 - 1)^2, \qquad (8.28)$$

where a_1, b_0, b_1 are as given in (8.27).

```
N ? 3

X(I)   I=1,2,...N
? 10000  10000  10000
  ERROR=    2.59460E+04

  X(I)=    1.09824E+04    1.09824E+04    1.09824E+04
  ERROR=   1.61135E+04

  X(I)=    1.32447E+04    1.03152E+04    1.06270E+04
  ERROR=   1.10851E+04

  X(I)=    1.35027E+04    1.25720E+04    1.12430E+04
  ERROR=   7.36973E+03

  X(I)=    1.50221E+04    1.12300E+04    1.34720E+04
  ERROR=   4.89402E+03

  X(I)=    1.96490E+04    1.21319E+04    1.33350E+04
  ERROR=   1.72462E+03

  X(I)=    2.15355E+04    1.52155E+04    1.66871E+04
  ERROR=   4.17308E+02

  X(I)=    2.89243E+04    1.34183E+04    2.08358E+04
  ERROR=   8.06558E+01

  X(I)=    3.17047E+04    1.59435E+04    2.04281E+04
  ERROR=   7.48690E+01

  X(I)=    3.19244E+04    1.44463E+04    2.12484E+04
  ERROR=   7.48069E+01

  X(I)=    3.04410E+04    1.35902E+04    1.98408E+04
  ERROR=   7.13897E+01
```

FIGURE 8.13. Coefficient matching by simplex.

The result of applying the simplex algorithm to minimize the error function is shown in Fig. 8.13. For the initial parameters $x_1 = x_2 = x_3 = 10000$ the optimization program yielded $x_1 = 30441$, $x_2 = 13590$, $x_3 = 19841$ as a better set after ten iterations; but the error function was still quite large.

In conclusion, the results of applying the simplex algorithm to the four test functions are shown in Figs. 8.8, 8.10, 8.11, and 8.13. Each of these figures shows ten iterations of the simplex optimization technique. If more iterations were allowed, the simplex method did converge to the minimum for each test function. However, the number of iterations was arbitrarily restricted to ten. This will also be done in later chapters when other optimization techniques are applied to the same test functions.

M. J. Box (1966) applied the simplex algorithm to many other test functions not described in this chapter. In fact, one of his test functions had twenty variables. He observed that (when compared with other optimization techniques such as Fletcher-Powell[7]) simplex did well for a small number of variables, but for more than three dimensions it was progressively less successful. However, in many applications it has been successfully used even for more than ten variables.

PROBLEMS

8.1 The simplex algorithm described in this chapter *minimizes* a function $E(\mathbf{x})$. If we instead want to *maximize* the function $f(\mathbf{x}) = 2 \sin x_1 \cos x_2 + (\cos x_1)^2 (\sin x_2)^4$, how should $E(\mathbf{x})$ be chosen?

8.2 Outline how optimization techniques can be used to solve the following set of linear equations:

$$x + y + z = 6, \qquad x + 2y + z = 8, \qquad 3x - y + z = 4.$$

8.3 Outline how optimization techniques can be used to solve the following set of nonlinear equations:

$$x^2 + y^2 = 13, \qquad y^3 - xy = 21.$$

8.4 If the initial parameters are chosen as $x_1 = 1$, $x_2 = 2$, and $x_3 = 3$, what are the four points that describe the initial simplex?

[7]See Chapter 9.

8.5 Let the error function for this problem be given as
$$E(\mathbf{x}) = x_1^2 + (2x_2 - 3)^2 + (x_3 - x_1 + 2)^2.$$
If a simplex is defined by
$$\mathbf{P}_0 = (0,0,0), \qquad \mathbf{P}_1 = (0, -1, 0), \qquad \mathbf{P}_2 = (0, 1, 0), \qquad \mathbf{P}_3 = (1, 1, 1),$$
what is the centroid?

8.6 If the four points of a simplex produce the error functions $E_1 = 2$, $E_2 = 5$, $E_3 = 2$, and $E_4 = 5$, then it is not obvious which points will be chosen as $\mathbf{P}_L$, $\mathbf{P}_H$, and $\mathbf{P}_{NH}$. In fact, the choice will depend on how the program is written. For the program in Fig. 8.3, what numbers would be determined for L, H, and NH?

8.7 The four points of a simplex are $\mathbf{P}_0 = (1,1,2)$, $\mathbf{P}_1 = (2,1,-1)$, $\mathbf{P}_2 = (0,1,2)$, $\mathbf{P}_3 = (1,1,0)$. Assume that $\mathbf{P}_H = \mathbf{P}_3$.

   (a) Find the centroid.

   (b) Reflect and find $\mathbf{P}_R$ (let $\alpha = 1$).

   (c) If reflection is highly successful (i.e., $E_R < E_L$), an expansion is attempted. Find $\mathbf{P}_{Ex}$ (let $\beta = 2$).

8.8 The following three points define a triangular simplex: $\mathbf{P}_0 = (1,0,4)$, $\mathbf{P}_1 = (8,2,5)$, $\mathbf{P}_2 = (3,2,6)$. Assume that $\mathbf{P}_H = \mathbf{P}_1$.

   (a) Find the centroid.

   (b) Reflect, and find $\mathbf{P}_R$ (let $\alpha = 1$).

   (c) Assume that the reflection in (b) resulted in an error function E_R described by $E_{NH} < E_R < E_H$. This implies that the highest point $\mathbf{P}_H$ should be replaced by $\mathbf{P}_R$ and reflection should be done again. Find the new point produced by reflection.

   (d) Assume that the reflection in (c) was unsuccessful ($E_R > E_H$). Contract and find $\mathbf{P}_C$ (let $\gamma = 0.5$).

8.9 In this problem the initial simplex is defined by $\mathbf{P}_0 = (0,2,4)$, $\mathbf{P}_1 = (4,2,0)$, $\mathbf{P}_2 = (2,-2,4)$. Assume that $\mathbf{P}_L = \mathbf{P}_1$, $\mathbf{P}_H = \mathbf{P}_0$, and therefore $\mathbf{P}_{NH} = \mathbf{P}_2$. If the result of reflecting (let $\alpha = 1$) is described by $\mathbf{P}_1 < \mathbf{P}_R < \mathbf{P}_2$, what is the new centroid?

8.10 (a) Draw a two-dimensional vector diagram to demonstrate that $\mathbf{P}_R = 2\mathbf{C} - \mathbf{P}_H$ produces a reflected point that is the same distance from the centroid as is $\mathbf{P}_H$, but on the oppostie side. (*Hint:* The drawing should be similar to Fig. 8.2.)

   (b) Draw a two-dimensional vector diagram to illustrate $\mathbf{P}_{Ex} = 2\mathbf{P}_R - \mathbf{C}$.

   (c) Draw a two-dimensional vector diagram to illustrate $\mathbf{P}_C = 0.5\mathbf{P}_H + 0.5\mathbf{P}_C$.

8.11 For this problem the simplex is defined by $P_0=(2,4,0)$, $P_1=(-2,4,2)$, $P_2=(0,1,0)$, $P_3=(2,2,-2)$. Assume that $P_L=P_1$, $P_H=P_3$, $P_{NH}=P_0$. If neither reflection nor contraction can produce a point better than P_H, then the simplex is scaled.

    (a) If $k=0.5$, what is the new simplex?

    (b) If $k=-1$, what is the new simplex? For this part, start with the original simplex and not the result of (a).

8.12 If the initial parameters are chosen as $x_1=0$, $x_2=0$, and $x_3=0$, what does the program in Fig. 8.3 find for an initial simplex?

8.13 If the simplex algorithm is applied to the error function

$$E(\mathbf{x})=(\cos x_2)^2+x_1(\sin x_2)^2,$$

what will $E(\mathbf{x})$ approach after many iterations?

8.14 Use the simplex program to solve the following set of nonlinear equations:

$$2x^2-4xy+y^2=-7, \qquad x^4+xy^2-y^3=7.$$

Use as the initial set of parameters $x=1=y$.

8.15 Solve the following three equations by using the simplex program with the initial parameters $x=y=z=1$:

$$x^2+y^2+z^2=21, \qquad xyz=-8, \qquad 2x+y^3+z^2=22.$$

8.16 Apply the simplex program to minimize

$$x^2-4x+y^2-6y+9.$$

8.17 Apply the simplex program to maximize

$$4x^2y+2xy^2+8x+4y-4x^2-y^2-8xy-x^2y^2.$$

Chapter Nine

Gradient Techniques

9.1 INTRODUCTION

The simplex algorithm described in the previous chapter was a collection of various rules: to find a minimum, reflection was tried first; if reflection was highly successful, an expansion was attempted; if reflection was only moderately successful, another reflection was performed; etc.

For a particular problem, the rate of convergence of an optimization technique depends on the initial parameters that are selected. In fact, if a poor set of initial parameters is used some optimization techniques will converge slowly so that they are useless. However, the simplex algorithm does not have this drawback: for any set of initial parameters it will proceed (although sometimes rather slowly) towards a minimum. Thus, if another optimization technique encounters convergence problems because of a poor set of initial parameters, the simplex algorithm can be used to provide a better set. In fact, practical optimization programs usually contain more than one optimization technique. This allows the user to first specify a "slow but sure" algorithm such as simplex and then automatically switch to a faster technique when sufficiently close to the minimum.

If one is sufficiently near a minimum, there are optimization techniques that will converge much more rapidly than the simplex algorithm. This chapter is an introduction to a class of optimization methods that can be viewed as a combination of two separate processes: first a decision is made to which direction to proceed in the parameter space, and then a decision is made as to how far to proceed in that direction.

There are many different rules that are used to determine the direction. In fact, the simplex algorithm could be modified so that it determines the direction. If Fig. 8.1 is reexamined, we can see that contraction, reflection, and expansion are all in the same direction from the high point $\mathbf{P}_H$. The simplex algorithm instructs the computer to proceed from $\mathbf{P}_H$ towards the centroid. How far it proceeds depends on which rule is used: reflection, expansion, or contraction (and, of course, the value of α, β, or γ).

The simplex rules are supposed to cause the parameters to proceed from the high point $\mathbf{P}_H$ in a "downhill" direction; that is, towards a minimum. In this chapter, we will next discuss a technique, steepest descent, that guarantees the direction is downhill. The Fletcher-Powell optimization technique modifies the steepest-descent direction slightly and thus may converge even faster. This method will also be discussed in this chapter. There are other methods which also modify the steepest-descent direction; they will not be discussed in detail in this book, but an important observation should be made: no matter which rule or set of rules used to determine the "proper" direction, the distance to proceed in that direction can be determined by the same method. The method commonly used is given in the next section.

9.2 QUADRATIC INTERPOLATION FOR A SPECIFIC DIRECTION

Many optimization methods seek the minimum of a function by choosing the parameter change $\delta\mathbf{x}$ to point in a certain direction. The direction $\mathbf{S}$ that is calculated will vary from method to method. However, once the direction of optimization has been determined, any of the optimization techniques can use the same algorithm to determine the magnitude of the parameter changes.

The following example is included to illustrate the meaning of direction and magnitude.

EXAMPLE 9.1

Find a vector $\mathbf{r} = (r_1, r_2)$ which is in the same direction as $\mathbf{S} = (3, 4)$ and is twice as long (i.e., has twice the magnitude).

SOLUTION

Since $\mathbf{r}$ should point in the same direction as $\mathbf{S}$, it follows that $\mathbf{r} = \alpha\mathbf{S}$, where α is a constant of proportionality. The fact that the magnitude of $\mathbf{r}$ is twice the magnitude of $\mathbf{S}$ implies that $\alpha = 2$, so that

$$\mathbf{r} = \alpha\mathbf{S} = 2\mathbf{S} = (6, 8).$$

This section will assume that the direction of the parameter change has been determined and is denoted as $\mathbf{S}$. The magnitude of the parameter changes will then be determined by selecting the proportionality constant in the following equation:

$$\delta\mathbf{x} = \alpha\mathbf{S}. \tag{9.1}$$

From this formulation of the problem it can be seen that the distance one goes in a specific direction can be determined by a single-parameter search. That is, the proportionality constant α can be found by using one of the single-parameter minimization methods that was described in Chapter 3. Because the single-parameter search can take a substantial amount of the total computational time, it should be chosen carefully. We will use the quadratic interpolation method.

The quadratic interpolation method can be used to approximate the minimum of the error function E by passing a parabola through three points. If the error function is quadratic, then the minimum of the parabola will also be the minimum of the error function (that is, the minimum in the direction **S**). However, the error function will not usually be quadratic, so the parabola minimum will just approximate the error minimum.

The rest of this section will be used to explain the statements shown in Fig. 9.1. These statements will be used in the steepest-descent program to apply quadratic interpolation. The statements are a generalization of the

```
49C     QUADRATIC INTERPOLATION
50C
51C         FIND ALPHA 1
52          A1=1.
53 53       DO 54 I=1,N
54 54       X1(I)=X(I)+A1*S(I)
55          E1=ERROR(X1)
57          IF(E1.LT.E0) GO TO 63
58          A1=.5*A1
59          GO TO 53
61C
62C         FIND ALPHA 2
63 63       A2=A1
64 64       A2=2.*A2
65          DO 66 I=1,N
66 66       X2(I)=X(I)+A2*S(I)
67          E2=ERROR(X2)
68          IF(E2.GT.E1) GO TO 74
69          A1=A2 $E1=E2
70          GO TO 64
72C
73C         FIND ALPHA
74 74       A=(A1*A1-A2*A2)*E0+A2*A2*E1-A1*A1*E2
76          A=.5*A/((A1-A2)*E0+A2*E1-A1*E2)
```

FIGURE 9.1. Some statements for quadratic interpolation in a specific direction.

original quadratic-interpolation program that was described in Chapter 3.

At the beginning of Fig. 9.1 it is assumed that the error function E_0 has been calculated at the initial point x; thus one of the three points of the parabola is by assumption x, E_0. The next point is found by evaluating the error function at $x_1 = x + \alpha_1 S$ with α_1 first set equal to unity. If this error E_1 is greater than E_0, then α_1 is repeatedly reduced by a factor of 2 until $E_1 < E_0$. In the original quadratic interpolation program of Fig. 3.5, α_1 was repeatedly reduced by a factor of -2 instead of 2. The minus sign was included so that the algorithm would first look for a minimum on one side of x and then on the other. In the application in this chapter we will know that the minimum is the direction S (not in the direction $-S$) and thus only need look on one side of x.

The last point x_2 is found by doubling the distance from x until $E_2 > E_1$. A parabola is then passed through the three points. The minimum of this parabola is given by

$$x_m = x + \alpha S,$$

where

$$\alpha = \frac{0.5\left(\alpha_1^2 - \alpha_2^2\right)E_0 + \alpha_2^2 E_1 - \alpha_1^2 E_2}{(\alpha_1 - \alpha_2)E_0 + \alpha_2 E_1 - \alpha_1 E_2}. \tag{9.2}$$

Summarizing, if the direction S is known, then quadratic interpolation can be used to find the constant of proportionality in $\delta x = \alpha S$. The direction S will be related to the gradient of the error function, which is discussed in the next section.

It should be noted that (9.2) only gives the exact minimum for a quadratic function. Applying quadratic interpolation many times could get one arbitrarily close to the minimum for the specific direction under consideration. However, in this chapter quadratic interpolation will be applied just once for each search direction that is considered. Then a new "optimum" direction will be determined and a new minimum estimated. Others have proposed algorithms that find the minimum in each direction more accurately, but they will not be treated here.

9.3 THE GRADIENT

If a function $f(x)$ depends on only one parameter x, then the first derivative (rate of change) of the function is called its slope. At a maximum or minimum the slope is zero.[1]

---

[1]However, the fact that the slope is zero does not necessarily imply that the function is at a maximum or minimum—it could be at a saddle point.

The error function $E(\mathbf{x})$ is a function of many parameters. That is, $\mathbf{x}$ is a vector which may be written as

$$\mathbf{x} = (x_1, x_2, \ldots, x_n) \tag{9.3}$$

For this multidemensional case, the concept of slope can be generalized by defining the gradient ∇E as

$$\nabla E = \left(\frac{\partial E}{\partial x_1}, \frac{\partial E}{\partial x_2}, \ldots, \frac{\partial E}{\partial x_n} \right). \tag{9.4}$$

The gradient is an n-dimensional vector, the ith component of which is obtained by finding the partial derivative of the function with respect to x_i.

EXAMPLE 9.2

The function $E(\mathbf{x}) = x_1^2 + x_2^2$ can be considered to define a set of circles centered at the origin. For example, if $E(\mathbf{x}) = 4$, then $x_1^2 + x_2^2 = 4$ is a circle of radius equal to 2.

By definition, the gradient of $E(\mathbf{x})$ for $\mathbf{x} = (x_1, x_2)$ is $\nabla E = (\partial E / \partial x_1, \partial E / \partial x_2)$. For this example

$$\frac{\partial E}{\partial x_1} = 2x_1, \qquad \frac{\partial E}{\partial x_2} = 2x_2.$$

Thus, the gradient is given by

$$\nabla E = (2x_1, 2x_2).$$

In general, the value of the gradient depends on the coordinates of the point at which the gradient is evaluated. For example, for this particular function

$$\nabla E |_{(2,3)} = (4, 6).$$

The concept of the gradient will be helpful when we try to find an expansion for $E(\mathbf{x} + \delta\mathbf{x})$. It will let us discover how to choose $\delta\mathbf{x}$, the change in the parameter vector $\mathbf{x}$, so as to minimize the error function E. This will be done by analogy to the following one-dimensional case.

If the error function is a function of only one variable, then it can be expanded in terms of a Taylor series as

$$E(x + \delta x) = E(x) + \frac{dE}{dx} \delta x + \frac{d^2E}{dx^2} \frac{(\delta x)^2}{2!} + \cdots. \tag{9.5}$$

If δx is small, then this can be approximated as

$$E(x + \delta x) \approx E(x) + \frac{dE}{dx} \delta x. \tag{9.6}$$

The approximation in (9.6) can be generalized to n dimensions. For this case, if the n parameter changes $\delta x_1, \delta x_2, \ldots, \delta x_n$ are sufficiently small, then it follows that

$$E(\mathbf{x} + \delta\mathbf{x}) \approx E(\mathbf{x}) + \frac{\partial E}{\partial x_1}\delta x_1 + \frac{\partial E}{\partial x_2}\delta x_2 + \cdots + \frac{\partial E}{\partial x_n}\delta x_n. \qquad (9.7)$$

This relation can be written in an extremely convenient form by recalling that the gradient is a vector which can be written as

$$\nabla E = \left(\frac{\partial E}{\partial x_1}, \frac{\partial E}{\partial x_2}, \ldots, \frac{\partial E}{\partial x_n}\right) = \left[\begin{array}{cccc} \dfrac{\partial E}{\partial x_1} & \dfrac{\partial E}{\partial x_2} & \cdots & \dfrac{\partial E}{\partial x_n} \end{array}\right]^T. \qquad (9.8)$$

Here we have used the notation that a vector can be treated as a column matrix. It follows that

$$\nabla E^T \delta\mathbf{x} = \left[\begin{array}{cccc} \dfrac{\partial E}{\partial x_1} & \dfrac{\partial E}{\partial x_2} & \cdots & \dfrac{\partial E}{\partial x_n} \end{array}\right]\begin{bmatrix} \delta x_1 \\ \delta x_2 \\ \vdots \\ \delta x_n \end{bmatrix}$$

$$= \frac{\partial E}{\partial x_1}\delta x_1 + \frac{\partial E}{\partial x_2}\delta x_2 + \cdots + \frac{\partial E}{\partial x_n}\delta x_n. \qquad (9.9)$$

Comparing this with (9.7), it follows that

$$E(\mathbf{x} + \delta\mathbf{x}) \approx E(\mathbf{x}) + \nabla E^T \delta\mathbf{x}. \qquad (9.10)$$

The above relation will be very important to us—in fact, it can be considered to be the foundation for the steepest-descent method which is described in the next section. However, before discussing the steepest-descent algorithm we will consider an example for (9.10) and also discuss the gradient in more detail.

EXAMPLE 9.3

If the function $E(\mathbf{x}) = x_1^2 + x_2^2$ is evaluated at $x_1 = 2$, $x_2 = 3$, one finds $E(2, 3) = 13$. If the parameters are changed slightly, choosing $\delta x_1 = 0.2$ and $\delta x_2 = 0.1$, then (9.10) can be applied to estimate a new error. In the following equation, the value of the gradient came from Example 9.2:

$$E(2.2, 3.1) \approx E(2, 3) + \begin{bmatrix} 4 & 6 \end{bmatrix}\begin{bmatrix} 0.2 \\ 0.1 \end{bmatrix} = 13 + 0.8 + 0.6 = 14.4.$$

The exact answer is 14.45.

It was mentioned at the beginning of this section that in the one-dimensional case the slope must be zero at a minimum (or at a maximum).

Similarly, in the n-dimensional case the gradient must be zero at a minimum (or at a maximum). That this is necessary can be seen by again examining

$$E(\mathbf{x} + \delta\mathbf{x}) \approx E(\mathbf{x}) + \nabla E^T \delta\mathbf{x}. \tag{9.10}$$

Consider the case of a minimum (a maximum could be treated in the same manner). If the gradient is not zero, then the parameter change $\delta\mathbf{x}$ can always be chosen so that $\nabla E^T \delta\mathbf{x}$ is a negative number. For example, if $\nabla E = (1, -2)$, then choosing $\delta\mathbf{x} = (-1, 1)$ yields $\nabla E^T \delta\mathbf{x} = -3$. If $\nabla E^T \delta\mathbf{x}$ can be made negative, then (9.10) implies that the parameter changes $\delta\mathbf{x}$ can be selected to reduce $E(\mathbf{x})$. That is, $E(\mathbf{x})$ can always be reduced unless the gradient is zero, so the gradient must be zero at a minimum.

In the next section we will learn how to iteratively choose the parameter change $\delta\mathbf{x}$ so as to make the gradient become zero and minimize the error function $E(\mathbf{x})$. However, before this can be done we must obtain an approximation that can be used by a computer to calculate the gradient.

The gradient is an n-dimensional vector, and a typical component of it is given by

$$\frac{\partial E}{\partial x_i} = \lim_{\delta x_i \to 0} \frac{E(\mathbf{x} + \delta\mathbf{x}_i) - E(\mathbf{x})}{\delta x_i}, \tag{9.11}$$

where $\delta\mathbf{x}_i$ is a vector which has all zero components except for the ith component, which is equal to δx_i.

The expression for the partial derivative in (9.11) is very similar to the expression for the derivative which was given in (3.8). We will evaluate this partial derivative by analogy with the method that was used to evaluate the derivative in Newton's method. That is, δx_i will be calculated via

$$\delta x_i = \varepsilon x_i, \tag{9.12}$$

where ε is a constant of proportionality. The same value for ε will be used here as in Chapter 3, namely $\varepsilon = 10^{-6}$.

9.4 THE STEEPEST-DESCENT OPTIMIZATION TECHNIQUE

For any optimization procedure, one must make an initial guess $\mathbf{x}$ for the parameter values. Next this guess is modified to $\mathbf{x} + \delta\mathbf{x}$ so as to reduce the error function. How the parameter change $\delta\mathbf{x}$ is calculated depends on the optimization procedure. In this section we will learn how $\delta\mathbf{x}$ is chosen for the steepest-descent technique.

Since $\delta\mathbf{x}$ is a vector, it can be described by two quantities: a direction and a magnitude. In order to choose the direction of $\delta\mathbf{x}$ we will use the *scalar product* (dot product) of vector algebra. By definition, the scalar product of $\mathbf{a}=(a_1,a_2,\ldots,a_n)$ and $\mathbf{b}=(b_1,b_2,\ldots,b_n)$ is

$$\mathbf{a}\cdot\mathbf{b}=a_1b_1+a_2b_2+\cdots+a_nb_n. \tag{9.13}$$

It can be shown that this definition implies

$$a\cdot b=|a||b|\cos\theta \tag{9.14}$$

where $|\mathbf{a}|$ is the magnitude of $\mathbf{a}$, $|\mathbf{b}|$ is the magnitude of $\mathbf{b}$, and θ is the angle between the two vectors.

EXAMPLE 9.4

If $\mathbf{a}=(3,4)$, choose a unit vector $\mathbf{b}$ such that

(a) $a_1b_1+a_2b_2$ is a maximum.
(b) $a_1b_1+a_2b_2$ is a minimum.

SOLUTION
(a) Comparing (9.13) and (9.14) yields $a_1b_1+a_2b_2=|\mathbf{a}||\mathbf{b}|\cos\theta$. This is a maximum when $\theta=0$—i.e., when $\mathbf{a}$ and $\mathbf{b}$ are in the same direction; thus $\mathbf{b}=\alpha(3,4)$. But $\mathbf{b}$ is a unit vector, so that

$$|\mathbf{b}|=|3\alpha,4\alpha|=\sqrt{9\alpha^2+16\alpha^2}=5\alpha=1.$$

Since therefore $\alpha=\frac{1}{5}$, it follows that

$$\mathbf{b}=(0.6,0.8).$$

(b) For the sum to be minimum we require $\cos\theta=-1$, to align $\mathbf{b}$ opposite to $\mathbf{a}$. Analogously to the above, we have

$$\mathbf{b}=-(0.6,0.8).$$

In order to see how the scalar product can be applied, consider again the relation

$$E(\mathbf{x}+\delta\mathbf{x})\approx E(\mathbf{x})+\nabla E^T\delta\mathbf{x}. \tag{9.15}$$

The last term in this expression can be rewritten as

$$\nabla E^T\delta\mathbf{x}=\frac{\partial E}{\partial x_1}\delta x_1+\frac{\partial E}{\partial x_2}\delta x_2+\cdots+\frac{\partial E}{\partial x_n}\delta x_n, \tag{9.16}$$

which [by comparison with (9.13)] is the scalar product of the gradient ∇E and the parameter change $\delta\mathbf{x}$.

Since $\nabla E^T\delta\mathbf{x}$ is equivalent to the scalar product of ∇E and $\delta\mathbf{x}$, it follows from Example 9.4 that a unit vector $\delta\mathbf{x}$ will produce a maximum change if it points in the direction of the gradient and will produce a minimum change (i.e., maximum negative change) if it points in the direction of the negative gradient. The steepest-descent method utilizes this information by choosing δx to point in the direction of the negative gradient.

In the steepest-descent optimization technique one first chooses an initial set of parameters x, which results in an error $E(x)$. Next the gradient ∇E is calculated at point x. The parameter changes are then chosen to be in the direction of the negative gradient; that is,

$$\delta x = -\alpha \nabla E, \qquad (9.17)$$

where α is a positive constant.

As explained in Section 9.2, the proportionality constant α can be determined by using quadratic interpolation for a specific direction. In the steepest-descent optimization technique the direction is that of

$$S = -\nabla E. \qquad (9.18)$$

In other optimization methods (e.g., the Fletcher-Powell method in Section 9.6) the direction may be calculated by an equation different from (9.18), but once the direction has been obtained, the same quadratic interpolation subroutine can be used to determine the constant of proportionality α. Finally, the new parameters can be calculated from the old parameters, α, and S by

$$x + \alpha S \rightarrow x. \qquad (9.19)$$

EXAMPLE 9.5

A previous example considered the error function $E(x) = x_1^2 + x_2^2$ and found that at $x = (2, 3)$ the error function had the gradient $\nabla E = (4, 6)$. In this example we will consider two different parameter changes, one which will be in the direction of the negative gradient and one in the direction of the positive gradient.

For the parameter changes in the direction of the negative gradient, $S = -\nabla E = (-4, -6)$. If the constant α is arbitrarily chosen as 0.01, then (9.19) yields

$$(2, 3) + 0.01(-4, -6) = (1.96, 2.94) = (x_1, x_2).$$

The error function for this is 12.49, which is smaller than the original error function $E = 13$.

If the parameter changes are instead in the direction of the positive gradient, then $S = \nabla E = (4, 6)$. Again choosing $\alpha = 0.01$ yields

$$(2, 3) + 0.01(4, 6) = (2.04, 3.06).$$

The error function for this set of parameters is 13.53, which is larger than the original error function.

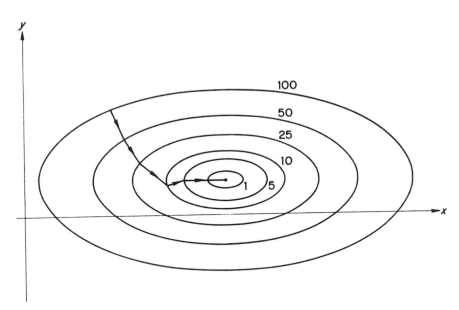

FIGURE 9.2. A steepest-descent optimization path for elliptical contours.

Choosing the parameter changes to be in the direction of the gradient results in a path that is orthogonal[2] to contours of constant error. This follows from (9.10) which was

$$E(\mathbf{x} + \delta\mathbf{x}) = E(\mathbf{x}) + \nabla E^T \delta\mathbf{x}.$$

If $\delta\mathbf{x}$ is chosen to be along a contour of constant error, then $E(\mathbf{x} + \delta\mathbf{x}) = E(\mathbf{x})$, so that $\nabla E^T\mathbf{x} = 0$. This implies that ∇E is orthogonal to $\delta\mathbf{x}$, i.e., the gradient is orthogonal to contours of constant error.

It is illustrated in Fig. 9.2 that the steepest-descent path is orthogonal to contours of constant error. The error contours for

$$E(\mathbf{x}) = (x_1 - 1)^2 + 4(x_2 - 2)^2.$$

are ellipses. The steepest-descent path originates on the $E(\mathbf{x}) = 100$ contour and is orthogonal to that contour. It continues in a straight line until the $E(\mathbf{x}) = 50$ contour, at which point calculating the gradient again makes the path orthogonal to the contour. Similarly, each time the gradient is recalculated at a contour the optimization path becomes orthogonal to that contour.

---

[2]If two vectors are orthogonal, then their scalar product is zero. That is, $\mathbf{a} \cdot \mathbf{b} = \mathbf{a}^T\mathbf{b} = ab\cos\theta = 0$. This implies that the angle between $\mathbf{a}$ and $\mathbf{b}$ is 90°.

```
01C     STEEPEST DESCENT
02      PROGRAM SD(INPUT,OUTPUT)
03 03   FORMAT(7H   X(I)=1P,4E14.5)
04 04   FORMAT(7H ERROR=,1P,E14.5,/)
06      DIMENSION E(10),GRAD(10),S(10),X(10),X1(10),X2(10)
09C
10C     INITIAL VALUES
11      PRINT,*N*, $READ,N
14      PRINT,/,*X(I)   I=1,2,...N*
15      READ,(X(I),I=1,N)
18      E0=ERROR(X)
19      PRINT 4,E0
20C
21C     FIND GRADIENT
22 22   DO 28 I=1,N
23      DELTA=.000001*X(I)
24      IF(ABS(X(I)).LT.1E-12) DELTA=.000001
25      XSAVE=X(I)
26      X(I)=X(I)+DELTA
27      GRAD(I)=(ERROR(X)-E0)/DELTA
28 28   X(I)=XSAVE
39C
40C     FIND DRECTION S   (EQ. 9.18)
41      DO 44 I=1,N
44 44   S(I)=-GRAD(I)
48C
49C     QUADRATIC INTERPOLATION
50C
51C         FIND ALPHA 1
52          A1=1.
53 53       DO 54 I=1,N
54 54       X1(I)=X(I)+A1*S(I)
55          E1=ERROR(X1)
57          IF(E1.LT.E0) GO TO 63
58          A1=.5*A1
59          IF(A1.LT.1E-8) STOP
60          GO TO 53
61C
62C         FIND ALPHA 2
63 63       A2=A1
64 64       A2=2.*A2
65          DO 66 I=1,N
66 66       X2(I)=X(I)+A2*S(I)
67          E2=ERROR(X2)
68          IF(E2.GT.E1) GO TO 74
69          A1=A2 $E1=E2
70          GO TO 64
72C
73C         FIND ALPHA
74 74       A=(A1*A1-A2*A2)*E0+A2*A2*E1-A1*A1*E2
76          A=.5*A/((A1-A2)*E0+A2*E1-A1*E2)
80C
```

(a)

FIGURE 9.3. A program for steepest descent.

```
81C    FIND NEW X
84     DO 85 I=1,N
85 85  X(I)=X(I)+A*S(I)
86     E0=ERROR(X)
87     IF(E0.LT.E1) GO TO 95
90     DO 9J I=1,N
91 91  X(I)=X(I)+(A1-A)*S(I)
93     E0=ERROR(X)
94C
95 95  PRINT 3,(X(I),I=1,N)
96     PRINT 4,E0
98     GO TO 22
99     END
897C
898    FUNCTION ERROR(X)
899    DIMENSION X(10)
900    ERROR=100.*(X(1)*X(1)-X(2))**2+(1.-X(1))**2
950    RETURN
999    END
```

(b)

FIGURE 9.3. (Continued.)

A program for the steepest-descent method is given in Fig. 9.3. The first part of the program indicates how the gradient can be approximated by applying (9.12) with the increment parameter ε equal to 0.000001. After the gradient is calculated, the negative gradient is defined to be S. A one-dimensional search for the minimum is then performed in this direction by employing quadratic interpolation, which was described in Section 9.2. This process yields the parameter α which indicates how far to proceed in the direction S. The parameter x is then incremented by αS.

The "minimum" that is obtained by the above process will probably not be *the* minimum of the error function. This is because (9.15) assumed that the parameter change δx is very small (in fact, infinitesimal). At the beginning of the steepest-descent method, δx will probably be quite large, because the initial guess for the parameter x may be poor. However, if the steepest-descent method is used iteratively, then as the minimum is approached, the parameter change will become smaller and smaller, so that the approximation in (9.15) will be very accurate.

Very infrequently it happens that the error function evaluated at $\mathbf{x}_m = \mathbf{x} + \alpha \mathbf{S}$ [where α is given by (9.2)] is larger than the original error function. This can occur far from a minimum where the assumption of a quadratic[3] error function is not sufficiently valid. In this case, line 87 of the steepest-descent program causes the point x_1 to be used as the next guess for the

[3]As a function of α.

location of the minimum, since $E(x_1)$ was found in such a manner that it is guaranteed to be less than the initial error E_0.

The function that is coded in statement 900 of Fig. 9.3 is the Rosenbrock function. The results of computer runs for this and the other test functions are given in Figs. 9.4–9.7. These figures indicate the minimum that steepest descent was able to attain (after ten iterations) for the various test

```
N ? 2

X(I)   I=1,2,...N
? -1.2   1
 ERROR=    2.42000E+01

   X(I)=   -1.01284E+00    1.07639E+00
 ERROR=    4.30709E+00

   X(I)=   -1.02891E+00    1.06651E+00
 ERROR=    4.12265E+00

   X(I)=   -8.13910E-01    6.58198E-01
 ERROR=    3.29207E+00

   X(I)=   -8.05820E-01    6.59570E-01
 ERROR=    3.27144E+00

   X(I)=   -8.02957E-01    6.41045E-01
 ERROR=    3.25202E+00

   X(I)=   -7.94927E-01    6.42283E-01
 ERROR=    3.23252E+00

   X(I)=   -7.92468E-01    6.24776E-01
 ERROR=    3.21399E+00

   X(I)=   -7.84461E-01    6.25899E-01
 ERROR=    3.19537E+00

   X(I)=   -7.82332E-01    6.09208E-01
 ERROR=    3.17751E+00

   X(I)=   -7.74318E-01    6.10229E-01
 ERROR=    3.15957E+00
```

FIGURE 9.4. Minimization of the Rosenbrock function by steepest descent.

```
N ? 2

X(I)   I=1,2,...N
? -1.2   1
  ERROR=    7.49038E+02

  X(I)=   -3.72447E-02    7.31346E-01
  ERROR=    5.45701E+01

  X(I)=   -2.38255E-02   -2.17332E-04
  ERROR=    1.04822E+00

  X(I)=    2.32122E-01    4.87883E-03
  ERROR=    5.95455E-01

  X(I)=    2.47363E-01    2.29155E-02
  ERROR=    5.72515E-01

  X(I)=    2.61018E-01    1.10520E-02
  ERROR=    5.50625E-01

  X(I)=    8.62417E-01    6.84183E-01
  ERROR=    2.01683E-01

  X(I)=    8.78017E-01    6.77291E-01
  ERROR=    1.48973E-02

  X(I)=    8.78377E-01    6.77222E-01
  ERROR=    1.48158E-02

  X(I)=    8.78676E-01    6.78807E-01
  ERROR=    1.47362E-02

  X(I)=    8.79030E-01    6.78740E-01
  ERROR=    1.46569E-02
```

FIGURE 9.5. Minimization of the "cube" function by steepest descent.

functions. If these results are compared with the corresponding results obtained by the simplex algorithm (see Figs. 8.8, 8.10, 8.11, 8.13), we are not able to conclude that one of these optimization techniques is always better than the other: The simplex algorithm was better for the Rosenbrock and cube functions, while steepest descent was better for the Powell function and coefficient matching.

```
N ? 4

X(I)   I=1,2,...N
? 3    -1    0    1
  ERROR=    7.07336E+05

  X(I)=    6.41034E-01   -9.99652E-01    4.83735E-06    1.23588E+00
  ERROR=   8.13063E+02

  X(I)=    2.22239E-01   -9.85161E-01    3.46988E-04    1.27696E+00
  ERROR=   1.02617E+02

  X(I)=    1.50222E-01   -1.25742E-02    2.56034E-02    1.23048E+00
  ERROR=   7.26477E+00

  X(I)=    1.23559E-01   -2.78714E-02    4.02785E-01    8.55751E-01
  ERROR=   1.55328E+00

  X(I)=    1.07730E-01    1.77109E-02    4.01929E-01    8.19492E-01
  ERROR=   1.33930E+00

  X(I)=    9.56487E-02   -1.84180E-02    4.04708E-01    7.79958E-01
  ERROR=   1.18252E+00

  X(I)=    9.52789E-02    1.63340E-02    3.97946E-01    7.47868E-01
  ERROR=   1.05018E+00

  X(I)=    8.69167E-02   -1.54803E-02    3.95124E-01    7.14234E-01
  ERROR=   9.35799E-01

  X(I)=    8.68037E-02    1.45339E-02    3.86480E-01    6.86602E-01
  ERROR=   8.36207E-01

  X(I)=    7.99820E-02   -1.35781E-02    3.81738E-01    6.57719E-01
  ERROR=   7.48938E-01
```

FIGURE 9.6. Minimization of the Powell function by steepest descent.

```
N ? 3

X(I)   I=1,2,...N
? 10000    10000    10000
    ERROR=    2.59460E+04

    X(I)=     2.98033E+04    1.98722E+04    1.97913E+04
    ERROR=    7.70003E+01

    X(I)=     2.79038E+04    1.86731E+04    1.81067E+04
    ERROR=    4.64119E+01

    X(I)=     2.74910E+04    1.92966E+04    1.66871E+04
    ERROR=    4.39795E+01

    X(I)=     2.80230E+04    1.98468E+04    1.68334E+04
    ERROR=    4.16719E+01

    X(I)=     2.78720E+04    2.04692E+04    1.54577E+04
    ERROR=    3.94360E+01

    X(I)=     2.84156E+04    2.09487E+04    1.56617E+04
    ERROR=    3.73815E+01

    X(I)=     2.83694E+04    2.13156E+04    1.47268E+04
    ERROR=    3.57458E+01

    X(I)=     2.88460E+04    2.17380E+04    1.48518E+04
    ERROR=    3.43825E+01

    X(I)=     2.88006E+04    2.19852E+04    1.40920E+04
    ERROR=    3.31333E+01

    X(I)=     2.92461E+04    2.23671E+04    1.42100E+04
    ERROR=    3.19864E+01
```

FIGURE 9.7. Coefficient matching by steepest descent.

9.5 APPLICATIONS OF STEEPEST DESCENT

The previous chapter discussed some applications of the simplex optimization technique. Steepest descent could also be applied to any of those applications. For some situations the simplex algorithm might be more efficient; for others, steepest descent. In this section some additional optimization problems will be solved by using the steepest-descent program. These, of course, could also be solved by using the simplex algorithm.

EXAMPLE 9.6

Minimize the following function by applying the steepest-descent program of Fig. 9.3:

$$E(\mathbf{x}) = x_1^2 + 0.1x_2^2 + (x_1 - 1)^2(x_1 - 5)^2 + x_2^2(x_2 - 4)^2. \qquad (9.20)$$

SOLUTION

Figure 9.8 shows two different steepest-descent computer runs for this error function. In Fig. 9.8(a) the initial parameters were chosen as $x_1 = 10$, $x_2 = 10$, which yielded a minimum $E(0.943, 3.975) = 2.533$. In Fig. 9.8(b) the initial parameters were instead chosen as $x_1 = 1$, $x_2 = 1$, which yielded $E(0.943, 0) = 0.943$.

This example was presented to introduce the concept of a local minimum versus a global minimum. The difference between these two minimums can be understood by picturing the steepest-descent algorithm as changing the parameters x in such a way that one goes down a mountain (that is, one reduces the error function) as quickly as possible. On the way down the mountain we may encounter a valley and conclude that we are at

```
N ? 2

X(I)    I=1,2,...N
? 10    10
 ERROR=      5.73500E+03

 X(I)=       4.85948E+00    2.28120E+00
 ERROR=      3.98028E+01

 X(I)=       2.01683E+00    4.25819E+00
 ERROR=      1.62909E+01

 X(I)=       1.01915E+00    3.58429E+00
 ERROR=      4.54937E+00

 X(I)=       9.17705E-01    3.91928E+00
 ERROR=      2.59120E+00

 X(I)=       9.47973E-01    3.97099E+00
 ERROR=      2.53324E+00

 X(I)=       9.43220E-01    3.97426E+00
 ERROR=      2.53266E+00

 X(I)=       9.43484E-01    3.97466E+00
 ERROR=      2.53266E+00
```

(a)

FIGURE 9.8. A local minimum is found in (a); the global minimum is found in (b).

```
N ? 2

X(I)    I=1,2,...N
? 1     1
  ERROR=      1.01000E+01

  X(I)=       8.70582E-01    2.10555E-01
  ERROR=      1.68458E+00

  X(I)=       9.63341E-01    2.06959E-02
  ERROR=      9.56749E-01

  X(I)=       9.42366E-01    1.61174E-03
  ERROR=      9.42785E-01

  X(I)=       9.43547E-01    8.18966E-05
  ERROR=      9.42722E-01

  X(I)=       9.43450E-01    7.58370E-06
  ERROR=      9.42721E-01

  X(I)=       9.43453E-01   -8.32343E-07
  ERROR=      9.42721E-01
```

(b)

FIGURE 9.8. (Continued.)

the bottom. However, it is possible that once we climb the other side of the valley we discover the mountain descends for another mile. In this discussion, the valley would be the local minimum, while the bottom of the mountain would be the global minimum. In Example 9.6, $E(0.943, 3.975) = 2.533$ was a local minimum, while $E(0.943, 0) = 0.943$ was the global minimum.

In an optimization problem one usually wants to find the global minimum and does not want to be trapped at a local minimum. Failing to find the global minimum is not just a difficulty associated with steepest-descent; any optimization technique can be plagued by this problem.

Sometimes one will know for physical reasons that the global minimum must be near a certain point, which should then be picked as the initial point. The computer will then improve on that point and hopefully attain the global minimum. Other times (see Chapter 11) the parameters will be constrained to remain within a certain region (perhaps for reasons of availability of component values) and this will imply there is only one allowable minimum.

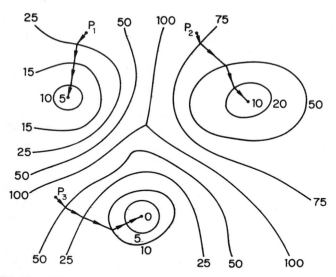

FIGURE 9.9. Different initial parameters can yield different minimums.

However, often many different computer runs must be done before one is satisfied with the minimum that is attained. If many different initial parameters produce the same minimum, then one is fairly confident that it is the lowest value that can be found. But in practical optimization problems that have many parameters that can be varied, there may be numerous local minimums.

A hypothetical case that has two local minimums in addition to the global minimum is portrayed in Fig. 9.9. Choosing the initial parameter values to be given by P_1 yields a minimum value of 5; starting at P_2 yields 10; and starting at P_3 yields the global minimum, which is zero.

In cases that have numerous local minimums, the initial parameters can be systematically picked for good distribution over the parameter space. In a practical problem one can never be positive that the global minimum has been found; however, after a sufficiently low value has been located one may decide his time can be spent more profitably on other tasks.

The rate of convergence of any search technique is highly dependent on the given function $E(\mathbf{x})$. It is for this reason that there is no optimal procedure for an arbitrary error function. The efficiency of a particular optimization technique is usually dependent on the scale used. To understand why this is so, consider the following function:

$$E(x_1, x_2) = (x_1 - 2)^2 + 0.01(x_2 - 30)^2. \tag{9.21}$$

A steepest-descent optimization printout for the initial condition $(1, 10)$ is shown in Fig. 9.10(a). The initial error was 5, and after ten iterations this was reduced to 0.44.

If $0.1x_2$ is replaced by x_3, then (9.21) can be rewritten as

$$E(x_1, x_3) = (x_1 - 2)^2 + (x_3 - 3)^2. \tag{9.22}$$

This function represents a family of concentric circles centered about $(2, 3)$. For a case such as this, steepest descent can find the minimum in one iteration, as demonstrated in Fig. 9.10(b). The initial error at $x_1 = 1$, $x_3 = 1$ was 5 (the same as it was at the equivalent unscaled point $x_1 = 1$, $x_2 = 10$), and after one iteration the error was essentially zero.

It has just been demonstrated that in some problems scaling can drastically affect the rate of convergence. In general, scaling should be done so as to make the contours of constant error be as circular as possible. Note that in (9.22) the contours were exact circles.

For a problem that has many parameters $x_1, x_2, \ldots, x_n$ one can examine the behavior of $E(\mathbf{x})$ as just x_1 and x_2 are varied. x_2 can then be scaled so that near the initial point $\mathbf{x}$ the error-function contours are nearly circular. Next just x_1 and x_3 can be varied so as to determine how to scale x_3; similarly for the remaining parameters $x_4, x_5, \ldots, x_n$.

Far from a minimum one will probably not be able to scale the parameters so that the error contours are circular. However, as the minimum is approached, the error function will behave as a quadratic form and thus can be scaled to yield circular contours. This discussion implies that as an optimization procedure advances, one may wish to change how it is scaled. In fact, some optimization techniques rescale the parameters after a certain number (e.g. $n + 1$) of iterations.

Very elaborate schemes exist for determining how to scale parameters for a particular problem. However, the reader of this text can usually ignore these techniques, since for our applications the computer will probably be able to optimize a poorly scaled problem faster than we can determine a satisfactory scaling. In fact, instead of attempting scaling if a particular problem is slow to converge, it may be more beneficial to apply a different optimization technique.

It was mentioned that scaling will *usually* affect the rate of convergence; however, the simplex optimization technique is an exception to this rule. As a demonstration of this, the error function

$$E(x_n, x_2) = (x_1 - 2)^2 + 0.01(x_2 - 30)^2$$

was reduced by using ten iterations of simplex. Similarly, ten iterations of simplex were applied to the scaled function

$$E(x_1, x_3) = (x_1 - 2)^2 + (x_3 - 3)^2.$$

```
N ? 2

X(I)   I=1,2,...N
? 1    10
 ERROR=    5.00000E+00

 X(I)=     2.03958E+00      1.02079E+01
 ERROR=    3.91883E+00

 X(I)=     1.21625E+00      1.43245E+01
 ERROR=    3.07148E+00

 X(I)=     2.03103E+00      1.44875E+01
 ERROR=    2.40735E+00

 X(I)=     1.38573E+00      1.77138E+01
 ERROR=    1.88685E+00

 X(I)=     2.02432E+00      1.78415E+01
 ERROR=    1.47888E+00

 X(I)=     1.51855E+00      2.03701E+01
 ERROR=    1.15915E+00

 X(I)=     2.01906E+00      2.04702E+01
 ERROR=    9.08538E-01

 X(I)=     1.62265E+00      2.24519E+01
 ERROR=    7.12127E-01

 X(I)=     2.01494E+00      2.25304E+01
 ERROR=    5.58177E-01

 X(I)=     1.70424E+00      2.40835E+01
 ERROR=    4.37520E-01
```

(a)

```
N ? 2

X(I)   I=1,2,...N
? 1    1
 ERROR=    5.00000E+00

 X(I)=     2.00000E+00      3.00000E+00
 ERROR=    4.94774E-14
```

(b)

FIGURE 9.10. Minimization of equivalent scaled functions by steepest descent.

```
N ? 2

X(I)    I=1,2,...N
? 1     10
  ERROR=      5.00000E+00

    X(I)=    1.14735E+00    1.14735E+01
  ERROR=     4.15930E+00

    X(I)=    1.02242E+00    1.36449E+01
  ERROR=     3.63056E+00

    X(I)=    1.25017E+00    1.55951E+01
  ERROR=     2.63726E+00
```
                                    (a)

```
N ? 2

X(I)    I=1,2,...N
? 1     1
  ERROR=      5.00000E+00

    X(I)=    1.14735E+00    1.14735E+00
  ERROR=     4.15930E+00

    X(I)=    1.02242E+00    1.36449E+00
  ERROR=     3.63056E+00

    X(I)=    1.25017E+00    1.55951E+00
  ERROR=     2.63726E+00
```
                                    (b)

FIGURE 9.11. Minimization of equivalent scaled functions by simplex.

As indicated in Fig. 9.11, the error functions are exactly the same at corresponding iterations. Scaling does not affect the simplex technique, because the initial simplex is determined by varying each parameter by the same percentage. Also, since the algorithm uses only discrete points, which one is discarded to form a new simplex is not affected by scaling.

9.6 THE FLETCHER-POWELL OPTIMIZATION TECHNIQUE

The steepest-descent optimization technique is based on the fact that the negative gradient points in the direction of the fastest rate of decrease. However, this direction is guaranteed to be the optimal direction only for an infinitesimal distance. After that infinitesimal distance, one should really calculate a new direction—but this of course is impractical.

In order to improve the steepest-descent method, (9.7) can be continued as

$$E(\mathbf{x} + \delta\mathbf{x}) \approx E(\mathbf{x}) + \sum_{i=1}^{n} \frac{\partial E}{\partial x_i} \delta x_i + \frac{1}{2} \sum_{i=1}^{n} \sum_{j=1}^{n} \frac{\partial^2 E}{\partial x_i \partial x_j} \delta x_i \delta x_j. \quad (9.23)$$

Not only does this equation contain the first-derivative terms, it also contains second-derivative terms. Steepest descent chose the direction to move in parameter space by considering the slope; any method based on (9.23) will use the slope and the curvature and thus should be more accurate.

The above equation can be used to improve (9.10), which was the foundation for the steepest-descent technique. The result is

$$E(\mathbf{x} + \delta\mathbf{x}) \approx E(\mathbf{x}) + \nabla E^T \delta\mathbf{x} + \tfrac{1}{2} \delta\mathbf{H}^T \mathbf{H} \delta\mathbf{x}, \quad (9.24)$$

where $\mathbf{H}$ is the Hessian matrix, which is defined as[4]

$$\mathbf{H} = \left[\frac{\partial^2 E}{\partial x_i \partial x_j} \right]. \quad (9.25)$$

Equation (9.24) implies that in the neighborhood of an optimum, the objective function is essentially a quadratic function. The theory of many optimization methods are based on this assumption. In particular, the Fletcher-Powell method leads to the minimum of a quadratic function in $n+1$ steps if n is the number of variables.[5] However, since most error functions are not quadratic, it usually takes longer to reach the minimum. Also adding to the number of iterations is the fact that for each search, quadratic interpolation finds the minimum search distance only approximately.

In the steepest-descent technique we searched for a minimum in the direction of the negative gradient, that is,

$$\mathbf{S} = -\nabla E. \quad (9.26)$$

Methods that are based on (9.24) modify this direction by the inverse of the Hessian, i.e.,

$$\mathbf{S} = -\mathbf{H}^{-1} \nabla E. \quad (9.27)$$

[4]Recall that at a minimum ∇E must be zero, so that $\nabla E^T \delta\mathbf{x}$ cannot be negative. Similarly it follows that $\delta\mathbf{x}^T \mathbf{H} \delta\mathbf{x}$ must be positive for any nonzero vector $\delta\mathbf{x}$. That is, $\mathbf{H}$ must be a positive definite matrix.

[5]This assumes that the derivatives are calculated analytically and not numerically.

This appears to be quite simple, but computationally it is very involved. First recall that the Hessian is a matrix which contains second-order partial derivatives. We know from the material in Chapter 5 that the evaluation of second derivatives by numerical methods is an inaccurate process. If we could evaluate the Hessian accurately, then the inverse could be obtained by the methods of Chapter 2, but this would require a substantial amount of computational time.

For the reasons just mentioned, one usually does not attempt to directly evaluate H^{-1} in an optimization technique; instead, approximations are used. The most famous approximation is used in the Fletcher-Powell optimization technique.[6] This approximates the inverse of the Hessian by another matrix G which iteratively approaches H^{-1}. Initially, the approximation is chosen to be the identity matrix I, so that S in (9.27) points in the direction of the negative gradient. Thus, the first Fletcher-Powell iteration is equivalent to steepest descent, but the following iterations use better and better approximations for H^{-1} to improve the search direction.

We shall now see how the approximation G is obtained. Assume we are at a point x and have a value for G (initially, this would be the identity matrix). We then go in the direction $S = -G \, GRAD \, (x)$ for a distance Δx (the distance can be found by quadratic interpolation)[7]. Thus, the next point is $x' = x + \Delta x$. At this point, a better approximation G' is found by using the parameter change Δx and also the gradient change

$$y = GRAD(x') - GRAD(x). \tag{9.28}$$

These changes are used to adjust G as follows:[8]

$$G' = G + \frac{\Delta x \, \Delta x^T}{d_1} - \frac{(Gy)(Gy)^T}{d_2}, \tag{9.29}$$

where the scale factors d_1 and d_2 are given by

$$d_1 = y^T \Delta x, \qquad d_2 = y^T Gy. \tag{9.30}$$

A program that implements these equations is given in Fig. 9.12. The following comments should help in understanding that program.

The definition

$$z = Gy \tag{9.31}$$

---

[6]This is also known as the DFP optimization technique after Davidon, Fletcher, and Powell. Davidon originally conceived the algorithm, but Fletcher and Powell presented it in a manner that made it famous.

[7]The notation $GRAD(x)$ is used to indicate that the gradient is evaluated at point x.

[8]For a derivation of this equation, the interested reader is referred to Gottfried, B. S., and J. Weisman (1973), *Introduction to Optimization Theory* (Englewood Cliffs, N.J.: Prentice-Hall).

```
01C      FLETCHER POWELL
02       PROGRAM FP(INPUT,OUTPUT)
03 03 FORMAT(7H  X(I)=1P,4E14.5)
04 04 FORMAT(7H ERROR=,1P,E14.5,/)
06       DIMENSION G(10,10),GRAD(10),GRAD1(10),S(10)
07       DIMENSION X(10),X1(10),X2(10),Y(10),Z(10),DELX(10)
09C
10C      INITIAL VALUES
11       PRINT,*N*, $READ,N
14       PRINT,/,*X(I)   I=1,2,...N*
15       READ,(X(I),I=1,N)
18       E0=ERROR(X)
19       PRINT 4,E0
20C
21C      FIND GRADIENT
22 22 DO 28 I=1,N
23       DELTA=.000001*X(I)
24       IF(ABS(X(I)).LT.1E-12) DELTA=.000001
25       XSAVE=X(I)
26       X(I)=X(I)+DELTA
27       GRAD(I)=(ERROR(X)-E0)/DELTA
28 28 X(I)=XSAVE
29C
30C      INITIALIZE G
31       K=0
33       DO 36 I=1,N
34       DO 35 J=1,N
35 35 G(I,J)=0.
36 36 G(I,I)=1.
39C
40C      FIND DIRECTION S   (EQ. 9.27)
41 41 DO 44 I=1,N
42       S(I)=0.
43       DO 44 J=1,N
44 44 S(I)=S(I)-G(I,J)*GRAD(J)
48C
49C      QUADRATIC INTERPOLATION
50C
51C         FIND ALPHA 1
52          A1=1.
53 53       DO 54 I=1,N
54 54       X1(I)=X(I)+A1*S(I)
55          E1=ERROR(X1)
57          IF(E1.LT.E0)GO TO 63
58          A1=.5*A1
59          GO TO 53
61C
62C         FIND ALPHA 2
63 63       A2=A1
64 64       A2=2.*A2
65          DO 66 I=1,N
66 66       X2(I)=X(I)+A2*S(I)
67          E2=ERROR(X2)
68          IF(E2.GT.E1) GO TO 74
69          A1=A2 $E1=E2
70          GO TO 64
72C
73C         FIND ALPHA
74 74       A=(A1*A1-A2*A2)*E0+A2*A2*E1-A1*A1*E2
76          A=.5*A/((A1-A2)*E0+A2*E1-A1*E2)
```

(a)

FIGURE 9.12. A program for the Fletcher-Powell optimization technique.

229

```
81C        FIND NEW X
82         DO 85 I=1,N
83         DELX(I)=A*S(I)
85 85      X(I)=X(I)+DELX(I)
86         E0=ERROR(X)
87         IF(E0.LT.E1) GO TO 95
89         DO 92 I=1,N
90         X(I)=X(I)+(A1-A)*S(I)
92 92      DELX(I)=A1*S(I)
93         E0=ERROR(X)
94C
95 95      PRINT 3,(X(I),I=1,N)
96         PRINT 4,E0
99C
100C       REINITIALIZE G EVERY 5 CYCLES
101        K=K+1
102        IF(K.EQ.5) GO TO 22
110C
111C       FIND NEW GRADIENT
112        DO 119 I=1,N
114        DELTA=.000001*X(I)
115        IF(ABS(X(I)).LT.1E-12) DELTA=.000001
116        XSAVE=X(I)
117        X(I)=X(I)+DELTA
118        GRAD1(I)=(ERROR(X)-E0)/DELTA
119 119    X(I)=XSAVE
122C
123C       FIND Y   (EQ. 9.28)
124        DO 126 I=1,N
125        Y(I)=GRAD1(I)-GRAD(I)
126 126    GRAD(I)=GRAD1(I)
129C
130C       FIND D1   (EQ. 9.30)
131        D1=0.
134        DO 135 I=1,N
135 135    D1=D1+Y(I)*DELX(I)
139C
140C       FIND Z   (EQ. 9.31)
141        DO 148 I=1,N
142        Z(I)=0.
144        DO 148 J=1,N
148 148    Z(I)=Z(I)+G(I,J)*Y(J)
149C
150C       FIND D2   (EQ. 9.31)
151        D2=0.
152        DO 155 I=1,N
154        DO 155 J=1,N
155 155    D2=D2+G(I,J)*Y(I)*Y(J)
199C
200C       FIND NEW G MATRIX   (EQ. 9.29)
201        DO 210 I=1,N
203        DO 210 J=1,N
210 210    G(I,J)=G(I,J)+DELX(I)*DELX(J)/D1-Z(I)*Z(J)/D2
212        GO TO 41
300        END
897C
898        FUNCTION ERROR(X)
899        DIMENSION X(10)
900        ERROR=100.*(X(1)*X(1)-X(2))**2+(1.-X(1))**2
950        RETURN
999        END
```

(b)

FIGURE 9.12. (Continued.)

is made to allow the vector **Gy** to be conveniently stored by the program. Lines 101 and 102 cause the matrix **G** to be set equal to the identity matrix every five iterations. The number five was chosen somewhat arbitrarily—the important fact is that periodic reinitialization is necessary to prevent numerical inaccuracies in **G** from accumulating. In order to observe how reinitialization of **G** can be beneficial, examine Figure 9.13, which is a Fletcher-Powell optimization of the Rosenbrock function. The

```
N ? 2

X(I)   I=1,2,...N
? -1.2    1
  ERROR=    2.42000E+01

   X(I)=  -1.01284E+00    1.07639E+00
  ERROR=    4.30709E+00

   X(I)=  -8.73203E-01    7.41217E-01
  ERROR=    3.55411E+00

   X(I)=  -8.15501E-01    6.24325E-01
  ERROR=    3.46184E+00

   X(I)=  -6.72526E-01    3.88722E-01
  ERROR=    3.20145E+00

   X(I)=  -7.12159E-01    4.94380E-01
  ERROR=    2.94785E+00

   X(I)=   1.05488E+00    1.13391E+00
  ERROR=    4.77510E-02

   X(I)=   1.06641E+00    1.13774E+00
  ERROR=    4.43687E-03

   X(I)=   1.06413E+00    1.13140E+00
  ERROR=    4.20725E-03

   X(I)=   1.02291E+00    1.04313E+00
  ERROR=    1.55704E-03

   X(I)=   1.02772E+00    1.05350E+00
  ERROR=    1.49666E-03
```

FIGURE 9.13. Minimization of the Rosenbrock function by the Fletcher-Powell program.

error did not change very much between the fourth iteration ($E = 3.20$) and the fifth ($E = 2.95$), but reinitializing **G** caused the error to be reduced dramatically ($E = 0.05$).

There are many other optimization techniques that are related to the Fletcher-Powell algorithm. These algorithms are referred to as conjugate-direction methods.[9] They all base their search direction on the assumption that sufficiently near a minimum the error function can be expressed as a second-degree equation as in (9.24). However, none of the practical methods directly evaluate the Hessian by evaluating second derivatives. In fact, some of the methods do not even evaluate the gradient by evaluating first derivatives. But of the conjugate-direction methods, the Fletcher-Powell optimization technique is the most popular.

In conclusion, there are many different optimization techniques. Even in a particular problem, the technique that works best may depend on the initial set of parameters. For example, far from a minimum, steepest descent may make more rapid improvements than Fletcher-Powell (because of a poor approximation to the inverse Hessian). In fact, far from a minimum the simplex optimization technique may be better than either steepest descent or Fletcher-Powell.

Organizations that must frequently solve optimization problems have general-purpose optimization programs that contain many different optimization algorithms. These programs can be written so they will automatically change from one optimization technique to another if the original one can not make sufficient reductions in the error function. Thus an error function might be reduced by steepest descent at first, and then by Fletcher-Powell as the minimum is approached.

The next chapter discusses another algorithm, the least-pth optimization technique, that is extremely popular. It is often used separately or as part of a general-purpose optimization program.

---

[9]S_1, S_2 are said to be conjugate with respect to the positive-definite matrix **H** if $S_1^T H S_2 = 0$.

PROBLEMS

9.1 If a vector $\mathbf{x}$ has components x_1, x_2, x_3, then its magnitude is defined as $|\mathbf{x}| = (x_1^2 + x_2^2 + x_3^2)^{1/2}$. Show that the magnitude of $\mathbf{x} = (2, 4, 6)$ is twice the magnitude of $\mathbf{y} = (1, 2, 3)$.

9.2 For the error function $E(\mathbf{x}) = (x_1 - 2)^2 + (x_2 - 4)^2$, what is the error at $\mathbf{x} + \alpha \mathbf{S}$ is $\mathbf{x} = (2.1, 4.2)$, $\alpha = 0.01$, and $\mathbf{S} = -(1, 2)$?

9.3 If the function $f(x)$ has $f'(x_0) = 0$ and $f''(x_0) = 0$, then x_0 is called a saddle point.

  (a) What is the saddle point of $f(x) = x^3 - 6x^2 + 12x + 1$?

  (b) For the saddle point found in (a), show that $f(x_0 + \delta) > f(x_0)$ if δ is a positive number and $f(x_0 + \delta) < f(x_0)$ if δ is a negative number (thus x_0 is neither a maximum nor minimum).

9.4 For $E(\mathbf{x}) = x_1^2 + 2x_2^2 + 3x_3^2$:

  (a) Calculate the gradient at $\mathbf{x} = (1, 2, 3)$.

  (b) Calculate the gradient at $\mathbf{x} = (1, 0, -1)$.

9.5 For $E(\mathbf{x}) = x_1^2 + 2x_1 x_3 + x_2 x_3^2$:

  (a) Calculate the gradient at $\mathbf{x} = (1, 1, 1)$.

  (b) Estimate $E(1.1, 1.05, 0.95)$ by using (9.10).

9.6 Find where the gradient of

$$E(\mathbf{x}) = x_1^2 - 2x_1 + x_2^2 - 8x_2 + 17$$

is equal to zero.

9.7 The gradient of $E(\mathbf{x}) = x_1^2 + 2x_1 x_3 + x_2 x_3^2$ was found analytically in Problem 9.5 to be $(4, 1, 4)$ at $\mathbf{x} = (1, 1, 1)$. In this problem it will be found by numerical methods.

  (a) Use (9.12) with $\varepsilon = 0.01$ to estimate the gradient at $\mathbf{x} = (1, 1, 1)$.

  (b) Instead of (9.12), use a central-difference formula to estimate the gradient at $\mathbf{x} = (1, 1, 1)$.

  (c) What is the disadvantage of using the central-difference formula to estimate the gradient?

9.8 What is the scalar product of the two vectors $\mathbf{a} = (1, 4, -2)$, $\mathbf{b} = (1, -1, 1)$?

9.9 What is $\mathbf{a} \cdot \mathbf{a}$?

9.10 For $\mathbf{a} = (1, 4, -2)$, choose a unit vector $\mathbf{b}$ such that
   (a) $a_1b_1 + a_2b_2 + a_3b_3$ is a maximum,
   (b) $a_1b_1 + a_2b_2 + a_3b_3$ is a minimum.
   (c) What are the maximum and minimum values?

9.11 For the error function $E(\mathbf{x}) = x_1^2 + 3x_1x_3 + 2x_2^2 + 4$:
   (a) Calculate the error at $\mathbf{x} = (1, 1, 2)$.
   (b) Calculate the gradient there.
   (c) Let $\delta\mathbf{x} = 0.01\,\nabla E$, and calculate the error at the new point.
   (d) Let $\delta\mathbf{x} = -0.01\,\nabla E$, and calculate the resulting error.

9.12 The Rosenbrock function was minimized by steepest descent in Fig. 9.4. This problem will verify that after one iteration $x_1 = -1.0128$, $x_2 = 1.0764$.
   (a) By analytical means, evaluate ∇E at $x_1 = -1.2$, $x_2 = 1$.
   (b) In what direction does steepest descent search for a minimum?
   (c) Quadratic interpolation finds it necessary to iterate to $\alpha_1 = (0.5)^{10}$ $= 9.765625 \times 10^{-4}$.
      (1) Find $\mathbf{x}_1$, $E(\mathbf{x}_1)$, where $\mathbf{x}_1$ is as identified in statement 54 of Fig. 9.3.
      (2) Find $\mathbf{x}_2$, $E(\mathbf{x}_2)$, where $\mathbf{x}_2$ is as identified in statement 66 of Fig. 9.3.
      (3) Find α.
   (d) For the value of α found in (c), calculate the new values of x_1, x_2.

9.13 What statement was included in the steepest-descent program in case any of the initial parameters were chosen as zero?

9.14 Solve Problem 8.14 by using the steepest-descent program.

9.15 Solve Problem 8.15 by using the steepest-descent program.

9.16 Solve Problem 8.16 by using the steepest-descent program.

9.17 Solve Problem 8.17 by using the steepest-descent program.

9.18 The amount of calculation performed by the quadratic-interpolation subroutine greatly affects the speed of the steepest-descent program. One way to reduce the number of calculations is to change the way α_1 is calculated.
   (a) Add an output statement to the steepest-descent program so that after $E_1 \leqslant E_0$ the value of α_1 is printed. Apply this program to the "cube" test function.
   (b) Change the $0.5\alpha_1 \rightarrow \alpha_1$ statement to $0.1\alpha_1 \rightarrow \alpha_1$ and apply this program to "cube". Did this increase the speed?

9.19 Instead of the modification suggested in Problem 9.18(b), another possibility is to change the initial value of α_1 from 1 to 0.01. Apply the resulting program to "cube" and determine whether or not this increased the speed.

9.20 The following function has two minimums:

$$E(x_1, x_2) = x_1^4 - 4x_1^2 + x_2^2 - 6x_2 + 20.$$

Use the steepest-descent program with different initial parameters so that both minimums are located.

9.21 The functions in the two parts of this problem are equivalent, since the variables were scaled according to $x_2 = 100x_3$. However, one form will be much easier for steepest descent to optimize than the other.

(a) Use the steepest-descent program to minimize

$$3x_1^2 - 4x_1 + 6 + (1 + x_1^2)(x_2 + 100)^2.$$

Choose the initial parameters as $x_1 = 1$, $x_2 = 100$.

(b) Use the steepest-descent program to minimize

$$3x_1^2 - 4x_1 + 6 + 10{,}000(1 + x_1^2)(x_3 + 1)^2.$$

Choose the initial parameters as $x_1 = 1$, $x_3 = 1$.

9.22 (a) Calculate the Hessian at $\mathbf{x} = (-1.2, 1)$ for the Rosenbrock function.

(b) Find the inverse of the Hessian.

(c) Find the direction that is given by $\mathbf{S} = -\mathbf{H}^{-1}\nabla E$.

Chapter Ten

The Least-pth Optimization Technique

10.1 INTRODUCTION

The steepest-descent optimization technique searches in the direction of the negative gradient for a minimum. Since the error function decreases most rapidly in that direction, this is a logical search direction. However, since the search must be for a finite distance, it will only be in the direction of the negative gradient at the beginning of the search (assuming that the gradient is not constant); other optimization techniques modify the search direction to attempt to predict changes in the gradient.

An optimization technique that is written for a specific type of problem is usually more efficient when applied to that type of problem than is a general-purpose optimization algorithm. The least-pth optimization technique is written for a particular class of problems. The theory used to develop it is very similar to that used for steepest descent, but it also assumes the the error function is of a particular form. This assumption is not very restrictive, but can drastically improve the rate of convergence.

In the least-pth optimization technique the assumption is made that the error function can be written as

$$E(x) = \sum_{i=1}^{m} \omega_i [e_i(x)]^p. \tag{10.1}$$

This form of the error function was discussed in Section 8.2. There it was mentioned that the individual error $e_i(x)$ is first raised to an even positive power p (to guarantee that each contribution to the total error E is positive) and then multiplied by a weight ω_i before the summation process. In this chapter we will assume that if any weights are used, the problem will first be transformed to a nonweighted problem by substituting

$$\omega_i [e_i(x)]^p \rightarrow [e_i(x)]^p. \tag{10.2}$$

Thus the error function will be assumed to be in the form

$$E(x) = \sum_{i=1}^{m} [e_i(x)]^p. \tag{10.3}$$

The least-*p*th method is the natural approach to use when one is attempting to match a polynomial to discrete data, because the errors are easy to formulate as in (10.3). Often this assumed form for the error function is not very restrictive; in fact, any of the test functions we have encountered can be put into this form.

EXAMPLE 10.1

The Rosenbrock function is

$$E(x_1, x_2) = 100(x_1^2 - x_2)^2 + (1 - x_1)^2.$$

This function can be put in the form (10.1) by choosing $m = 2 = p$, $\omega_1 = 100$, $\omega_2 = 1$, $e_1 = x_1^2 - x_2$, $e_2 = 1 - x_1$. However, it can also be written as a non-weighted problem by rewriting it as

$$E(x_1, x_2) = [10(x_1^2 - x_2)]^2 + (1 - x_1)^2.$$

Thus for this nonweighted formulation the individual error contributions are

$$e_1 = 10(x_1^2 - x_2), \qquad e_2 = (1 - x_1).$$

In this example, the error functions were raised to the power $p = 2$. For this case, the least-*p*th optimization technique is often referred to as the least-squares optimization technique. Most of the problems that will be solved in this chapter will use the least-squares method, but generalizing to obtain the least-*p*th technique will lead to important applications in the last section.

The least-squares optimization technique is derived in the next section. Starting first with $p = 2$ will help keep the derivation relatively simple. However, we will see in the following section that the more general case of p being any even integer is not much more complicated.

10.2 THE LEAST-SQUARES ALGORITHM

In this section we will assume that the error function can be written in the form

$$E(\mathbf{x}) = \sum_{i=1}^{m} [e_i(\mathbf{x})]^2 = \sum_{i=1}^{m} e_i^2. \tag{10.4}$$

In order to simplify notation, the second form of the equation will commonly be used.

From Chapter 9 we know that the gradient of the error function must be zero at a minimum. It will be made zero by proceeding in an iterative manner. Parameter changes for **x** will be chosen. These increments will usually not reduce ∇E to zero at the first step, because a linear approximation must be made; however, by iterating, the gradient may be made as close to zero as desired.

To learn how to choose the parameter change $\delta \mathbf{x}$, it is necessary to calculate the gradient of the error function. For the special form that was assumed in (10.4) it follows that

$$
\nabla E(\mathbf{x}) =
\begin{bmatrix}
\dfrac{\partial E}{\partial x_1} \\[2ex]
\dfrac{\partial E}{\partial x_2} \\[2ex]
\vdots \\[2ex]
\dfrac{\partial E}{\partial x_n}
\end{bmatrix}
= 2
\begin{bmatrix}
\displaystyle\sum_{i=1}^{m}\left(e_i \dfrac{\partial e_i}{\partial x_1}\right) \\[3ex]
\displaystyle\sum_{i=1}^{m}\left(e_i \dfrac{\partial e_i}{\partial x_2}\right) \\[3ex]
\vdots \\[3ex]
\displaystyle\sum_{i=1}^{m}\left(e_i \dfrac{\partial e_i}{\partial x_n}\right)
\end{bmatrix} .
\tag{10.5}
$$

In this equation it has been assumed that the error function depends on n parameters, so that the gradient vector has n components. Any of these n components can be found by evaluating a summation of m terms, where m represents the number of individual error functions.

EXAMPLE 10.2

The error function

$$
E(\mathbf{x}) = \left(x_1^2 + x_2^2 + x_1 x_2 - 4\right)^2 + 4x_1^2 x_2^2 + 9x_1^2 x_2^4
$$

can be written as

$$
E(\mathbf{x}) = \sum_{i=1}^{3} e_i^2,
$$

where

$$
e_1 = x_1^2 + x_2^2 + x_1 x_2 - 4, \qquad e_2 = 2x_1 x_2, \qquad e_3 = 3x_1 x_2^2 .
$$

For these individual error functions, the gradient can be determined by applying (10.5):

$$
\nabla E =
\begin{bmatrix}
\dfrac{\partial E}{\partial x_1} \\[2ex]
\dfrac{\partial E}{\partial x_2}
\end{bmatrix}
= 2
\begin{bmatrix}
(2x_1 + x_2)e_1 + 2x_2 e_2 + 3x_2^2 e_3 \\[2ex]
(2x_2 + x_1)e_1 + 2x_1 e_2 + 6x_1 x_2 e_3
\end{bmatrix} .
$$

The result in (10.5) can be rewritten in a simpler form if we introduce the $m \times n$ Jacobian matrix, which is defined to be

$$
\mathbf{J}(\mathbf{x}) = \begin{bmatrix}
\dfrac{\partial e_1}{\partial x_1} & \dfrac{\partial e_1}{\partial x_2} & \cdots & \dfrac{\partial e_1}{\partial x_n} \\[2ex]
\dfrac{\partial e_2}{\partial x_1} & \dfrac{\partial e_2}{\partial x_2} & \cdots & \dfrac{\partial e_2}{\partial x_n} \\[2ex]
\vdots & \vdots & & \vdots \\[2ex]
\dfrac{\partial e_m}{\partial x_1} & \dfrac{\partial e_m}{\partial x_2} & \cdots & \dfrac{\partial e_m}{\partial x_n}
\end{bmatrix} = \left[\dfrac{\partial e_i}{\partial x_k} \right].
\tag{10.6}
$$

That is, the element in the ith row and kth column is $\partial e_i / \partial x_k$.

Since for a least-squares error formulation the gradient can be written as in (10.5), we have

$$
\nabla E(\mathbf{x}) = 2\mathbf{J}^t(\mathbf{x})\mathbf{e}(\mathbf{x}),
\tag{10.7}
$$

where $\mathbf{e}(\mathbf{x})$ is a vector that has the individual errors e_i as components. That is, $\mathbf{e}(\mathbf{x}) = (e_1, e_2, \ldots, e_n)$.

Recall that at a minimum of the error function E, the gradient should be zero. The initial parameter vector $\mathbf{x}$ will usually not be at the minimum; thus $\nabla E(\mathbf{x})$ will not be zero. However, (10.7) can be used to obtain a change $\delta\mathbf{x}$ such that the magnitude of the gradient is reduced. The increment $\delta\mathbf{x}$ can be found by using (10.7) to express the gradient at $\mathbf{x} + \delta\mathbf{x}$ as

$$
\nabla E(\mathbf{x} + \delta\mathbf{x}) = 2\mathbf{J}^t(\mathbf{x} + \delta\mathbf{x})\mathbf{e}(\mathbf{x} + \delta\mathbf{x}).
\tag{10.8}
$$

It often happens that the Jacobian does not vary very much as the parameters are changed. Even if this is not true at the start of an iterative search for the minimum, it will be true as the minimum is approached. Thus we can use the approximation

$$
\nabla E(\mathbf{x} + \delta\mathbf{x}) \approx 2\mathbf{J}^t(\mathbf{x})\mathbf{e}(\mathbf{x} + \delta\mathbf{x}).
\tag{10.9}
$$

In order to choose the parameter change $\delta\mathbf{x}$ so that the gradient becomes zero, we must find an approximation for $\mathbf{e}(\mathbf{x} + \delta\mathbf{x})$. Expanding this in a Taylor series and keeping the first-order terms yields

$$
\mathbf{e}(\mathbf{x} + \delta\mathbf{x}) \approx \mathbf{e}(\mathbf{x}) + \sum_{k=1}^{n} \frac{\partial \mathbf{e}}{\partial x_k} \delta x_k.
\tag{10.10}
$$

This approximation can be written in the following simpler form by using the Jacobian defined in (10.6):

$$
\mathbf{e}(\mathbf{x} + \delta\mathbf{x}) \approx \mathbf{e}(\mathbf{x}) + \mathbf{J}(\mathbf{x})\delta\mathbf{x}.
\tag{10.11}
$$

The approximations (10.9) and (10.11) can be used to estimate the parameter changes δx that will produce a zero gradient at $x + \delta x$. Substituting (10.11) into (10.9), setting $\nabla E(x + \delta x)$ equal to zero, and rearranging yields

$$J'J\delta x \approx -J'e(x). \tag{10.12}$$

EXAMPLE 10.3

The error functions in Example 10.2 were

$$e_1 = x_1^2 + x_2^2 + x_1 x_2 - 4, \qquad e_2 = 2x_1 x_2, \qquad e_3 = 3x_1 x_2^2.$$

At $x = (1, 1)$ the total error is

$$E = (-1)^2 + (2)^2 + (3)^2 = 14.$$

In this example we will use (10.12) to yield parameter changes that will reduce the error.

From (10.6) the Jacobian is

$$J = \begin{bmatrix} 2x_1 + x_2 & 2x_2 + x_1 \\ 2x_2 & 2x_1 \\ 3x_2^2 & 6x_1 x_2 \end{bmatrix}_{x=(1,1)} = \begin{bmatrix} 3 & 3 \\ 2 & 2 \\ 3 & 6 \end{bmatrix},$$

so that

$$J'J = \begin{bmatrix} 3 & 2 & 3 \\ 3 & 2 & 6 \end{bmatrix} \begin{bmatrix} 3 & 3 \\ 2 & 2 \\ 3 & 6 \end{bmatrix} = \begin{bmatrix} 22 & 31 \\ 31 & 49 \end{bmatrix}.$$

Substituting into (10.12),

$$\begin{bmatrix} 22 & 31 \\ 31 & 49 \end{bmatrix} \delta x = -\begin{bmatrix} 3 & 2 & 3 \\ 3 & 2 & 6 \end{bmatrix} \begin{bmatrix} -1 \\ 2 \\ 3 \end{bmatrix}.$$

Solving for δx yields $(\frac{99}{117}, -\frac{108}{117})$, so that the new point is $x = (1, 1) + \delta x = (1.8462, 0.0769)$. The error function at this new point is

$$E = (-0.4437)^2 + (0.2839)^2 + (0.0328)^2 = 0.279.$$

The error function in this example was reduced, but not minimized. The minimum was not found in one application of the least-squares technique, because (10.12) was an approximate relation and not an exact one. However, it can be the basis of an iterative procedure to minimize error functions. Instead of developing a least-squares program, we will develop a more general least-pth program in the next sections.

10.3   THE LEAST-pTH ALGORITHM

The iterative least-squares optimization technique can be used to minimize functions of the form

$$E(\mathbf{x}) = \sum_{i=1}^{m} e_i^2. \tag{10.4}$$

This can be generalized to yield the least-pth optimization technique, which can be used to minimize

$$E(\mathbf{x}) = \sum_{i=1}^{m} e_i^p. \tag{10.4$'$}$$

The equations in this section will be very similar to the equations in the previous section, and thus will be only briefly discussed. They will be numbered in such a way that the corresponding least-squares equations may be obtained by removing the prime. For example, for the least-squares case we had

$$\nabla E(\mathbf{x}) = 2\mathbf{J}^t(\mathbf{x})\mathbf{e}(\mathbf{x}), \tag{10.7}$$

while for the least-pth case this becomes

$$\nabla E(\mathbf{x}) = p\mathbf{J}^t(\mathbf{x})\mathbf{e}^{p-1}(\mathbf{x}), \tag{10.7$'$}$$

where $\mathbf{e}^{p-1}(\mathbf{x})$ is a vector that has components equal to e_i^{p-1}.

In order to make the gradient become zero, as it must at a minimum, we substitute $\mathbf{x} + \delta\mathbf{x}$ into (10.7$'$) to yield

$$\nabla E(\mathbf{x} + \delta\mathbf{x}) = p\mathbf{J}^t(\mathbf{x} + \delta\mathbf{x})\mathbf{e}^{p-1}(\mathbf{x} + \delta\mathbf{x}) \tag{10.8$'$}$$

$$\approx p\mathbf{J}^t(\mathbf{x})\mathbf{e}^{p-1}(\mathbf{x} + \delta\mathbf{x}). \tag{10.9$'$}$$

To solve for $\delta\mathbf{x}$ we use the Taylor approximation

$$\mathbf{e}^{p-1}(\mathbf{x} + \delta\mathbf{x}) \approx \mathbf{e}^{p-1}(\mathbf{x}) + (p-1)\mathbf{D}\mathbf{J}(\mathbf{x})\delta\mathbf{x}, \tag{10.11$'$a}$$

where $\mathbf{D}$ is a diagonal matrix which has the diagonal elements

$$e_1^{p-2}, e_2^{p-2}, \ldots, e_m^{p-2}. \tag{10.11$'$b}$$

The approximations (10.9$'$) and (10.11$'$) can be used to estimate the parameter change $\delta\mathbf{x}$ that will produce a zero gradient at $\mathbf{x} + \delta\mathbf{x}$. Substituting (10.11$'$) into (10.9$'$), setting $\nabla E(\mathbf{x} + \delta\mathbf{x})$ equal to zero, and rearranging yields

$$\mathbf{J}^t\mathbf{D}\mathbf{J}\,\delta\mathbf{x} \approx -\frac{1}{p-1}\mathbf{J}^t\mathbf{e}^{p-1}(\mathbf{x}). \tag{10.12$'$}$$

This equation can be the foundation for an iterative procedure that minimizes an error function $E = \sum_{i=1}^{m} e_i^p$. One first chooses initial values for the parameter vector $\mathbf{x}$. The gradient $\nabla E(\mathbf{x})$ will not be zero, but its magnitude can be reduced by using a new parameter vector $\mathbf{x} + \delta\mathbf{x}$, where $\delta\mathbf{x}$ is found from (10.12'). Using this equation iteratively can make the magnitude of the gradient as small as desired.

The next section will describe a program that is based on (10.12'); but before presenting the program an example will be discussed. In the example, as in the program, the following definitions are used:

$$\mathbf{A} = \mathbf{J}'\mathbf{DJ}, \qquad \mathbf{C} = -\frac{1}{p-1}\mathbf{J}'e^{p-1}(\mathbf{x}), \qquad (10.13)$$

so that solving (10.12') is equivalent to solving

$$\mathbf{A}\,\delta\mathbf{x} = \mathbf{C}. \qquad (10.14)$$

EXAMPLE 10.4

Example 10.3 had the error functions

$$e_1 = x_1^2 + x_2^2 + x_1 x_2 - 4, \qquad e_2 = 2x_1 x_2, \qquad e_3 = 3x_1 x_2^2.$$

This example will raise these individual error functions to the fourth power and use one iteration of the least-pth algorithm to obtain a lower error function. That is, we will reduce $E(\mathbf{x}) = e_1^4 + e_2^4 + e_3^4$.

At $\mathbf{x} = (1, 1)$ the total error is

$$E = (-1)^4 + (2)^4 + (3)^4 = 98.$$

In this example we will use (10.12') to yield parameter changes that will reduce the error.

From Example 10.3 the Jacobian is

$$\mathbf{J}' = \begin{bmatrix} 3 & 2 & 3 \\ 3 & 2 & 6 \end{bmatrix},$$

so that

$$\mathbf{C} = -\frac{1}{p-1}\mathbf{J}'e^{p-1} = -\frac{1}{3}\begin{bmatrix} 3 & 2 & 3 \\ 3 & 2 & 6 \end{bmatrix}\begin{bmatrix} -1 \\ 8 \\ 27 \end{bmatrix} = -\frac{1}{3}\begin{bmatrix} 94 \\ 175 \end{bmatrix},$$

$$\mathbf{A} = \mathbf{J}'\mathbf{DJ} = \begin{bmatrix} 3 & 2 & 3 \\ 3 & 2 & 6 \end{bmatrix}\begin{bmatrix} 1 & 0 & 0 \\ 0 & 4 & 0 \\ 0 & 0 & 9 \end{bmatrix}\begin{bmatrix} 3 & 3 \\ 2 & 2 \\ 3 & 6 \end{bmatrix}$$

$$= \begin{bmatrix} 106 & 187 \\ 187 & 349 \end{bmatrix}.$$

Thus

$$\begin{bmatrix} 106 & 187 \\ 187 & 349 \end{bmatrix}\delta\mathbf{x} = -\frac{1}{3}\begin{bmatrix} 94 \\ 175 \end{bmatrix}.$$

Solving this set of equations yields $\delta x = (-\frac{1}{75}, -0.16)$, so that the new point is $x = (1, 1) + \delta x = (0.9867, 0.84)$. The error at this new point is

$$E = (-1.492)^4 + (1.6577)^4 + (2.0886)^4 = 31.5.$$

In the above example, the new point $x = (0.9867, 0.84)$ resulted in an error of 31.5 when the individual errors were raised to the fourth power. Even if these same individual errors were squared instead of raised to the fourth power, the total error would be 11.7, which is much larger than the error of 0.279 found in Example 10.3.

A general property of the least-pth optimization technique is that the larger the power p, the slower the rate of convergence. However, when an optimum is finally attained, having p large can produce favorable results. To understand why this is possible, recall that the total error E is found by summing some individual error functions, each of which is raised to the pth power. If p is a large number (e.g., 10), then when the largest individual error is raised to the pth power, its contribution to E will be much larger than that of another individual error which is only slightly smaller. Thus when p is large, the least-pth optimization technique tends to minimize the maximum error. Much more will be said about this property when Chebyshev theory is presented in Section 10.6.

10.4   A LEAST-pTH PROGRAM

Any least-pth program that is based on (10.12′) must be able to evaluate the Jacobian matrix $\mathbf{J}$. Recall that the element in the ith row and kth column of $\mathbf{J}$ is $\partial e_i / \partial x_k$; thus a typical component of $\mathbf{J}$ is

$$J_{ik} = \frac{\partial e_i}{\partial x_k} = \lim_{\delta x_k \to 0} \frac{e_i(\mathbf{x} + \delta \mathbf{x}_k) - e_i(\mathbf{x})}{\delta x_k}, \qquad (10.15)$$

where $\delta \mathbf{x}_k$ is a vector which has all zero components except for the kth component, which is equal to δx_k.

The partial derivative in (10.15) will be approximated in the same way we have approximated previous partial derivatives, namely by

$$J_{ik} \approx \frac{e_i\left[x_1, x_2, \ldots, (1 + \varepsilon)x_k, \ldots, x_n \right] - e_i(\mathbf{x})}{\varepsilon x_k}, \qquad (10.16)$$

where ε is a constant of proportionality. The same value for ε will be used as in Chapter 3, namely $\varepsilon = 10^{-6}$. The expression in (10.16) for an element of the Jacobian matrix is very similar to the expression in (9.12) for an element of the gradient vector; thus a computer implementation can be similar.

The least-*p*th program is given in Fig. 10.1. In this program line 26 indicates that the elements in the first column of **J** are evaluated first, then the elements in the second column are evaluated, etc. That is, J_{i1} ($i = 1, 2, \ldots, m$) is found first, then J_{i2} ($i = 1, 2, \ldots, m$) is found, etc. Calculating the elements of the Jacobian in this order means that error function subroutine $e(\mathbf{x})$ only has to be used n times. Since the command $\mathbf{e}(\mathbf{x}) \rightarrow e_i$ is only encountered n times, the evaluation of the Jacobian is not too time consuming.

Recall that the least-*p*th algorithm is based on

$$\mathbf{J}^T \mathbf{DJ} \, \delta\mathbf{x} \approx -\frac{1}{p-1} \mathbf{J}' \mathbf{e}^{p-1}, \qquad (10.17)$$

which can be rewritten as

$$\mathbf{A} \, \delta\mathbf{x} \approx \mathbf{C}, \qquad (10.18)$$

where

$$\mathbf{A} = \mathbf{J}^T \mathbf{DJ}, \qquad \mathbf{C} = -\frac{1}{p-1} \mathbf{J}^T \mathbf{e}^{p-1}. \qquad (10.19)$$

The vector **C** is found in lines 50 to 60. **D** is an $n \times n$ diagonal matrix of terms e_i^{p-2}. Because **D** has only m nonzero terms, it can be found very simply as indicated in lines 61 to 63.

The set of equations $\mathbf{A} \, \delta\mathbf{x} = \mathbf{C}$ is solved by using the Gauss elimination method.[1] In terms of this solution $\delta\mathbf{x}$, the new set of parameters could be expressed as $\mathbf{x}_1 = \mathbf{x} + \delta\mathbf{x}$. However, for some initial conditions, the error function may vary so rapidly that the assumption of small parameter changes is a poor approximation. In this case, the error function may actually get worse if the new parameters are found from $\mathbf{x}_1 = \mathbf{x} + \delta\mathbf{x}$. Because of this, it may be necessary to reduce $\delta\mathbf{x}$ by a scale factor, that is,

$$\mathbf{x}_1 = \mathbf{x} + \mathrm{SF} \, \delta\mathbf{x}. \qquad (10.20)$$

Initially, the scale factor SF can be chosen as unity. If the error function is not reduced, then SF can be repeated halved until the error function finally is reduced. The halving of the scale factor is accomplished in line 202, and equation (10.20) is implemented in line 204.

The first application of the least-*p*th program is shown in Fig. 10.2, which is a printout for the following error functions:

$$e_1 = x_1^2 + x_2^2 + x_1 x_2 - 4, \qquad e_2 = 2x_1 x_2, \qquad e_3 = 3x_1 x_2^2.$$

These error functions were studied in Example 10.4, which showed that for $p = 4$ the initial error $E(1, 1) = 98$ could be reduced to $E(0.9867, 0.84) =$

---

[1]Since **A** is symmetric, it would be more efficient to use the square-root method that was mentioned in Section 2.6.

```
01C         LEAST-PTH OPTIMIZATION
02          PROGRAM LP(INPUT,OUTPUT)
03 03       FORMAT(7H  X(I)=,1P,4E14.5)
04 04       FORMAT(7H ERROR=,1P,E14.5,/)
06          DIMENSION A(20,40),C(20),D(20),E(20),E0(20),X(20),X1(20)
07          INTEGER P,P1,P2
08          REAL JA(20,20)
09C
10C         INITIAL VALUES
11          PRINT,*M,N,P*, $READ,M,N,P
12          N1=N+1   $P1=P-1   $P2=P-2
14          PRINT,/,*X(I)   I=1,2,...N*
15          READ,(X(I),I=1,N)
16          CALL ERROR(X,E0)
17          EX=0.
18          DO 19 I=1,M
19 19       EX=EX+E0(I)**P
22          PRINT 4,EX
24C
25C         FIND JACOBIAN
26 26       DO 46 K=1,N
30          DELTA=.000001*X(K)
32          IF(ABS(X(K)).LT.1E-12) DELTA=.000001
34          XSAVE=X(K)
36          X(K)=X(K)+DELTA
38          CALL ERROR(X,E)
40          X(K)=XSAVE
42          DO 46 I=1,M
46 46       JA(I,K)=(E(I)-E0(I))/DELTA
49C
50C         FIND C
52          DO 58 K=1,N
54          C(K)=0.
56          DO 57 I=1,M
57 57       C(K)=C(K)+JA(I,K)*E0(I)**P1
58 58       C(K)=-C(K)/P1
60C
61C         FIND D
62          DO 63 I=1,M
63 63       D(I)=E0(I)**P2
69C
70C         FIND A
71          DO 79 I=1,N
72          DO 79 K=1,M
73          A(I,K)=A(I,M+K)=0.
77          DO 79 L=1,M
79 79       A(I,K)=A(I,K)+D(L)*JA(L,I)*JA(L,K)
99C
100C        GAUSS ELIMINATION
130C
131C            DEFINE AUGMENTED MATRIX
132            DO 135 I=1,N
135 135        A(I,N1)=C(I)
142            DO 175 I=1,N
144            IF(A(I,I).NE.0) GO TO 164
```

(a)

FIGURE 10.1. A program for the least-*p*th algorithm.

```
146C            INTERCHANGE ROWS I,J
148             J=I
149 149         J=J+1
151             IF(J.GT.N) GO TO 298
152             IF(A(J,I).EQ.0) GO TO 149
153             DO 157 K=1,N1
155             SAVE=A(I,K)
156             A(I,K)=A(J,K)
157 157         A(J,K)=SAVE
162C
163C            NORMALIZE ROW I
164 164         Y=A(I,I)
165             DO 166 K=I,N1
166 166         A(I,K)=A(I,K)/Y
169C
170C            FORWARD ELIMINATION
171             I1=I+1
172             DO 175 J=I1,N
174             DO 175 K=I1,N1
175 175         A(J,K)=A(J,K)-A(J,I)*A(I,K)
177C
178C            BACK SUBSTITUTION
179             DO 184 L=2,N
180             I=N+2-L $I1=I-1 $I2=I+1
181             DO 184 J=1,I1
184 184         A(J,N1)=A(J,N1)-A(J,I)*A(I,N1)
186C
199C
200C            FIND NEW X
201             J=0 $SF=2.
202 202         SF=.5*SF
203             DO 204 I=1,N
204 204         X1(I)=X(I)+SF*A(I,N1)
245             CALL ERROR(X1,E0)
247             EX1=0.
248             DO 249 I=1,M
249 249         EX1=EX1+E0(I)**P
251             J=J+1
252             IF(J.EQ.10) GO TO 281
270             IF(EX1.GE.EX) GO TO 202
280C
281 281 DO 282 I=1,N
282 282 X(I)=X1(I)
284             PRINT 3,(X(I),I=1,N)
286             EX=EX1
287             PRINT 4,EX
288             GO TO 26
290C
298 298 PRINT,*DET=0*
299             STOP
300             END
897C
898             SUBROUTINE ERROR(X,E)
899             DIMENSION X(10),E(10)
900             E(1)=10.*(X(1)*X(1)-X(2))
910             E(2)=1.-X(1)
950             RETURN
999             END
```

(b)

FIGURE 10.1. (Continued.)

```
M,N,P ? 3   2   4

X(I)   I=1,2,...N
? 1    1
  ERROR=      9.80000E+01

  X(I)=        9.86667E-01    8.40000E-01
  ERROR=       3.15344E+01

  X(I)=        1.32081E+00    5.48988E-01
  ERROR=       8.73832E+00

  X(I)=        1.56725E+00    3.62529E-01
  ERROR=       2.32095E+00

  X(I)=        1.73376E+00    2.25155E-01
  ERROR=       4.69911E-01

  X(I)=        1.83417E+00    1.39328E-01
  ERROR=       8.53242E-02

  X(I)=        1.89393E+00    8.85433E-02
  ERROR=       1.58390E-02

  X(I)=        1.93103E+00    5.73137E-02
  ERROR=       3.01056E-03

  X(I)=        1.95474E+00    3.75078E-02
  ERROR=       5.80598E-04

  X(I)=        1.97012E+00    2.47102E-02
  ERROR=       1.12954E-04

  X(I)=        1.98021E+00    1.63470E-02
  ERROR=       2.20937E-05
```

FIGURE 10.2. Application of the least-*p*th program to the function in Example 10.4.

31.5. This result is confirmed by the data in Fig. 10.2, which also indicates that after ten iterations $E(1.98), 0.016) = 2.2 \times 10^{-5}$.

Insight into the efficiency of the least-*p*th algorithm relative to simplex or steepest descent can be obtained by applying it to our various test functions. The Rosenbrock function is shown coded in statements 900 and 910 of Fig. 10.1.

The least-*p*th computer output for the Rosenbrock function is shown in Fig. 10.3. As is customary for the Rosenbrock function, the initial parameters were chosen as $\mathbf{x} = (-1.2, 1)$, which yielded the error 24.2. The first few iterations of the least-*p*th algorithm reduced the error function slowly, but the last one was extremely successful—it found the minimum.

The least-*p*th algorithm was even more successful with "cube", as indicated in Fig. 10.4. The exact minimum $(1, 1)$ was essentially found after six iterations. Neither simplex nor steepest descent approached this efficiency.

```
M,N,P ? 2     2     2

X(I)   I=1,2,...N
? -1.2    1
 ERROR=     2.42000E+01

  X(I)=   -1.06250E+00    6.97500E-01
 ERROR=     2.28651E+01

  X(I)=   -9.33594E-01    4.50537E-01
 ERROR=     2.14680E+01

  X(I)=   -6.91895E-01    5.18714E-02
 ERROR=     2.10823E+01

  X(I)=   -4.80408E-01   -1.87426E-01
 ERROR=     1.96822E+01

  X(I)=   -2.95357E-01   -3.12949E-01
 ERROR=     1.76927E+01

  X(I)=    2.84824E-02   -4.04199E-01
 ERROR=     1.73472E+01

  X(I)=    2.71362E-01   -2.89111E-01
 ERROR=     1.36895E+01

  X(I)=    6.35681E-01    8.99879E-02
 ERROR=     9.99875E+00

  X(I)=    1.00000E+00    8.67272E-01
 ERROR=     1.76168E+00

  X(I)=    1.00000E+00    1.00000E+00
 ERROR=     6.00261E-18
```

FIGURE 10.3. Minimization of the Rosenbrock function by the least-*p*th program.

```
M,N,P ? 2    2    2

X(I)    I=1,2,...N
? -1.2    1
  ERROR=    7.49038E+02

   X(I)=  -9.25000E-01   1.84700E+00
  ERROR=   6.99850E+02

   X(I)=  -4.43750E-01   2.42270E+00
  ERROR=   6.32134E+02

   X(I)=   1.00000E+00   7.65504E-01
  ERROR=   5.49883E+00

   X(I)=   1.00000E+00   1.00000E+00
  ERROR=   7.77389E-18

   X(I)=   1.00000E+00   1.00000E+00
  ERROR=   2.02453E-26

   X(I)=   1.00000E+00   1.00000E+00
  ERROR=   0.
```

FIGURE 10.4. Minimization of the "cube" function by the least-pth program.

```
M,N,P ? 4    4    2

X(I)    I=1,2,...N
? 3   -1    0    1
  ERROR=    7.07336E+05

   X(I)=   1.46766E+00  -1.46766E-01   1.76617E-01   1.76617E-01
  ERROR=   4.42052E+04

   X(I)=   7.33832E-01  -7.33832E-02   8.83085E-02   8.83085E-02
  ERROR=   2.76283E+03

   X(I)=   3.66916E-01  -3.66916E-02   4.41542E-02   4.41542E-02
  ERROR=   1.72677E+02

   X(I)=   1.83458E-01  -1.83458E-02   2.20771E-02   2.20771E-02
  ERROR=   1.07924E+01

   X(I)=   9.17291E-02  -9.17291E-03   1.10386E-02   1.10386E-02
  ERROR=   6.74524E-01

   X(I)=   4.58646E-02  -4.58646E-03   5.51928E-03   5.51928E-03
  ERROR=   4.21578E-02

   X(I)=   2.29323E-02  -2.29323E-03   2.75964E-03   2.75964E-03
  ERROR=   2.63487E-03

   X(I)=   1.14662E-02  -1.14662E-03   1.37982E-03   1.37982E-03
  ERROR=   1.64680E-04

   X(I)=   5.73308E-03  -5.73308E-04   6.89911E-04   6.89911E-04
  ERROR=   1.02925E-05

   X(I)=   2.86654E-03  -2.86654E-04   3.44956E-04   3.44956E-04
  ERROR=   6.43282E-07
```

FIGURE 10.5. Minimization of the Powell function by the least-pth program.

For the Powell test function in Fig. 10.5 and the coefficient-matching test function in Fig. 10.6, the optimization required more iterations than for Rosenbrock or "cube", but the results were still extremely successful.

Usually the least-pth optimization technique is quite efficient in locating minimums. If a poor initial guess for the location of the minimum causes the algorithm to converge too slowly, then simplex or steepest descent can be applied to yield a better starting location. They can also be used if the error function cannot be put into the least-pth format. Thus we now have some very practical tools that can be applied to many different types of problems. The next section indicates one application.

```
M,N,P ?  3     3     2

X(I)   I=1,2,...,N
?  10000    10000    10000
 ERROR=     2.59460E+04

  X(I)=     1.37917E+04    1.45833E+04    5.83333E+03
 .ERROR=    1.80888E+04

  X(I)=     2.26507E+04    2.73944E+04    4.82724E+03
 ERROR=     4.58639E+03

  X(I)=     3.25978E+04    4.85351E+04    5.24397E+03
 ERROR=     6.19031E+02

  X(I)=     4.05497E+04    7.74397E+04    5.71401E+03
 ERROR=     4.05724E+01

  X(I)=     4.37610E+04    1.04905E+05    5.91843E+03
 ERROR=     6.43089E-01

  X(I)=     4.41341E+04    1.18101E+05    5.94405E+03
 ERROR=     1.68864E-03

  X(I)=     4.41391E+04    1.19970E+05    5.94449E+03
 ERROR=     2.92233E-07

  X(I)=     4.41391E+04    1.20000E+05    5.94449E+03
 ERROR=     1.79019E-14

  X(I)=     4.41391E+04    1.20000E+05    5.94449E+03
 ERROR=     5.57378E-26

  X(I)=     4.41391E+04    1.20000E+05    5.94449E+03
 ERROR=     5.16988E-26
```

FIGURE 10.6. Coefficient matching by the least-pth program.

10.5 APPLICATION TO LEAST-SQUARES DATA FITTING

Section 4.9 introduced the concept of least-squares data fitting. In that section it was assumed that measurements were taken at m points[2] $x_1, x_2, \ldots, x_m$ and the data $y_1, y_2, \ldots, y_m$ were recorded. The measurements contained "noise", which was smoothed by fitting the following nth-degree polynomial to the data:

$$f(x) = \sum_{j=0}^{n} a_j x^j. \tag{10.21}$$

The difference between the experimental data and the polynomial at point x_i is the error

$$e_i = y_i - f(x_i), \qquad i = 1, 2, \ldots, m. \tag{10.22}$$

The least-squares error criterion seeks to minimize the sum of the squared errors,

$$E = \sum_{i=1}^{m} e_i^2. \tag{10.23}$$

This is in a form which is ideal for applying the least-pth optimization technique. By using (10.21) and (10.22), the individual error functions are expressed as

$$e_i = y_i - \left(a_0 + a_1 x_i + a_2 x_i^2 + \cdots + a_n x_i^n \right), \tag{10.24}$$

where it should be recalled that x_i is the ith measurement point. In this section the parameters to be optimized are *not* x_i; they are instead[3] $a_0, a_1, a_2, \ldots, a_n$.

EXAMPLE 10.5

In Example 4.6 we chose the coefficients a_0, a_1, a_2 of $f(x) = a_0 + a_1 x + a_2 x^2$ to minimize the mean-square error for the following data:

$x =$	0	0.5	1	1.5	2
$y =$	−2.9	−1.8	0.2	2.0	5.2

In that example we solved for the coefficients by applying the Gauss elimination method to a set of three linear equations.

In this example the coefficients will be solved for by applying the least-squares optimization technique. The general form for the individual error function e_i is given in (10.24). For this example, the error functions are shown in Fig. 10.7(a).

---

[2]Beware! In this section, the initial value of x is identified as x_1, and not x_0 as it was in Chapter 4.

[3]Beware! In this section, the number of parameters is $n + 1$ and not n.

```
898          SUBROUTINE ERROR(X,E)
899          DIMENSION X(10),E(10)
900          E(1)=-2.'9-X(1)
910          E(2)=-1.8-(X(1)+.5*X(2)+.25*X(3))
920          E(3)=.2-(X(1)+X(2)+X(3))
930          E(4)=2.-(X(1)+1.5*X(2)+2.25*X(3))
940          E(5)=5.2-(X(1)+2.*X(2)+4.*X(3))
950          RETURN
999          END
```

(a)

```
M,N,P ? 5   3   2

X(I)   I=1,2,...N
? 1    1   1
 ERROR=    4.64550E+01

  X(I)=  -2.88857E+00   1.71429E+00   1.14286E+00
 ERROR=   1.29143E-01

  X(I)=  -2.88857E+00   1.71429E+00   1.14286E+00
 ERROR=   1.29143E-01
```

(b)

FIGURE 10.7. An illustration of least-squares data fitting by applying the least-pth program.

An application of the least-pth program is shown in Fig. 10.7(b). Since there are five error functions and three adjustable parameters, we have $m=5$ and $n=3$. Since we want to minimize the mean-square error, p must be selected as 2. For the initial parameters $x=(1,1,1)$ the algorithm was able to find the minimum in one iteration. It is indicated in Fig. 10.7 that the minimum is located at $a_0=-2.88857$, $a_1=1.71429$, $a_3=1.14286$, so that the second-degree polynomial is

$$f(x)=-2.88857+1.71429x+1.14286x^2.$$

In the above example, the least-squares optimization technique was able to find the minimum in just one iteration. It is proven in Problem 10.19 that if the individual error functions are of the form (10.24), then the minimum can always be found by applying just one iteration of the least-squares algorithm. This proof of course must assume that there are no roundoff errors introduced by the computer.

Unfortunately, any computer will introduce roundoff errors. In Example 10.5 the errors were negligible, but this will not always be the case. If there are substantial roundoff errors, nothing catastrophic happens in the least-squares algorithm: instead of reaching the minimum in one iteration, a few more may be required. The least-squares algorithm will eventually reach the minimum because the parameter changes will become smaller and the effect of roundoff errors will decrease.

The ability of the least-squares algorithm to find the minimum should be contrasted with the approach that was described in Chapter 4. In that chapter the coefficients in

$$f(x) = \sum_{j=0}^{n} a_j x^j \qquad (10.25)$$

were found by solving a set of n linear equations; thus, theoretically, the solution could be obtained by using some standard approach such as the Gauss elimination method. However, for high order (e.g., for $n=8$), the equations are ill conditioned; thus there may be substantial roundoff errors in the solution. The least-squares algorithm can also have ill-conditioned equations, but it has the advantage of being able to iterate the linear equation solving.[4]

Better accuracy is one reason for applying the least-pth program instead of attempting to find an analytical solution as in Chapter 4. Another reason is that the approach that was described in Chapter 4 was only for functions $f(x)$ which are power series as in (10.25). The method can be extended to other types of functions, but there is a limit to the functions that can be used for least-squares data fitting when analytical means are used.

As an example of a data-fitting function that would present problems for the analytical approach consider

$$f(x) = \frac{a_0 + a_1 x}{1 + b_1 x}. \qquad (10.26)$$

This is a special case of the more general function

$$f(x) = \frac{\sum a_j x^j}{\sum b_i x^i}. \qquad (10.27)$$

This function is not a polynomial as in (10.25), but is instead a ratio of polynomials. However, the least-pth program can be easily applied to such functions, as demonstrated in the next example.

EXAMPLE 10.6

The function $y(x) = 100(e^x - 1)/(e^x + 1)$ could be approximated by a power series; but e^x can also be represented as a power series, therefore a

---

[4]Also, see Forsythe (1977) for the "singular valued decomposition" which can be used to avoid ill conditioning.

better approximation for $y(x)$ is possible by using a ratio of power series. In this example we will approximate $y(x) = 100(e^x - 1)/(e^x + 1)$ by $f(x) = (a_0 + a_1 x)/(1 + b_1 x)$.

The coefficients a_0, a_1, b_1 will be chosen so as to minimize the mean-square error for the following data:

$$y(0.2) = y_1 = 9.967, \quad y(0.4) = y_2 = 19.74, \quad y(0.6) = y_3 = 29.13,$$
$$y(0.8) = y_4 = 37.99, \quad y(1.0) = y_5 = 46.21.$$

```
898        SUBROUTINE ERROR(X,E)
899        DIMENSION X(10),E(10)
900        E(1)=9.967-(X(1)+.2*X(2))/(1.+.2*X(3))
910        E(2)=19.74-(X(1)+.4*X(2))/(1.+.4*X(3))
920        E(3)=29.13-(X(1)+.6*X(2))/(1.+.6*X(3))
930        E(4)=37.99-(X(1)+.8*X(2))/(1.+.8*X(3))
940        E(5)=46.21-(X(1)+1.*X(2))/(1.+1.*X(3))
950        RETURN
999        END
```

(a)

```
M,N,P ? 5    3    2

X(I)    I=1,2,...,N
? 0     50     .5
  ERROR=     3.01371E+02

  X(I)=     5.73498E-02     4.89583E+01    -1.09513E-01
  ERROR=    1.09323E+02

  X(I)=    -1.70491E-01     5.14107E+01     7.37450E-02
  ERROR=    2.81954E+00

  X(I)=    -5.23130E-01     5.37790E+01     1.49232E-01
  ERROR=    2.28780E-02

  X(I)=    -5.53010E-01     5.39835E+01     1.55312E-01
  ERROR=    1.19690E-02

  X(I)=    -5.52727E-01     5.39826E+01     1.55308E-01
  ERROR=    1.19688E-02

  X(I)=    -5.52727E-01     5.39826E+01     1.55308E-01
  ERROR=    1.19688E-02
```

(b)

FIGURE 10.8. Least-squares data fitting with a ratio of polynomials.

That is, the coefficients will be chosen so as to minimize

$$E = \sum_{i=1}^{5} e_i^2 = \sum_{i=1}^{5} \left[y_i - f(x_i) \right]^2.$$

The individual error functions e_i for this example are shown in Fig. 10.8(a), and a computer output is shown in Fig. 10.8(b). The initial values for a_0, a_1, b_1 were picked by using the approximation

$$100 \frac{e^x - 1}{e^x + 1} \approx \frac{100x}{2 + x} = \frac{50x}{1 + 0.5x}.$$

This implies that good starting parameters would be $a_0 = 0$, $a_1 = 50$, $b_1 = 0.5$.

The output in Fig. 10.8 indicates that a good approximation for the function in this example is

$$100 \frac{e^x - 1}{e^x + 1} \approx \frac{-0.5527 + 53.98x}{1 + 0.1553x}. \tag{10.28}$$

This is a good example of the importance of choosing the initial parameters wisely. The initial parameters $a_0 = 0$, $a_1 = 50$, $b_1 = 0.5$ were based on knowledge about the behavior of $y(x)$ for small values of x. If the initial parameters were instead picked poorly, then the least-*p*th algorithm would not have been able to locate the minimum. For example, choosing $a_0 = a_1 = b_1 = 1$ led to the least-*p*th program attempting to make the parameters approach infinity.

Example 10.6 was the first time we did not restrict an approximating function to be a polynomial: we instead used a ratio of polynomials. This approximating function can be used to estimate the value of $y(x) = 100(e^x - 1)/(e^x + 1)$ at any value of x. As usual, the approximation will be better if x is located within the range of the given data. As a demonstration of using the approximating function for interpolation, consider

$$f(0.5) = \frac{-0.5527 + 53.98 \times 0.5}{1 + 0.1553 \times 0.5} = 24.53.$$

This agrees very well with the analytical answer $y(0.5) = 24.49$.

10.6 CHEBYSHEV APPROXIMATIONS

Chebyshev approximations occur in many different branches of science and engineering. The diverse applications of the theory due to Chebyshev provide a remarkable example of how an elegant mathematical development can have important practical results. For example, millions of electrical networks termed Chebyshev filters have been manufactured.

Chebyshev approximations were originally studied by means of Chebyshev polynomials. These polynomials are obtained by solving a differential equation which describes an approximation problem. The theory of Chebyshev polynomials is both interesting and time consuming. Those caring to pursue the subject further are referred to Daniels (1974).

The least-pth optimization technique offers a way of obtaining Chebyshev approximations without resorting to Chebyshev polynomials. In this section we will learn an easy way of finding Chebyshev approximations and also come to appreciate intuitively why this type of approximation is so important.

For the sake of comparison, we will first study the Maclaurin series. A function $y(x)$ can be approximated by the Maclaurin series

$$y(x) \approx \sum_{j=0}^{n} \frac{y^{(j)}(0)x^j}{j!}, \tag{10.29}$$

where $y^{(j)}(0)$ is the jth derivative of $y(x)$ evaluated at x equal to zero. The Maclaurin series is of course just a special case of the Taylor series.

The Maclaurin series is expressed in terms of powers of x and thus can be written as

$$y(x) \approx \sum_{j=0}^{n} a_j x^j = f(x). \tag{10.30}$$

The difference between the true function $y(x)$ and the approximation $f(x)$ can be defined to be the error $e(x)$. That is,

$$e(x) = y(x) - f(x). \tag{10.31}$$

The power series matches $y(x)$ and the first n derivatives at $x=0$; thus it is an extremely good match at the origin. However, the quality of the match decreases as we proceed away from the origin.

EXAMPLE 10.7

The function $y(x) = (100e^x)^2$ can be expanded in a Maclaurin series as

$$y(x) = 10^4 \left[1 + 2x + \frac{(2x)^2}{2} + \frac{(2x)^3}{3!} + \frac{(2x)^4}{4!} + \cdots \right].$$

It is of course not practical to continue the series indefinitely, so it must be truncated. In this example we will truncate the Maclaurin series to yield a fourth-degree polynomial $f(x)$ that approximates $(100e^x)^2$. This Maclaurin series is

$$f_m(x) = 10^4(1 + 2x + 2x^2 + 4x^3/3 + 2x^4/3). \tag{10.32}$$

The error of this approximation can be defined as

$$e(x) = 10^4 \left[e^{2x} - (1 + 2x + 2x^2 + 4x^3/3 + 2x^4/3) \right]. \tag{10.33}$$

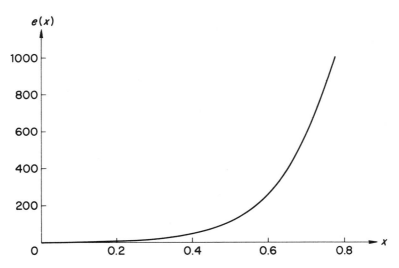

FIGURE 10.9. The error function for a Maclaurin series approximation.

This error is plotted in Fig. 10.9. Note that the error is zero at the origin, but the magnitude of the error increases as we proceed away from the origin.

The Maclaurin series concentrated its approximating power at the origin, where it matched $y(x)$ and the first three derivatives. This type of approximation is sometimes referred to as a maximally flat approximation. Instead of concentrating all the approximating power at the origin, we usually would prefer to have a better approximation over a specified region. Two ways of accomplishing this are illustrated in the next example.

EXAMPLE 10.8

The function $y(x) = (100e^x)^2$ can be approximated by a power series as

$$f(x) = a_0 + a_1 x + a_2 x^2 + a_3 x^3 + a_4 x^4. \tag{10.34}$$

The error of the approximation is

$$e(x) = 10^4 e^{2x} - (a_0 + a_1 x + a_2 x^2 + a_3 x^3 + a_4 x^4). \tag{10.35}$$

The coefficients in (10.35) can be found by applying optimization techniques.

For example, let individual error functions e_i be defined at $x = 0, 0.1, 0.2, \ldots, 1.0$. These error functions are shown in Fig. 10.10(a). The total error was optimized in a least-squares sense by choosing p equal to

```
898         SUBROUTINE ERROR(X,E)
899         DIMENSION X(20),E(20)
900         E(01)=10000.0- X(1)
902         E(02)=12214.0-(X(1)+.1*X(2)+.01*X(3)+.001*X(4)+.0001*X(5))
903         E(03)=14918.2-(X(1)+.2*X(2)+.04*X(3)+.008*X(4)+.0016*X(5))
904         E(04)=18221.2-(X(1)+.3*X(2)+.09*X(3)+.027*X(4)+.0081*X(5))
905         E(05)=22255.4-(X(1)+.4*X(2)+.16*X(3)+.064*X(4)+.0256*X(5))
906         E(06)=27182.8-(X(1)+.5*X(2)+.25*X(3)+.125*X(4)+.0625*X(5))
907         E(07)=33201.2-(X(1)+.6*X(2)+.36*X(3)+.216*X(4)+.1296*X(5))
908         E(08)=40552.0-(X(1)+.7*X(2)+.49*X(3)+.343*X(4)+.2401*X(5))
909         E(09)=49530.3-(X(1)+.8*X(2)+.64*X(3)+.512*X(4)+.4096*X(5))
910         E(10)=60496.5-(X(1)+.9*X(2)+.81*X(3)+.729*X(4)+.6561*X(5))
911         E(11)=73890.6-(X(1)+1.*X(2)+1.0*X(3)+1.00*X(4)+1.000*X(5))
950         RETURN
999         END
```

(a)

```
M,N,P ? 11   5   2

X(I)   I=1,2,...N
? 10000  20000  20000   13333  6667
  ERROR=    2.17750E+07

   X(I)=     1.00087E+04   1.93643E+04   2.49640E+04   4.89352E+02
   X(I)=     1.90548E+04
   ERROR=    1.43101E+03

   X(I)=     1.00087E+04   1.93643E+04   2.49640E+04   4.89382E+02
   X(I)=     1.90548E+04
   ERROR=    1.43101E+03
```

(b)

```
M,N,P ? 11   5   10

X(I)   I=1,2,...N
? 10008.7  19364.3  24964.0   489.352   19054.8
  ERROR=    1.00952E+13

   X(I)=     1.00157E+04   1.92936E+04   2.51726E+04   2.64280E+02
   X(I)=     1.91305E+04
   ERROR=    4.46970E+12

   X(I)=     1.00142E+04   1.93270E+04   2.50970E+04   2.88580E+02
   X(I)=     1.91507E+04
   ERROR=    2.44471E+12

   X(I)=     1.00135E+04   1.93296E+04   2.51002E+04   2.72466E+02
   X(I)=     1.91611E+04
   ERROR=    2.29063E+12

   X(I)=     1.00133E+04   1.93308E+04   2.50990E+04   2.70757E+02
   X(I)=     1.91630E+04
   ERROR=    2.28841E+12

   X(I)=     1.00133E+04   1.93308E+04   2.50989E+04   2.71022E+02
   X(I)=     1.91629E+04
   ERROR=    2.28840E+12
```

(c)

FIGURE 10.10. (a) The error functions used in Example 10.8. (b) Least-squares optimization for Example 10.8. (c) Least-tenth optimization for Example 10.8.

259

two as shown in Fig. 10.10(b). Note that the initial values for the parameters were selected from the Maclaurin series of (10.32). For the least-squares error criterion, Fig. 10.10(b) indicates that the approximating function is

$$f_2(x) = 10008.7 + 19364.3x + 24964x^2 + 489.382x^3 + 19054.8x^4. \quad (10.36)$$

Instead of choosing the power p equal to 2, it can be selected as any positive even integer. An example of this is indicated in Fig. 10.10(c), where p was 10. Note that this time the initial values for the parameters were selected from the least-squares function of (10.34). For the "least-tenth" error criterion, Fig. 10.10(c) indicates that the approximating function is

$$f_{10}(x) = 10013.3 + 19330.8x + 25098.9x^2 + 271.022x^3 + 19162.9x^4. \quad (10.37)$$

From the material in Examples 10.7 and 10.8 we now have three different fourth-degree polynomials that can be used to approximate $100e^{2x}$. We can decide which is best by comparing the error functions. The error function for the Maclaurin series was shown in Fig. 10.9; the error functions for $f_2(x)$ and $f_{10}(x)$ are shown in Fig. 10.11.

Comparing Fig. 10.11 with Fig. 10.9 indicates that the maximum error of the least-squares function $f_2(x)$ is smaller than the maximum error of the Maclaurin function $f_m(x)$. That is, the magnitude of the maximum error of $f_2(x)$ is approximately 20, while the magnitude of the maximum error of $f_m(x)$ is much greater than 1000.

The least-squares error criterion was able to produce a smaller maximum error than that due to the Maclaurin series. However, choosing $p = 10$ reduced the maximum error even more. From Fig. 10.11, the maximum error was reduced to approximately 15.

The Chebyshev error criterion seeks to minimize the maximum error. One way of doing this is to use Chebyshev polynomials to yield an approximating function. However, our previous work has indicated another way: we can use the least-pth program and choose p to be a large number (for example, $p = 10$). If errors that are almost equal are raised to a large power such as ten, then the largest error will be magnified and will contribute much more to the total error function.

We now see why it is so useful to have a least-pth program instead of a more restrictive least-squares program. As demonstrated in the first part of this chapter, the least-pth program can be applied to minimize errors in a least-squares sense. However, as just demonstrated, the same program can also be used to yield a Chebyshev error criterion.

As illustrated in Fig. 10.11, the Chebyshev error criterion seeks to minimize the maximum error by making the peak errors have equal

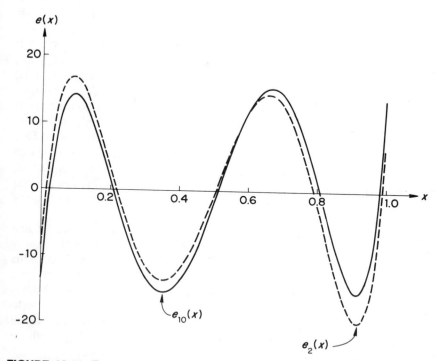

FIGURE 10.11. Error functions for a least-squares approximation (dashed curve) and a least-tenth approximation (solid curve).

magnitudes; that is, it produces an *equiripple* error function. The least-pth program can be used to produce equiripple error functions not only for polynomials as in (10.34), but also for more general functions such as ratios of polynomials. However, there are a couple of pitfalls that must be avoided.

In the least-pth program, the error function is only calculated at discrete points. For example, in Ex. 10.8 it was calculated at $x = 0, 0.1, 0.2, \ldots, 1$. By choosing p as a large number we can minimize the maximum error at *these* points, but it is possible that a larger error occurs between the points. However, if a sufficient number of points is specified, it is unlikely that a much larger error will occur between the points. A good rule of thumb is that twice as many points should be specified as arbitrary constants. Whether or not this number of points is sufficient can be determined by plotting the error function and observing whether or not it is equiripple. If it is not equiripple, then more points should be added. Note that these points need not be equally spaced. Usually it is best to have more near the ends of the approximation interval, where the approximating function varies most rapidly.

Another problem that may be encountered when applying the least-*p*th algorithm to yield an equiripple error function is that the process may not converge. When *p* is selected as a large number, the initial parameters must be selected very carefully or one of the individual errors may be much larger than any other—this can cause the least-*p*th algorithm to diverge. If convergence problems are encountered, the least-*p*th program can first be applied with $p = 2$. A good set of initial parameters is relatively easy to find for this case. Then the optimized parameters for the least-squares case can be used as initial parameters for a higher power *p*. In this way *p* can be increased until the error function is sufficiently equiripple (assuming that increasing *p* does not cause numerical overflow problems; then scaling would be necessary).

The least-*p*th algorithm that has been developed in this chapter is just one of many possible ones. This one was described because it is closely related to the previous material on the steepest-descent method. This least-*p*th method converged extremely rapidly for the examples that were given in this chapter; but in other examples it could encounter difficulties because of the approximation of derivatives by finite differences. Peckham[5] has described a method which does not require the calculation of derivatives. It can get around potential difficulties by using methods similar to those described in the simplex optimization method.

---

[5]Peckham, G. (Nov. 1970), "A New Method for Minimizing a Sum of Squares Without Calculating Gradients", *Computer J.*, pp. 418–420.

PROBLEMS

10.1 The error function $E(\mathbf{x}) = 25(x_1 - 10)^2 + 100(x_1 x_2)^2$ can be considered to be of the form $E(\mathbf{x}) = w_1 e_1^2 + w_2 e_2^2$, where $w_1 = 25$, $w_2 = 100$, $e_1 = x_1 - 10$, and $e_2 = x_1 x_2$. Instead of these individual error functions e_1, e_2, define new error functions by using the substitution in (10.2).

10.2 For the individual error functions $e_1 = x_1 - 10$ and $e_2 = x_1 x_2$, use (10.5) to determine an expression for ∇E.

10.3 (a) What is the Jacobian for the error functions in Problem 10.2?

(b) Use (10.7) to determine an expression for ∇E.

10.4 For the individual error functions

$$e_1 = x_1(x_2 + 10) \quad \text{and} \quad e_2 = (x_1 + 5)x_2:$$

(a) Find $\nabla E(1, 1)$ by using (10.7).

(b) Find $\nabla E(1.01, 1.02)$ by using (10.8).

(c) Approximate $\nabla E(1.01, 1.02)$ by using (10.9).

10.5 For the individual error functions $e_1 = x_1(x_2 + 10)$ and $e_2 = (x_1 + 5)x_2$, use the approximation in (10.11) to estimate $\mathbf{e}(1.01, 1.02)$. Choose the initial point as $\mathbf{x} = (1, 1)$.

10.6 The number of error functions, m, need not be equal to the number of parameters, n. In this problem $m = 3$ while $n = 2$. If $e_1 = x_1$, $e_2 = x_2$, and $e_3 = x_1 x_2$:

(a) Find $\nabla E(1, 2)$ by using (10.7).

(b) Use the approximation in (10.11) to estimate $\mathbf{e}(1.01, 2.02)$.

10.7 If $e_1 = x_1(x_2 + 10)$ and $e_2 = (x_1 + 5)x_2$, what would the least-squares optimization technique yield for $\delta \mathbf{x}$ if the initial parameters are $\mathbf{x} = (1, 1)$?

10.8 If $e_1 = x_1$, $e_2 = x_2$, and $e_3 = x_1 x_2$, what would the least-squares optimization technique yield for $\delta \mathbf{x}$ if the initial parameters are $\mathbf{x} = (1, 2)$?

10.9 For $e_1 = x_1$, $e_2 = x_2$, and $e_3 = x_1 x_2$ calculate $\mathbf{H} = \mathbf{J}' \mathbf{e}^{p-1}$. Let the initial parameters be $\mathbf{x} = (1, 2)$ and choose $p = 4$.

10.10 Apply one iteration of the least-pth algorithm with $p = 4$ to yield $\delta \mathbf{x}$ for the following conditions: $e_1 = x_1(x_2 + 10)$, $e_2 = (x_1 + 5)x_2$, initial parameter $\mathbf{x} = (1, 1)$.

10.11 For the following test functions, give the individual error functions that would be required for least-pth optimization:

263

(a) Rosenbrock

(b) "Cube"

(c) Powell

(d) Coefficient matching

10.12 If one never uses the least-*p*th method for any case except $p=2$, then the program in Fig. 10.1 can be simplified considerably. Simplify the program for the least-squares case.

10.13 What is the purpose of statement 32 in Fig. 10.1?

10.14 Solve Problem 8.14 by using the least-*p*th program (with $p=2$).

10.15 Solve Problem 8.15 by using the least-*p*th program (with $p=2$). Use as initial conditions $x=(-1, -1, -1)$.

10.16 Re-solve Example 8.4 by using the least-*p*th program (with $p=2$).

10.17 Re-solve Example 9.6 by using the least-*p*th program (with $p=2$).

10.18 In Example 10.6 the function $y(x)=100(e^x-1)/(e^x+1)$ was approximated by $f(x)=(a_0+a_1x)/(1+b_1x)$. Find a better approximation by applying the least-*p*th program to minimize the mean-square error due to $f(x)=(a_0+a_1x)/(1+b_1x+b_2x^2)$. Use the same data points as in Example 10.6.

10.19 For the individual error function

$$e_i(\mathbf{a})=y_i-\left(a_0+a_1x_i+a_2x_i^2\right):$$

(a) Show that $\dfrac{\partial e_i(\mathbf{a}+\delta\mathbf{a})}{\partial a_k}=\dfrac{\partial e_i(\mathbf{a})}{\partial a_k}$.

(b) Show that $e_i(\mathbf{a}+\delta\mathbf{a})=e_i(\mathbf{a})+\displaystyle\sum_{k=0}^{2}\dfrac{\partial e_i(\mathbf{a})}{\partial a_k}\delta a_k$.

Note that (a) implies the approximation in (10.9) would be exact for this error function, while (b) implies the approximation in (10.10) would likewise be exact.

10.20 Use the least-squares program to find the coefficients in the following approximation: $\cos x \approx a_0+a_1x+a_2x^2=f(x)$. Define the error function as $e(x)=\cos x-f(x)$, and let $x=0,0.1,0.2,\ldots,0.5$.

10.21 Use the least-squares program to find the coefficients in the following approximation: $\sin x \approx a_0+a_1x+a_2x^2+a_3x^3=f(x)$. Define the error functions as $e(x)=\sin x-f(x)$, and let $x=0,0.1,0.2,\ldots,0.5$.

10.22 Proceed as in Problems 10.20 and 10.21, except this time approximate $\tan x$ as $\tan x \approx (a_0+a_1x)/(1+b_1x+b_2x^2)$. (*Hint:* Use a Maclaurin series for $\sin x$ to yield initial values for a_0, a_1, and use a Maclaurin series for $\cos x$ to yield initial values for b_1, b_2.)

Chapter Eleven

Constrained Optimization Problems

11.1 INTRODUCTION

In the previous three chapters we have studied different techniques that can be applied to solve optimization problems. In the material presented thus far it has been assumed that all of the parameters were unconstrained. However, in practical problems the parameter values usually are not allowed to attain any value that a designer might like to specify.

A chemical engineer might use an optimization technique to determine the temperature, pressure, and duration of a certain process. If a computer indicates that the optimum process requires a temperature so high that the container would melt, then the engineer must settle for a lower temperature. One solution would be to fix the temperature at the highest allowable value and then optimize the remaining parameters; but this is not necessarily the best solution.

We have just observed that in some situations a parameter might be constrained to be less than an upper bound. In other cases, a parameter might be constrained to be greater than a lower bound. For example, returning to our hypothetical chemical process, the apparatus may be capable of reducing the pressure to only one-half an atmosphere which would thus be a lower bound. Similarly, a parameter may have both an upper bound and a lower bound. In this chapter we will learn how to treat any of these three cases. The approach we will use will be to transform a bounded problem to an unbounded one; then any of the previously discussed optimization techniques can be applied to the unconstrained problem.

Not only can there be constraints on individual parameters; there can be a constraint on a function of the parameters. For example, consider an electrical network that is constructed by putting many resistors on a thin-film circuit. There is an upper bound to the total amount of resistance that can be put onto such a circuit. If this upper bound is denoted as U, then the constraint can be written as

$$\sum_i R_i \leqslant U, \tag{11.1}$$

where R_i is a resistance. In this chapter we will also learn how to optimize problems when there are constraints such as these.

11.2   ACTIVE CONSTRAINTS VERSUS INACTIVE CONSTRAINTS

Assume that the error function $E(\mathbf{x})$ is a function of the two parameters x_1, x_2. Furthermore, assume that the parameters are constrained as indicated below:

$$-2 \leqslant x_1 \leqslant 0.5, \qquad x_1 + x_2 \leqslant 1, \qquad x_1 - x_2 \leqslant 1. \qquad (11.2)$$

These constraints are illustrated in Fig. 11.1. The region inside the shaded area is referred to as the *feasible region*. By definition, no constraints are violated within the feasible region.

In any constrained optimization problem the first task will be to select an initial set of parameters that is located in the feasible region. Sometimes this can be simply done by randomly choosing points and having good luck. Other times a systematic approach of varying the parameters one at a time will be necessary. Often insight into the practical problem will be necessary. In some cases it may not even be possible to obtain a feasible

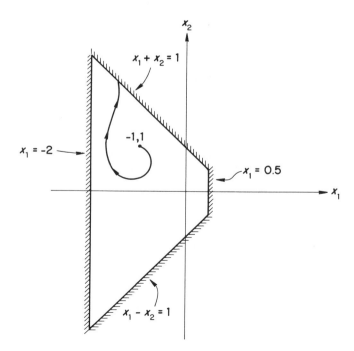

FIGURE 11.1. A possible optimization path in a feasible region.

set of parameters. One may then be forced to find ways of modifying the constraints.

Once a feasible set of initial parameters has been determined, then one can start the optimization procedure by applying an optimization program and monitoring the way the parameters are varied. As long as no constraints are violated, everything is fine. However, if the optimization procedure attempts to force the parameters into the forbidden region, then something must be done.

Different optimization techniques use different methods to guarantee that the parameters always remain in the feasible region. For example, at a constraint boundary the *gradient-projection* method chooses a *feasible direction* by projecting the negative gradient onto the constraint boundary and then proceeding in that projected direction. A detailed description of the gradient-projection method is beyond the scope of this text, but a simple feasible-direction method will be discussed next.

As an illustration of how the parameter could be kept in the feasible region, consider again Fig. 11.1. This indicates that from the initial point $x = (-1, 1)$ an optimization procedure varied the parameters until the constraint $x_1 + x_2 \leq 1$ was encountered. Until that point, the optimization procedure had progressed as if there were no constraints; that is, the constraints were *inactive*. However, when the boundary between the feasible and forbidden region was encountered the constraint $x_1 + x_2 \leq 1$ became *active*.

When a constraint is active, often it can be used to remove one of the parameters from the error function. For example, if the constraint $x_1 + x_2 \leq 1$ is active, then one can make the substitution $x_2 = 1 - x_1$. One can then proceed and use an unconstrained optimization program. However, care must be taken in this approach, because even though a constraint becomes active in a minimization search, it may later become inactive.

The above procedure varies the parameters, which are related by the active constraints, until a minimum is reached. If one knew ahead of time what constraints would be active at the minimum, then the constrained optimization problem would be greatly simplified. The active constraints could be used to simplify the error function, which could then be minimized by an unconstrained optimization program.

Although one may not be able to predict which constraints will be active at the minimum, there are only a finite number of combinations of constraints that can be active. For example, if there are three constraints, a, b, c, then

(1) none might be active;

(2) a, (3) b, or (4) c might be active;

(5) a and b, (6) a and c, or (7) b and c might be active;

(8) a, b, and c might be active.

The optimization problem could be solved for each of these cases and the results examined. Any proposed solution that violates constraints which were assumed to be inactive should be discarded. The remaining solutions can be compared, and the one with the smallest error function is the correct answer.

EXAMPLE 11.1

Minimize

$$E(\mathbf{x}) = x_1^2 + 2x_2^2 + 3x_3^2 + 4x_4^2 \tag{11.3}$$

subject to the constraints

(a) $x_1 \geqslant 0.4$, (b) $x_2 + x_3 \geqslant 0.5$, (c) $x_3 + x_4 \geqslant 0.6$.

SOLUTION

There are eight different combinations of these constraints, and thus eight different optimization problems must be solved. The different possibilities are indicated in Table 11.1. The first couple of possibilities were so simple that an optimization program did not have to be applied to yield the solution vector. For example, if it is assumed that no constraints are active, then it is obvious that the minimum is located at $\mathbf{x} = (0,0,0,0)$. However, all three constraints are violated at that location, so it is not a feasible point.

As another possibility, assume that constraints a and b are active at the minimum. Substituting $x_1 = 0.4$ and $x_2 = 0.5 - x_3$ into (11.3) yields

$$E(\mathbf{x}) = 0.16 + 2(0.5 - x_3)^2 + 3x_3^2 + 4x_4^2. \tag{11.4}$$

Table 11.1

ACTIVE CONSTRAINTS	SOLUTION VECTOR	CONSTRAINTS VIOLATED
None	0, 0, 0, 0	a,b,c
a	0.4, 0, 0, 0	b,c
b	0, 0.3, 0.2, 0	a,c
c	0, 0, 0.34, 0.26	b,c
a,b	0.4, 0.3, 0.2, 0	c
a,c	0.4, 0, 0.34, 0.26	b
b,c	0, 0.12, 0.38, 0.22	a
a,b,c	0.4, 0.12, 0.38, 0.22	None

Applying the least-pth program to this error function yields $x = (0.4, 0.3, 0.2, 0)$.

Table 11.1 indicates if (and only if) all constraints were active, then the minimum point was in the feasible region; so the minimum is $E(0.4, 0.12, 0.38, 0.22) = 0.82$.

Although it is true that for a finite number of constraints there is a finite number of possibilities as to which constraints will be active, it may also be true that the number of possibilities is so large that it is impractical to analyze them all. Fortunately, as indicated in the following sections, there are other approaches that can be used.

11.3 TRANSFORMATIONS

Many of the constraints that are encountered can be eliminated by using special transformations. In the transformed problem, no parameters are constrained, and thus the standard optimization programs can be used. Once the transformed problem has been optimized, the unconstrained parameters (which are guaranteed to be in the feasible region) can be determined from the transformed parameters.

The notation that will be used is that $\mathbf{x} = (x_1, x_2, \dots, x_n)$ are the constrained parameters and $\mathbf{z} = (z_1, z_2, \dots, z_n)$ are the unconstrained parameters. As an example, assume that x_1 is constrained to be greater than the lower bound x_{1l}; that is, $x_1 \geqslant x_{1l}$. We can thus express x_1 as

$$x_1 = x_{1l} + z_1^2 \qquad (11.5)$$

Here the parameter z_1 is unconstrained ($-\infty < z_1 < \infty$), but the parameter x_1 is constrained to be greater than (or equal to) x_{1l}, as required.

Generalizing, if parameters are constrained to be greater than (or equal to) lower bounds as indicated by

$$x_i \geqslant x_{il}, \qquad (11.6)$$

then the constrained problem can be transformed to an unconstrained problem by introducing the substitutions

$$x_i = x_{il} + z_i^2. \qquad (11.7)$$

EXAMPLE 11.2

Minimize the Rosenbrock function $E(\mathbf{x}) = 100(x_1^2 - x_2)^2 + (1 - x_1)^2$ subject to the constraints $x_1 \geqslant -2$ and $x_2 \geqslant 2$.

SOLUTION

For this example, the transformations in (11.7) are

$$x_1 = -2 + z_1^2, \qquad x_2 = 2 + z_2^2,$$

so that the transformed error function is

$$E(\mathbf{z}) = 100\left[\left(-2+z_1^2\right)^2 - \left(2+z_2^2\right)\right]^2 + \left[1-\left(-2+z_1^2\right)\right]^2.$$

The simplex program was applied to this (see Fig. 11.2) and yielded that the minimum is at $\mathbf{z} = (1.848, 0.07)$, where $E = 0.17$. Thus in terms of the constrained parameters, the minimum is where

$$x_1 = -2 + (1.848)^2 = 1.39, \qquad x_2 = 2 + (0.07)^2 \approx 2.$$

In this example, both parameters x_1 and x_2 were constrained. However, the optimized answer $\mathbf{x} = (1.4136, 2)$ indicates that only the constraint $x_2 \geqslant 2$ was active. We can now use hindsight to verify the optimized answer. Since the constraint $x_2 \geqslant 2$ is active, we can set $x_2 = 2$ in the error function to yield

$$E(\mathbf{x}) = 100\left(x_1^2 - 2\right)^2 + (1 - x_1)^2.$$

Because this is a function of only one variable, it can be minimized by applying the quadratic interpolation program of Fig. 3.5. The result is $x_1 = 1.4137$, which verifies the answer in Example 11.2.

The transformation for lower bounds was applied so that only a positive quantity could be added to a lower bound. The quantity was guaranteed to be positive, since it was the square of a real number. It is very easy to proceed by analogy to this approach and obtain a transformation for upper bounds. This time a positive quantity should be subtracted from the upper bound. Again, the quantity can be guaranteed to be positive if it is the square of a real number.

The above discussion indicates that if parameters are constrained to be less than (or equal to) upper bounds as indicated by

$$x_i \leqslant x_{iu}, \tag{11.8}$$

then the constrained problem can be transformed to an unconstrained problem by introducing the substitutions

$$x_i = x_{iu} - z_i^2. \tag{11.9}$$

EXAMPLE 11.3

Minimize the cube test function $E(\mathbf{x}) = 100(x_1^3 - x_2)^2 + (1 - x_1)^2$ subject to the constraints $x_1 \leqslant 0.5$ and $x_2 \leqslant 0.6$. Choose as initial parameters $\mathbf{x} = (0.4, 0.5)$.

SOLUTION

For this example, the transformations in (11.9) are

$$x_1 = 0.5 - z_1^2, \qquad x_2 = 0.6 - z_2^2,$$

```
N ? 2

X(I)   I=1,2,...N
?  2        .2
  ERROR=    3.85160E+02

    X(I)=   1.80030E+00    2.19985E-01
  ERROR=    2.58761E+01

    X(I)=   1.84983E+00    2.27500E-01
  ERROR=    2.68001E-01

    X(I)=   1.84965E+00    2.07554E-01
  ERROR=    2.31640E-01

    X(I)=   1.85279E+00    2.17375E-01
  ERROR=    1.90630E-01

    X(I)=   1.85118E+00    2.07484E-01
  ERROR=    1.87314E-01

    X(I)=   1.85068E+00    1.95089E-01
  ERROR=    1.86122E-01

    X(I)=   1.85161E+00    2.03119E-01
  ERROR=    1.83630E-01

    X(I)=   1.85108E+00    1.82788E-01
  ERROR=    1.82106E-01

    X(I)=   1.84995E+00    1.59748E-01
  ERROR=    1.78994E-01

    X(I)=   1.84955E+00    1.26972E-01
  ERROR=    1.77777E-01

    X(I)=   1.84842E+00    1.03992E-01
  ERROR=    1.75115E-01

    X(I)=   1.84802E+00    7.12828E-02
  ERROR=    1.72928E-01
```

FIGURE 11.2. A transformed version of a lower-bounded problem.

so that the transformed error function is

$$E(\mathbf{z}) = 100\left[\left(0.5 - z_1^2\right)^3 - \left(0.6 - z_2^2\right)\right]^2 + \left[1 - \left(0.5 - z_1^2\right)\right]^2.$$

The optimization will be done in terms of this error function because z_1, z_2 are unconstrained. However, the initial parameter values were given in terms of $\mathbf{x}$, so they must be transformed to equivalent parameter values in terms of $\mathbf{z}$.

For any value of $\mathbf{x}$, an equivalent value for $\mathbf{z}$ can be found by applying (11.9) to yield[1]

$$z_i = \left(x_{iu} - x_i\right)^{\frac{1}{2}}. \tag{11.10}$$

If the parameter x_i is in the feasible region, then it cannot be greater than the upper bound, so that we need not worry about requiring the square root of a negative number. Equation (11.10) can be applied to yield equivalent initial parameters for this problem:

$$z_1 = (0.5 - 0.4)^{\frac{1}{2}} \approx 0.32, \qquad z_2 = (0.6 - 0.5)^{\frac{1}{2}} \approx 0.32.$$

For the above initial parameters, the steepest-descent program was applied to the transformed error function, and the results are shown in Fig. 11.3. The results indicate that the minimum is at $\mathbf{z} = (0.051, 0.689)$, where $E = 0.253$. Thus in terms of the constrained parameters, the minimum is where

$$x_1 = 0.5 - (0.051)^2 \approx 0.5, \qquad x_2 = 0.6 - (0.689)^2 = 0.125.$$

The transformations in (11.7) and (11.9) allow one to treat constraints that are either upper bounds or lower bounds. We will now learn how to transform parameters x_i that have both upper bounds and lower bounds:

$$x_{il} \leqslant x_i \leqslant x_{iu}. \tag{11.11}$$

A transformation that can be used to restrict a parameter to such a range of values is

$$x_i = x_{il} + \left(x_{iu} - x_{il}\right)\left(\sin z_i\right)^2. \tag{11.12}$$

In this equation the parameter z_i is unconstrained; but because $(\sin z_i)^2$ varies between zero and unity, the parameter x_i is constrained. In particular, when $\sin z_i = 0$, x_i then has its minimum value of x_{il}. On the other hand, when $\sin z_i = \pm 1$, x_i then has its maximum value of x_{iu}.

The inverse transformation for the relation in (11.12) is

$$z_i = \sin^{-1}\left[\frac{x_i - x_{il}}{x_{iu} - x_{il}}\right]^{\frac{1}{2}}. \tag{11.13}$$

---

[1]Note that the negative square root could have been selected instead.

```
N ? 2

X(I)   I=1,2,...N
? .32     .32
  ERROR=    1.92632E+01

   X(I)=    1.07795E-01    7.54745E-01
  ERROR=    1.00353E+00

   X(I)=    1.13674E-01    6.92011E-01
  ERROR=    2.66185E-01

   X(I)=    1.12594E-01    6.96033E-01
  ERROR=    2.62842E-01

   X(I)=    8.96238E-02    6.90534E-01
  ERROR=    2.59770E-01

   X(I)=    8.88595E-02    6.93526E-01
  ERROR=    2.57961E-01

   X(I)=    7.30132E-02    6.89793E-01
  ERROR=    2.56346E-01

   X(I)=    7.24387E-02    6.92109E-01
  ERROR=    2.55276E-01

   X(I)=    6.07960E-02    6.89387E-01
  ERROR=    2.54333E-01

   X(I)=    6.03457E-02    6.91239E-01
  ERROR=    2.53656E-01

   X(I)=    5.13904E-02    6.89156E-01
  ERROR=    2.53062E-01
```

FIGURE 11.3. A transformed version of an upper-bounded problem.

EXAMPLE 11.4

Minimize the Rosenbrock function

$$E(\mathbf{x}) = 100(x_1^2 - x_2)^2 + (1 - x_1)^2 \tag{11.14}$$

subject to the constraint

$$-2 \leq x_1 \leq 0.8.$$

SOLUTION

For this example, the transformation in (11.12) is

$$x_1 = -2 + 2.8(\sin z_1)^2. \tag{11.15}$$

Substituting this transformation into the Rosenbrock function yields the following error function:

$$E = 100\left\{\left[-2 + 2.8(\sin z_1)^2\right]^2 - x_2\right\}^2 + \left[3 - 2.8(\sin z_1)^2\right]^2. \tag{11.16}$$

The result of using the simplex program for this error function is shown in Fig. 11.4, which indicates that the minimum for the constrained error function is located at $z_1 = \pi/2$, $x_2 = 0.64$. We can use (11.12) to obtain the value of x_1 that corresponds to z_1:

$$x_1 = -2 + 2.8\sin(\pi/2) = 0.8.$$

The error function at $\mathbf{x} = (0.8, 0.64)$ is equal to 0.04.

Example 11.2 applied the transformation in (11.7) for lower bounds, Example 11.3 applied the transformation in (11.9) for upper bounds, and Example 11.4 applied the transformation in (11.12) for a parameter that was restricted to a range of values. It is of course possible to encounter the three types of bounds in the same problem. This presents no added difficulty; the proper transformation is simply selected for each type of constraint.

In the preceding pages, the possibility that the optimization procedure may not converge was ignored. However, the transformations introduced in this section often scale the parameters in such a way as to introduce convergence problems. The rest of this section will discuss various remedies for this situation.

If transforming a constrained optimization problem into an unconstrained optimization problem creates difficulties, the first solution that may come to mind is "don't transform". We saw in the previous section that constrained problems can be solved by examining all the different combinations of active and inactive constraints. This is an attractive approach for a small number of constraints, but is too time consuming for many constraints.

Another approach is to use different transformations. The transformations described in this section are not unique: there are many others that can be used to transform a constrained problem to an unconstrained one. For some other transformations see Box (1966).

If a particular optimization program (for example, steepest descent) encounters convergence problems, another optimization technique can be

```
N ? 2

X(I)   I=1,2,...N
? 2      .5
ERROR=     1.65260E+01

   X(I)=    1.61059E+00     5.73677E-01
   ERROR=   3.92896E-01

   X(I)=    1.41697E+00     5.72921E-01
   ERROR=   1.84672E-01

   X(I)=    1.46545E+00     5.97988E-01
   ERROR=   5.76557E-02

   X(I)=    1.48509E+00     6.14325E-01
   ERROR=   5.31571E-02

   X(I)=    1.52920E+00     6.28757E-01
   ERROR=   4.31982E-02

   X(I)=    1.54440E+00     6.37791E-01
   ERROR=   4.08667E-02

   X(I)=    1.54824E+00     6.36565E-01
   ERROR=   4.07060E-02

   X(I)=    1.55295E+00     6.39661E-01
   ERROR=   4.04755E-02

   X(I)=    1.56266E+00     6.38738E-01
   ERROR=   4.01674E-02

   X(I)=    1.57704E+00     6.40906E-01
   ERROR=   4.01606E-02
```

FIGURE 11.4. A transformed version of a problem with upper and lower bounds.

applied. As noted many times, no one optimization technique is always best. In this book four optimization techniques have been described in detail: simplex, steepest descent, Fletcher-Powell, and least pth. Many others have been described in the literature.

Instead of applying a new optimization technique, a reader of this book may have more immediate success by modifying one of the programs described in this text. Since this is an introductory text, the algorithms have been kept relatively simple. If convergence problems are encountered in a particular application, the reader may now have enough insight into the algorithm to be able to modify it so that it will converge.

11.4 PENALTY FUNCTIONS

The previous section described a constrained problem that had constraints of the form

$$x_{il} \leqslant x_i, \qquad x_i \leqslant x_{iu}, \qquad x_{il} \leqslant x_i \leqslant x_{iu}. \tag{11.17}$$

We were able to transform problems of this type into equivalent unconstrained problems. However, these are not the only types of constraints that may be encountered. For example, in (11.2) we had the constraint $x_1 + x_2 \leqslant 1$, which is not of the form of any of the constraints in (11.17).

In this section we will learn how to apply unconstrained optimization programs to constraints that are much more general than those that were studied in the previous section. In particular, we will learn how to:

Minimize $E(\mathbf{x})$

Subject to $\qquad\qquad C_i(\mathbf{x}) \geqslant 0, \qquad i = 1, 2, \ldots, c. \tag{11.18}$

This notation indicates that there are c different constraints: $C_1, C_2, \ldots, C_c$. Any of these constraints can be a function of more than one parameter.

EXAMPLE 11.5

The constraints in (11.2) were

$$-2 \leqslant x_1 \leqslant 0.5, \qquad x_1 + x_2 \leqslant 1, \qquad x_1 - x_2 \leqslant 1.$$

These constraints can be put into the form of (11.18) as indicated below:

$$C_1(x) = x_1 + 2 \geqslant 0, \qquad C_3(x) = 1 - x_1 - x_2 \geqslant 0,$$
$$C_2(x) = 0.5 - x_1 \geqslant 0, \qquad C_4(x) = 1 - x_1 + x_2 \geqslant 0.$$

The constrained problem will be solved by minimizing an error function $E^*(\mathbf{x})$ which is related to the original error function $E(\mathbf{x})$ via a *penalty function*:

$$E^*(\mathbf{x}) = E(\mathbf{x}) + \text{penalty function}. \tag{11.19}$$

The penalty function is introduced so that $E^*(\mathbf{x})$ can be an unconstrained problem. This will be done by choosing the initial set of points $\mathbf{x}$ to be in the feasible region (i.e., $\mathbf{x}$ satisfies the constraints). If the optimization procedure tries to find a minimum by going out of the feasible region, then the penalty function will become large and "force" the parameters to stay in the feasible region.

There are many different forms that are possible for the penalty function; we will choose the simple one

$$\text{penalty function} = r \sum_{i=1}^{c} \frac{1}{C_i(\mathbf{x})},\qquad(11.20)$$

where r is a positive constant. To understand why this is a possible penalty function, recall that in the feasible region $C_i(\mathbf{x})$ is positive. However, as $\mathbf{x}$ approaches a boundary of the feasible region the penalty function will become very large—which is exactly what is desired.

The parameter r is a "constant" that will initially be chosen quite large, e.g., $r = 100$. If an optimization run is done for r large, the penalty function will be quite large even far from the boundary of the feasible region. Thus the minimum of $E^*(\mathbf{x})$ in (11.19) will not also be the minimum of $E(\mathbf{x})$. However, because the penalty function is quite large even far from the boundary, we do not have to worry about a finite change in parameters causing us to jump across the boundary.

Now suppose r is reduced and the parameters $\mathbf{x}$ found in the previous paragraph are used for initial parameters in another optimization run. Because r is smaller, the new optimum will be a little closer to the boundary of the feasible region. If r is reduced slowly enough, the changes will be small, so $\mathbf{x}$ will always stay in the feasible region.

Summarizing, instead of minimizing the error function $E(\mathbf{x})$ subject to the constraints $C_i(\mathbf{x}) \geqslant 0$, we will minimize the unconstrained problem

$$E^*(\mathbf{x}) = E(\mathbf{x}) + r \sum_{i=1}^{c} \frac{1}{C_i(\mathbf{x})}.\qquad(11.21)$$

This will be done by sequentially solving a series of optimization problems. The parameter r will initially be quite large and then be gradually reduced. It should be noted that as r approaches zero the unconstrained problem for $E^*(\mathbf{x})$ approaches the constrained problem for $E(\mathbf{x})$. Because r is sequentially reduced, this method has been called SUMT (sequential unconstrained minimization technique).

Before an example can be done, it will be necessary to modify one of our optimization programs. As the programs are presently written, large parameter changes at early stages of optimization may cause the parameters to leave the feasible region and enter the forbidden region. Once the parameters are in the forbidden region, at least one of the constraints $C_i(\mathbf{x})$ will be negative, and the parameters may then be adjusted so that $E^*(\mathbf{x})$ of (11.21) approaches minus infinity.

As an illustration of how a program can be modified to keep the parameters in the feasible region, consider the least-pth program. This will be discussed with reference to the following problem:

$$\text{Minimize} \qquad E(\mathbf{x}) = x_1^2 + 2x_2^2 + 3x_3^2 + 4x_4^2,$$

$$\text{subject to} \qquad x_1 + x_2 \geqslant 0.4. \tag{11.22}$$

The penalty function will be defined as $[k/(x_1 + x_2 - 0.4)]^2$, so that the unconstrained error function is

$$E^*(\mathbf{x}) = x_1^2 + 2x_2^2 + 3x_3^2 + 4x_4^2 + \left[\frac{k}{x_1 + x_2 - 0.4} \right]^2. \tag{11.23}$$

It should be noted that the penalty function was not defined as equal to the reciprocal of the constraint, but instead as the square of the reciprocal. This allowed the error function $E^*(x)$ to be written as a sum of squares, which is necessary for a least-squares solution.

For this example, the constraint can be added to the least-pth program (Fig. 10.1) via

$$210 \quad \text{IF(X1(1)} + \text{X1(2) .LT. 4.) GO TO 202}$$

and the error functions can be written as (assuming $k = 1$)

```
900   E(1) = X(1)
910   E(2) = SQRT(2.)*X(2)
920   E(3) = SQRT(3.)*X(3)
930   E(4) = 2.*X(4)
940   E(5) = 1./(X(1) + X(2) − .4)
```

The results of applying the modified least-squares program are shown in Table 11.2. It should be noted that each separate value of k required a different optimization run. For each new run, statement 940 was modified to reflect the change in k.

It should be mentioned that for the data in Table 11.2, the optimized values were obtained by allowing the computer to use two iterations of the

Table 11.2

k	INITIAL VALUES					OPTIMIZED VALUES				
	X_1	X_2	X_3	X_4	E^*	X_1	X_2	X_3	X_4	E^*
1	1.000	2.000	3.000	4.000	100.15	0.794	0.397	0.000	0.000	25.89
0.1	0.794	0.397	0.000	0.000	0.96	0.483	0.241	0.000	0.000	0.44
0.01	0.483	0.241	0.000	0.000	0.35	0.302	0.151	0.000	0.000	0.17
0.001	0.302	0.151	0.000	0.000	0.14	0.275	0.137	0.000	0.000	0.12
0.0001	0.275	0.137	0.000	0.000	0.11	0.269	0.134	0.000	0.000	0.11

least-squares algorithm. For example, when k was equal to unity, two iterations reduced $E^*(1, 2, 3, 4) = 100.15$ to $E^*(0.794, 0.397, 0, 0) = 25.89$. More iterations of the least-squares algorithm would not have reduced the error E^* much further, because $k = 1$ corresponds to a large penalty function.

A much larger reduction in the error function was possible by reducing k to the value 0.1. The initial values for this optimization problem were chosen as the previous optimized values. The least-squares algorithm then adjusted these parameters to yield $E^*(0.483, 0.241, 0, 0) = 0.44$.

By gradually reducing the value of k, the error function was eventually reduced to $E^*(0.269, 0.134, 0.000, 0.001) = 0.11$. The value of k for this error function was 0.0001, which is so small that the unconstrained error function E^* essentially corresponds to the constrained function E. In fact, notice that the optimized values of x_1, x_2 are such that their sum is equal to 0.403, which is extremely close to the constraint of 0.4.

We have just seen that by gradually reducing the value of the penalty constant r (or equivalently the value of k), the unconstrained optimization problem E^* can be made to approach the constrained optimization problem E. If one attempts to write a noninteractive batch program that automatically selects an initial value for r and then automatically reduces r, difficulty may be encountered in making the program foolproof. However, in an interactive program[2] one can use many different strategies for varying the penalty constant r, and thus one should be able to finally make the unconstrained problem for E^* approach the constrained problem for E.

The constrained optimization technique that was just discussed is referred to as an interior-point algorithm. The initial point was selected to be in the feasible region, and then penalty functions were designed to keep the parameters interior to the feasible region. These penalty functions can be viewed as barriers which keep the parameters within certain regions.

In an exterior-point algorithm penalty functions are used again as barriers, but this time to prevent a parameter (or parameters) from entering the feasible region. Thus the minimum can be approached from either side of the boundary, since penalty functions can be made to keep the parameters interior to the feasible region or exterior to it.

In closing this section it should be pointed out that the penalty-function approach is not limited just to inequality constraints of the form $C_i(x) \geq 0$. Equality constraints such as $D_i(\mathbf{x}) = 0$ can be treated by introducing the

---

[2]One should be aware that in many optimization problems the running time may be so great that it is impractical to use an interactive mode.

following penalty function:

$$\text{penalty function} = \sum_{i=1}^{d} \frac{\left[D_i(\mathbf{x}) \right]^2}{r}. \tag{11.24}$$

Again the penalty constant r should be initially chosen large and then gradually reduced.

11.5 CONCLUDING COMMENTS ABOUT OPTIMIZATION TECHNIQUES

Since this is an introductory text, none of the examples that were discussed required a computer to do very much work. However, in practical applications it is not uncommon for problems to take a substantial amount of computation effort. One such type of program will be discussed next in order to illustrate how circumstances can combine to cause an optimization problem to tax even a large computer.

Electrical networks called filters are used to modify the amplitude of electrical signals. These filters can be investigated experimentally by changing the frequency of the signal that is applied to the filter's input and measuring the amplitude of the output signal. Test sets exist that automatically change the frequency of the input signal and record the amplitude of the output.

The relation that is desired between the input signal and the output signal will depend on the application for which the filter is designed. It is the responsibility of the filter designer to choose the network parameters (e.g. capacitors and inductors) so as to synthesize the proper response.

Sometimes the filter designer can apply analytic expressions to calculate the network parameters, but in other cases optimization techniques must be used. This can be done by simulating the filter response on a computer. However, there is a fundamental difference between what can be done experimentally and what can be simulated on a computer. In a laboratory it is possible to vary the frequency of the input signal continuously— e.g. from 1000 to 4000 Hz. However, this is not possible if one is simulating the response on a computer. Instead, the input must be varied in discrete steps—e.g. from 1000 to 4000 Hz in 100-Hz increments (i.e. 1000, 1100, 1200, ..., 4000). For this example there are thirty-one different frequencies. At each one of these frequencies the filter response must be calculated, the calculated value compared with the desired value, and the error determined. The individual errors e_i can then be combined to produce the total error

$$E = \sum_{i=1}^{31} (e_i)^p,$$

where the power p is often selected to be 2.

Next consider what must be done if optimization techniques are to be applied to this problem. Assume that twenty network parameters[3] should be adjusted to minimize the total error E. Requiring twenty parameters to be simultaneously optimized by a computer is a large request; but this is only part of the difficulty. Since we are simulating the frequency response by using thirty-one different frequencies, each calculation of the total error E requires that the network be analyzed thirty-one different times.

Just to analyze a twenty-parameter network one time can require a substantial amount of computer time. Thirty-one such analyses will take almost 31 times longer. Because of this, much time has been spent developing efficient analysis programs. Some of the popular ones are described by Jensen (1976). Many modern network analysis programs use "sparse-matrix techniques"[4] to reduce the number of computations that are necessary.

Generalizing, if evaluating the error function E requires a substantial amount of computer time (e.g. because a complicated network must be analyzed many different times) then it may be worthwhile to develop sophisticated analysis tools (e.g. by using sparse-matrix techniques). Similarly, if an optimization program is applied to minimize such an error function, then considerable effort should be spent to assure that a rapidly convergent algorithm is used.

---

[3]This is not an unreasonably large number; in fact, it could be considered as only a moderate-size network.

[4]By definition, a sparse matrix has very few nonzero terms. For an introduction to this subject see Calahan, D. A. (1972), *Computer-Aided Network Design* (New York: McGraw-Hill).

PROBLEMS

11.1 In Example 11.1 it was mentioned that the least-pth program could be used to minimize $E(x)=0.16+2(0.5-x_3)^2+3x_3^2+4x_4^2$. However, this is an unnecessary application of the program, as the minimum is easily found by other methods. Find the minimum by analytical means.

11.2 If there are four different constraints, what is the number of possibilities as to which constraints will be active?

11.3 Minimize the Rosenbrock function $E(x)=100(x_1^2-x_2)^2+(1-x_1)^2$ subject to the constraint $0.6 \leqslant x_1 \leqslant 0.8$. The minimum can be found by solving the following parts to this problem:

(a) Assume the constraint $0.6 \leqslant x_1$ is active and find the minimum by analytical means.

(b) Assume the constraint $x_1 \leqslant 0.8$ is active and find the minimum by analytical means.

11.4 Minimize the Rosenbrock function subject to the constraint $0.6 \leqslant x_2 \leqslant 0.8$. The minimum can be found by solving the following parts to this problem:

(a) Assume the constraint $0.6 \leqslant x_2$ is active, and find the minimum by using the quadratic interpolation program.

(b) Assume the constraint $x_2 \leqslant 0.8$ is active, and find the minimum by using the quadratic interpolation program.

11.5 Example 11.3 minimized $E(x)=100(x_1^3-x_2)^2+(1-x_1)^2$ subject to the constraints $x_1 \leqslant 0.5$ and $x_2 \leqslant 0.6$.

(a) Assume that the constraint $x_1 \leqslant 0.5$ is active, and write the error function in terms of just x_2. Apply quadratic interpolation to minimize the error.

(b) Assume that the constraint $x_2 \leqslant 0.6$ is active, and write the error function in terms of just x_1. Apply quadratic interpolation to minimize the error.

(c) Discuss whether or not the results in (a) and (b) confirm the results in Example 11.3.

11.6 Example 11.4 minimized $E(x)=100(x_1^2-x_2)^2+(1-x_1)^2$ subject to the constraint $-2 \leqslant x_1 \leqslant 0.8$.

(a) Assume that the constraint $-2 \leqslant x_1$ is active, and write the error function in terms of just x_2. Use analytical methods to minimize the error.

(b) Repeat part (a) assuming that $x_1 \leqslant 0.8$ is active.

(c) Discuss whether or not the results in (a) and (b) confirm the results in Example 11.4.

11.7 For each of the following parts, find transformations to change the constrained problem to an unconstrained one.

(a) $x \geqslant -4$.

(b) $x_1 \leqslant 2$, $x_2 \leqslant 4$.

(c) $1 \leqslant x_1 \leqslant 3$, $-1 \leqslant x_2 \leqslant 5$.

(d) $x_1 \leqslant 2$, $x_2 \geqslant -4$.

11.8 If the transformation in (11.7) is used to change the constrained problem $x_1 \geqslant 4$ into an unconstrained problem, what is the value of x_1 that corresponds to $z_1 = 2$?

11.9 If the transformations in (11.9) and (11.12) are used to change the constrained problem $x_1 \leqslant 2$, $0 \leqslant x_2 \leqslant 10$ into an unconstrained problem, what is the value of $\mathbf{x}$ that corresponds to $\mathbf{z} = (1,2)$?

11.10 Define a penalty function of the type shown in (11.20) for the constraints $x_1 \leqslant 4$, $x_1 + x_2 \geqslant 2$.

11.11 Define a penalty function of the type shown in (11.20) for the constraint $-2 \leqslant x_1 \leqslant 4$.

11.12 For the constraint $1 \leqslant x_2 \leqslant 10$, define two error functions that could be used as penalty functions in the least-squares program.

11.13 Example 11.2 minimized the Rosenbrock function subject to the constraints $x_1 \geqslant -2$ and $x_2 \geqslant 2$ by transforming the problem to an unconstrained example. Verify the result by instead minimizing the following function, which has penalty functions:

$$E^*(\mathbf{x}) = 100(x_1^2 - x_2)^2 + (1 - x_1)^2 + \frac{K^2}{x_1 + 2} + \frac{K^2}{x_2 - 2},$$

where $k = 0.000001$. Choose as initial parameters $\mathbf{x} = (5,5)$.

Hint: Add two statements that are similar to statement 210 on p. 278. These statements should describe the constraints for this problem.

11.14 Verify the results in Example 11.3 by minimizing

$$E^*(\mathbf{x}) = 100(x_1^3 - x_2)^2 + (1 - x_1)^2 + \frac{K^2}{(0.5 - x_1)^2} + \frac{K^2}{0.6 - x_2},$$

where $K = 0.000001$. Choose as initial parameters $\mathbf{x} = (-1, -1)$.

11.15 Verify the results in Example 11.4 by defining an error function $E^*(\mathbf{x})$ that is similar to the error function in Problem 11.13, except have the penalty functions be defined for $-2 \leqslant x_1 \leqslant 0.8$. Choose as initial parameters $\mathbf{x} = (-1.2, 1)$.

11.16 Equation (11.2) listed the following constraints:

$$-2 \leqslant x_1 \leqslant 0.5, \qquad x_1 + x_2 \leqslant 1, \qquad x_1 - x_2 \leqslant 1.$$

Minimize the Rosenbrock function subject to these constraints. Do this by defining four error functions for the least-pth program. These error functions should be of the form $e(\mathbf{x}) = 0.000001/C(\mathbf{x})$. Choose as initial parameters $\mathbf{x} = (-1.2, 1)$.

REFERENCES

Some of the following references were specifically mentioned in this text; others are included because they serve as good general references for the reader who wants more detailed information about a numerical method or an optimization technique.

Box, M. J. (1966), "A Comparison of Several Current Optimization Methods and the Use of Transformations in Constrained Problems", *Computer J.*, No. 1, p. 67.

Brigham, E. O. (1974), *The Fast Fourier Transform.* Englewood Cliffs, N.J.: Prentice-Hall.

Calahan, D. A. (1972), *Computer-Aided Network Design.* New York: McGraw-Hill.

Carnahan, B., Luther, H. A., and Wilkes, J. O. (1968), *Applied Numerical Methods.* New York: John Wiley.

Charalambous, C. (March 1974), "A Unified Review of Optimization", *IEEE Trans. Microwave Theory Tech.*, pp. 289–300.

Chua, L. O. and Lin, P. (1975), *Computer-Aided Analysis of Electronic Circuits: Algorithms & Computational Techniques.* Englewood Cliffs, N.J.: Prentice-Hall.

Conte, S. D. and deBoor, C. (1972), *Elementary Numerical Analysis.* New York: McGraw-Hill.

Daniels, R. W. (1974), *Approximation Methods for Electronic Filter Design.* New York: McGraw-Hill.

Fiacco, A. V. and McCormick, G. P. (1968), *Nonlinear Programming.* New York: John Wiley.

Forsythe, G. E., Malcolm, M. A., and Moler, C. B. (1977), *Computer Methods for Mathematical Computations.* Englewood Cliffs, N.J.: Prentice-Hall.

Fowler, M. E. and Warten, R. M. (September 1967), "A Numerical Integration Technique for Ordinary Differential Equations with Widely Separated Eigenvalues", *IBM J. Res. Develop.*, pp. 537–543.

Fox, R. L. (1971), *Optimization Methods for Engineering Design.* Reading, Mass.: Addison-Wesley.

Gear, C. W. (1971), *Numerical Initial Value Problems in Ordinary Differential Equations.* Englewood Cliffs, N.J.: Prentice-Hall.

Gerald, C. F. (1973), *Applied Numerical Analysis.* Reading, Mass.: Addison-Wesley.

Gottfried, B. S. and Weisman, J. (1973), *Introduction to Optimization Theory.* Englewood Cliffs, N.J.: Prentice-Hall.

GROVE, W. E. (1963), *Brief Numerical Methods*. Englewood Cliffs, N.J.: Prentice-Hall.

GUNSTON, M. A. R. (1970), *Practical Matrix Algebra*. New York: American Elsevier.

HAMMING, R. W. (1973), *Numerical Methods for Scientists and Engineers*. New York: McGraw-Hill.

HILDEBRAND, F. B. (1974), *Introduction to Numerical Analysis*. New York: McGraw-Hill.

HOUSEHOLDER, A. (1953), *Principles of Numerical Analysis*, New York: McGraw-Hill.

JENSEN, R. W. and MCNAMEE, L. P. (1976), *Handbook of Circuit Analysis Languages and Techniques*. Englewood Cliffs, N.J.: Prentice-Hall.

KOWALIK, J. and OSBORNE, M. R. (1968), *Methods for Unconstrained Optimization Problems*. New York: American Elsevier.

LIOU, M. L. (May 1976), "Spline Fit Made Easy", *IEEE Trans. Computers*, pp. 522–527.

MCCORMICK, J. M. and SALVADORI, M. G. (1965), *Numerical Methods in* FORTRAN. Englewood Cliffs, N.J.: Prentice-Hall.

NELDER, J. A. and MEAD, R. (January 1965), "A Simplex Method for Function Minimization", *Computer J.*, pp. 308–313.

PECKHAM, G. (November 1970), "A New Method for Minimizing a Sum of Squares Without Calculating Derivatives", *Computer J.*, pp. 418–420.

PENNINGTON, P. H. (1970), *Introductory Computer Methods and Numerical Analysis*. London: MacMillan.

PIERRE, D. A. (1969), *Optimization Theory with Applications*. New York: John Wiley.

POLAK, E. (1971), *Computational Methods in Optimization*. New York: Academic.

RAINVILLE, E. D. (1969), *Elementary Differential Equations*. New York: MacMillan.

RALSTON, A. (1965), *A First Course in Numerical Analysis*. New York: McGraw-Hill.

SCHEID, F. (1968), *Theory and Problems of Numerical Analysis*. New York: McGraw-Hill.

SHAMPINE, L. F. and GORDAN, M. K. (1975), *Computer Solution of Ordinary Differential Equations*. San Francisco: W. H. Freeman.

STEWART, G. W. (1973), *Introduction to Matrix Computations*. New York: Academic.

STROUD, A. H. and SECREST, D. (1966), *Gaussian Quadrature Formulas*. Englewood Cliffs, N.J.: Prentice-Hall.

WHITTLE, P. (1971), *Optimization Under Constraints: Theory and Applications of Nonlinear Programming*. New York: Wiley-Interscience.

ANSWERS TO SELECTED PROBLEMS

Chapter 1

1.2 (a) 7.07 (b) 7.071
1.4 (a) 0.02, 0.01 (b) 2, 0.01 (c) relative error
1.6 1.5%
1.8 -75%
1.10 (a) $3.102E-4$ (b) $4.016E-5$ (c) 7.72 (d) 0.3
1.12 (a) $-5.25E-4$ (b) $-6.406E-5$ (c) 8.2
1.14 error $(0.1)/$error $(0.05)=(-0.0517)/(-0.0254)=2.04$

Chapter 2

2.2 The unique solution is $(0,0,0)$
2.3 (b) $x_3=-2x_2=0$ (c) $x_3=-1x_2=0$
2.8 $(4,2)$
2.9 $A=B=-6$
2.10 $A=-6$ $B=-18$
2.11 $A=-6$ $B=+6$
2.17 9484
2.19 $(2.85714, -2.28571, 11.2857, 4)$
2.20 (a) $(-0.75, 2.25, -1.25)$ (b) $(-1.375, 1.625, -8.125)$
2.23 $(39, 10, 5)$

Chapter 3

3.1 1.103 versus 1.1
3.3 3.73
3.7 $0.618034, -1.61803, 1.73205, -1.73205$
3.10 1.41667
3.12 $-1, -3, -1$
3.14 (a) $-0.352, -0.576, -0.448$ (b) 1.533 (c) 1.54858
3.16 -0.901
3.19 $R=A_2$ $S=A_3$
3.24 x^*x+x+2
3.26 $2(x^*x+x+7)(x+1)$
3.28 (a) $(x^*x+x+4)(x^*x+2x+9)$ (b) $(x^*x+2x+9)(x^*x+x+4)$

Chapter 4

4.2 -3.3
4.4 0

4.6   (a) 1 (b) -2
4.7 $f_{s+5} - 5f_{s+4} + 10f_{s+3} - 10f_{s+2} + 5f_{s+1} - f_s$
4.12 $a_0 = -3 \ a_1 = 25 \ a_2 = -12 \ a_3 = 2$
4.14 $a_0 = 41 \ a_1 = 52 \ a_2 = 16$
4.16 $f(x) = x$
4.18 17
4.20 2.22, 2.47, 3.22, 2.47, 2.22, 8.47
4.22 $r!$
4.24 15
4.26 179
4.28 44.99
4.30 0.129
4.32 $-1.645 + 3.765x + 0.825x*x$
4.35 2.396, 3, 3.104

Chapter 5

5.2   6.002
5.4   (a) 0.0036 (b) 0.0009
5.6   (a) 0.106 (b) 0.051
5.8 $(f_{-2} - 8f_{-1} + 8f_1 - f_2)/(12h)$
5.10 $(-7f_0 + 15f_4 - 8f_5)/(20h)$
5.12 (a) 17 (b) 14
5.14 11
5.16 (a) 35 42 (b) 35 35

Chapter 6

6.2   14
6.4   0.882
6.6   2.45
6.9   1.88571
6.11 0.23255
6.12 0.8821
6.16 0.1747
6.18 1.68575
6.20 0.174754
6.22 $[16\text{INT}(h/2) - \text{INT}(h)]/15$
6.26 11.9375
6.28 23.1
6.30 6.361 versus 6.389
6.32 156.83

Chapter 7

7.2	0.0128
7.3	0.0185
7.5	0.0003175
7.6	-8.38906
7.8	-8.3890561
7.10	0.0176687
7.13	$\exp(x) - 4y\,y_2 - \sin y$
7.15	(a) $h = 0.3\ y = 0.2225$ (b) $h = 0.1\ y = 0.2226$
7.17	0.2208
7.19	0.4802

Chapter 8

8.1	$-2\sin x_1 \cos x_2 - (\cos x_1)**2(\sin x_2)**4$
8.4	$(1,2,3)\ (1.1,2,3)\ (1,2.2,3)\ (1,2,3.3)$
8.5	$(1/3, 2/3, 1/3)$
8.7	(a) $(1,1,1)$ (b) $(1,1,2)$ (c) $(1,1,3)$
8.9	$(5,0,0)$
8.11	(a) $(0,4,1)\ (-2,4,2)\ (-1,2.5,1)\ (0,3,0)$
	(b) $(6,4,-2)\ (-2,4,2)\ (2,-2,-2)\ (6,0,-6)$
8.14	After ten iterations $x = (2.03, 2.96)$
8.16	If initial $x = (1,1)$ then ten iterations gives $(2.00, 3.03)$ at which point the minimum is approximately -4.

Chapter 9

9.2	0.0405
9.4	(a) $(2,8,18)$ (b) $(2,0,-6)$
9.6	$(1,4)$
9.8	-5
9.11	(a) 13 (b) $(8,4,3)$ (c) 13.9068 (d) 12.1268
9.13	Statement 24
9.20	$E(1.422, 2.958) = E(-1.422, 2.958) = 7.002$
9.21	(a) $E(0.666663, -100) = 4.66667$ (b) $E(0.664175, -0.999753) = 4.66756$

Chapter 10

10.1	$e_1 = 5(x_1 - 10)\ e_2 = 10x_1x_2$
10.4	(a) $(254, 94)$ (b) $(257.815, 96.168)$ (c) $(257.125, 95.823)$
10.6	(a) $(10, 8)$ (b) $(1.01, 2.02, 2.04)$

10.8 $(-1/3, -5/3)$

10.10 $(-0.3077, -0.2821)$

10.18 $a_0 = -0.02670$ $a_1 = 50.2236$ $b_1 = 0.01050$ $b_2 = 0.07579$

10.20 $a_0 = 1.00012$ $a_1 = -4.48E-3$ $a_2 = -0.48161$

10.22 $a_0 = -6.8E-6$ $a_1 = 1.00033$ $b_1 = 5.10E-3$ $b_2 = -0.348$

Chapter 11

11.1 $E(0.4, 0.3, 0.2, 0) = 0.36$

11.3   (a) $E(0.6, 0.36) = 0.16$ (b) $E(0.8, 0.64) = 0.04$ which is the constrained minimum.

11.5   (a) $E(0.5, 0.125) = 0.25$ (b) $E(0.8438, 0.6) = 0.02446$

11.8   8

11.10 $r[1/(4-x_1) + 1/(x_1 + x_2 - 2)]$

11.12 $E(1) = [k/(x_2-1)]**2$ $E(2) = [k/(x_2-10)]**2$

Index